AN INTRODUCTION TO
CYBERNETICS

AN INTRODUCTION TO
CYBERNETICS

by

W. ROSS ASHBY
M.A., M.D.(Cantab.), D.P.M.

LONDON

CHAPMAN & HALL LTD

37 ESSEX STREET WC2

1961

First published 1956
Second impression 1957
Third impression 1958
Fourth impression 1961
Fifth impression 1963

Catalogue No. 567/4

MADE AND PRINTED BY OFFSET IN GREAT BRITAIN BY
WILLIAM CLOWES AND SONS, LIMITED, LONDON AND BECCLES

PREFACE

Many workers in the biological sciences—physiologists, psychologists, sociologists—are interested in cybernetics and would like to apply its methods and techniques to their own speciality. Many have, however, been prevented from taking up the subject by an impression that its use must be preceded by a long study of electronics and advanced pure mathematics; for they have formed the impression that cybernetics and these subjects are inseparable.

The author is convinced, however, that this impression is false. The basic ideas of cybernetics can be treated without reference to electronics, and they are fundamentally simple; so although advanced techniques may be necessary for advanced applications, a great deal can be done, especially in the biological sciences, by the use of quite simple techniques, provided they are used with a clear and deep understanding of the principles involved. It is the author's belief that if the subject is founded in the common-place and well understood, and is then built up carefully, step by step, there is no reason why the worker with only elementary mathematical knowledge should not achieve a complete understanding of its basic principles. With such an understanding he will then be able to see exactly what further techniques he will have to learn if he is to proceed further; and, what is particularly useful, he will be able to see what techniques he can safely ignore as being irrelevant to his purpose.

The book is intended to provide such an introduction. It starts from common-place and well-understood concepts, and proceeds, step by step, to show how these concepts can be made exact, and how they can be developed until they lead into such subjects as feedback, stability, regulation, ultrastability, information, coding, noise, and other cybernetic topics. Throughout the book no knowledge of mathematics is required beyond elementary algebra; in particular, the arguments nowhere depend on the calculus (the few references to it can be ignored without harm, for they are intended only to show how the calculus joins on to the subjects discussed, if it should be used). The illustrations and examples are mostly taken from the biological, rather than the physical, sciences. Its overlap with *Design for a Brain* is small, so that the two books are almost independent. They are, however, intimately related, and are best treated as complementary; each will help to illuminate the other.

v

It is divided into three parts.

Part I deals with the principles of Mechanism, treating such matters as its representation by a transformation, what is meant by "stability", what is meant by "feedback", the various forms of independence that can exist within a mechanism, and how mechanisms can be coupled. It introduces the principles that must be followed when the system is so large and complex (e.g. brain or society) that it can be treated only statistically. It introduces also the case when the system is such that not all of it is accessible to direct observation—the so-called Black Box theory.

Part II uses the methods developed in Part I to study what is meant by "information", and how it is coded when it passes through a mechanism. It applies these methods to various problems in biology and tries to show something of the wealth of possible applications. It leads into Shannon's theory; so after reading this Part the reader will be able to proceed without difficulty to the study of Shannon's own work.

Part III deals with mechanism and information as they are used in biological systems for regulation and control, both in the inborn systems studied in physiology and in the acquired systems studied in psychology. It shows how hierarchies of such regulators and controllers can be built, and how an amplification of regulation is thereby made possible. It gives a new and altogether simpler account of the principle of ultrastability. It lays the foundation for a general theory of complex regulating systems, developing further the ideas of *Design for a Brain*. Thus, on the one hand it provides an explanation of the outstanding powers of regulation possessed by the brain, and on the other hand it provides the principles by which a designer may build machines of like power.

Though the book is intended to be an easy introduction, it is not intended to be merely a chat about cybernetics—it is written for those who want to work themselves into it, for those who want to achieve an actual working mastery of the subject. It therefore contains abundant easy exercises, carefully graded, with hints and explanatory answers, so that the reader, as he progresses, can test his grasp of what he has read, and can exercise his new intellectual muscles. A few exercises that need a special technique have been marked thus: *Ex. Their omission will not affect the reader's progress.

For convenience of reference, the matter has been divided into sections; all references are to the section, and as these numbers are shown at the top of every page, finding a section is as simple and direct as finding a page. The section is shown thus: S.9/14—ndicating the fourteenth section in Chapter 9. Figures, Tables, and

Exercises have been numbered within their own sections; thus
Fig. 9/14/2 is the second figure in S.9/14. A simple reference, e.g.
Ex. 4, is used for reference within the same section. Whenever a
word is formally defined it is printed in **bold-faced** type.

I would like to express my indebtedness to Michael B. Sporn, who
checked all the Answers. I would also like to take this opportunity
to express my deep gratitude to the Governors of Barnwood House
and to Dr. G. W. T. H. Fleming for the generous support that made
these researches possible. Though the book covers many topics,
these are but means; the end has been throughout to make clear
what principles must be followed when one attempts to restore
normal function to a sick organism that is, as a human patient, of
fearful complexity. It is my faith that the new understanding may
lead to new and effective treatments, for the need is great.

Barnwood House   W. ROSS ASHBY
Gloucester

CONTENTS

CONTENTS

Chapter   1

WHAT IS NEW

1/1. Cybernetics was defined by Wiener as "the science of control
and communication, in the animal and the machine"—in a
word, as the art of *steermanship*, and it is to this aspect that the
book will be addressed. Co-ordination, regulation and control
will be its themes, for these are of the greatest biological and practical
interest.

We must, therefore, make a study of mechanism; but some
introduction is advisable, for cybernetics treats the subject from a
new, and therefore unusual, angle. Without introduction, Chapter
2 might well seem to be seriously at fault. The new point of view
should be clearly understood, for any unconscious vacillation between the old and the new is apt to lead to confusion.

1/2. *The peculiarities of cybernetics.* Many a book has borne the
title "Theory of Machines", but it usually contains information
about *mechanical* things, about levers and cogs. Cybernetics, too,
is a "theory of machines", but it treats, not things but *ways of
behaving*. It does not ask "what *is* this thing?" but "*what does it
do?*". Thus it is very interested in such a statement as "this variable
is undergoing a simple harmonic oscillation", and is much less
concerned with whether the variable is the position of a point on a
wheel, or a potential in an electric circuit. It is thus essentially
functional and behaviouristic.

Cybernetics started by being closely associated in many ways with
physics, but it depends in no essential way on the laws of physics or
on the properties of matter. Cybernetics deals with all forms of
behaviour in so far as they are regular, or determinate, or reproducible. The materiality is irrelevant, and so is the holding or not
of the ordinary laws of physics. (The example given in S.4/15 will
make this statement clear.) *The truths of cybernetics are not
conditional on their being derived from some other branch of science.*
Cybernetics has its own foundations. It is partly the aim of this
book to display them clearly.

1

1/3. Cybernetics stands to the real machine—electronic, mechanical, neural, or economic—much as geometry stands to a real object in our terrestrial space. There was a time when "geometry" meant such relationships as could be demonstrated on three-dimensional objects or in two-dimensional diagrams. The forms provided by the earth—animal, vegetable, and mineral—were larger in number and richer in properties than could be provided by elementary geometry. In those days a form which was suggested by geometry but which could not be demonstrated in ordinary space was suspect or inacceptable. Ordinary space *dominated* geometry.

Today the position is quite different. Geometry exists in its own right, and by its own strength. It can now treat accurately and coherently a range of forms and spaces that far exceeds anything that terrestrial space can provide. Today it is geometry that contains the terrestrial forms, and not vice versa, for the terrestrial forms are merely special cases in an all-embracing geometry.

The gain achieved by geometry's development hardly needs to be pointed out. Geometry now acts as a framework on which all terrestrial forms can find their natural place, with the relations between the various forms readily appreciable. With this increased understanding goes a correspondingly increased power of control.

Cybernetics is similar in its relation to the actual machine. It takes as its subject-matter the domain of "all possible machines", and is only secondarily interested if informed that some of them have not yet been made, either by Man or by Nature. What cybernetics offers is the framework on which all individual machines may be ordered, related and understood.

1/4. Cybernetics, then, is indifferent to the criticism that some of the machines it considers are not represented among the machines found among us. In this it follows the path already followed with obvious success by mathematical physics. This science has long given prominence to the study of systems that are well known to be non-existent—springs without mass, particles that have mass but no volume, gases that behave perfectly, and so on. To say that these entities do not exist is true; but their non-existence does not mean that mathematical physics is mere fantasy; nor does it make the physicist throw away his treatise on the Theory of the Massless Spring, for this theory is invaluable to him in his practical work. The fact is that the massless spring, though it has no physical representation, has certain properties that make it of the highest importance to him if he is to understand a system even as simple as a watch.

The biologist knows and uses the same principle when he gives to *Amphioxus*, or to some extinct form, a detailed study quite out of proportion to its present-day ecological or economic importance.

In the same way, cybernetics marks out certain types of mechanism (S.3/3) as being of particular importance in the general theory; and it does this with no regard for whether terrestrial machines happen to make this form common. Only after the study has surveyed adequately the *possible* relations between machine and machine does it turn to consider the forms actually found in some particular branch of science.

1/5. In keeping with this method, which works primarily with the comprehensive and general, cybernetics typically treats any given, particular, machine by asking not "what individual act will it produce here and now?" but "what are *all* the possible behaviours that it can produce?"

It is in this way that information theory comes to play an essential part in the subject; for information theory is characterised essentially by its dealing always with a *set* of possibilities; both its primary data and its final statements are almost always about the set as such, and not about some individual element in the set.

This new point of view leads to the consideration of new types of problem. The older point of view saw, say, an ovum grow into a rabbit and asked "why does it do this?—why does it not just stay an ovum?" The attempts to answer this question led to the study of energetics and to the discovery of many reasons why the ovum should change—it can oxidise its fat, and fat provides free energy; it has phosphorylating enzymes, and can pass its metabolites around a Krebs' cycle; and so on. In these studies the concept of energy was fundamental.

Quite different, though equally valid, is the point of view of cybernetics. It takes for granted that the ovum.has abundant free energy, and that it is so delicately poised metabolically as to be, in a sense, explosive. Growth of some form there will be; cybernetics asks "why should the changes be to the rabbit-form, and not to a dog-form, a fish-form, or even to a teratoma-form?" Cybernetics envisages a set of possibilities much wider than the actual, and then asks why the particular case should conform to its usual particular restriction. In this discussion, questions of energy play almost no part—the energy is simply taken for granted. Even whether the system is closed to energy or open is often irrelevant; what *is* important is the extent to which the system is subject to determining and controlling factors. So no information or signal or determining factor may pass from part to part without its being recorded as a significant event. Cybernetics might, in fact, be defined as *the study of systems that are open to energy but closed to information and control*—systems that are "information-tight" (S.9/19.).

1/6.   The uses of cybernetics.   After this bird's-eye view of cybernetics we can turn to consider some of the ways in which it promises to be of assistance.   I shall confine my attention to the applications that promise most in the biological sciences.   The review can only be brief and very general.   Many applications have already been made and are too well known to need description here; more will doubtless be developed in the future.   There are, however, two peculiar scientific virtues of cybernetics that are worth explicit mention.

One is that it offers a single vocabulary and a single set of concepts suitable for representing the most diverse types of system.   Until recently, any attempt to relate the many facts known about, say, servo-mechanisms to what was known about the cerebellum was made unnecessarily difficult by the fact that the properties of servo-mechanisms were described in words redolent of the automatic pilot, or the radio set, or the hydraulic brake, while those of the cerebellum were described in words redolent of the dissecting room and the bedside—aspects that are irrelevant to the *similarities* between a servo-mechanism and a cerebellar reflex.   Cybernetics offers one set of concepts that, by having exact correspondences with each branch of science, can thereby bring them into exact relation with one other.

It has been found repeatedly in science that the discovery that two branches are related leads to each branch helping in the development of the other.   (Compare S.6/8.)   The result is often a markedly accelerated growth of both.   The infinitesimal calculus and astronomy, the virus and the protein molecule, the chromosomes and heredity are examples that come to mind.   Neither, of course, can give *proofs* about the laws of the other, but each can give suggestions that may be of the greatest assistance and fruitfulness.   The subject is returned to in S.6/8.   Here I need only mention the fact that cybernetics is likely to reveal a great number of interesting and suggestive parallelisms between machine and brain and society. And it can provide the common language by which discoveries in one branch can readily be made use of in the others.

1/7.   The complex system.   The second peculiar virtue of cybernetics is that it offers a method for the scientific treatment of the system in which complexity is outstanding and too important to be ignored. Such systems are, as we well know, only too common in the biological world!

In the simpler systems, the methods of cybernetics sometimes show no obvious advantage over those that have long been known. It is chiefly when the systems become complex that the new methods reveal their power.

Science stands today on something of a divide. For two centuries it has been exploring systems that are either intrinsically simple or that are capable of being analysed into simple components. The fact that such a dogma as "vary the factors one at a time" could be accepted for a century, shows that scientists were largely concerned in investigating such systems as *allowed* this method; for this method is often fundamentally impossible in the complex systems. Not until Sir Ronald Fisher's work in the '20s, with experiments conducted on agricultural soils, did it become clearly recognised that there are complex systems that just do not allow the varying of only one factor at a time—they are so dynamic and interconnected that the alteration of one factor immediately acts as cause to evoke alterations in others, perhaps in a great many others. Until recently, science tended to evade the study of such systems, focusing its attention on those that were simple and, especially, reducible (S.4/14).

In the study of some systems, however, the complexity could not be wholly evaded. The cerebral cortex of the free-living organism, the ant-hill as a functioning society, and the human economic system were outstanding both in their practical importance and in their intractability by the older methods. So today we see psychoses untreated, societies declining, and economic systems faltering, the scientist being able to do little more than to appreciate the full complexity of the subject he is studying. But science today is also taking the first steps towards studying "complexity" as a subject in its own right.

Prominent among the methods for dealing with complexity is cybernetics. It rejects the vaguely intuitive ideas that we pick up from handling such simple machines as the alarm clock and the bicycle, and sets to work to build up a rigorous discipline of the subject. For a time (as the first few chapters of this book will show) it seems rather to deal with truisms and platitudes, but this is merely because the foundations are built to be broad and strong. They are built so that cybernetics can be developed vigorously, without the primary vagueness that has infected most past attempts to grapple with, in particular, the complexities of the brain in action.

Cybernetics offers the hope of providing effective methods for the study, and control, of systems that are intrinsically extremely complex. It will do this by first marking out what is achievable (for probably many of the investigations of the past attempted the impossible), and then providing generalised strategies, of demonstrable value, that can be used uniformly in a variety of special cases. In this way it offers the hope of providing the essential methods by which to attack the ills—psychological, social, economic—which at present are defeating us by their intrinsic complexity. Part III of this book does not pretend to offer such methods perfected, but it attempts to offer a foundation on which such methods can be constructed, and a start in the right direction.

PART ONE

MECHANISM

The properties commonly ascribed to any object are, in last analysis, names for its behavior.

(Herrick)

Chapter   **2**

CHANGE

2/1. The most fundamental concept in cybernetics is that of "difference", either that two things are recognisably different or that one thing has changed with time. Its range of application need not be described now, for the subsequent chapters will illustrate the range abundantly. All the changes that may occur with time are naturally included, for when plants grow and planets age and machines move some change from one state to another is implicit. So our first task will be to develop this concept of "change", not only making it more precise but making it richer, converting it to a form that experience has shown to be necessary if significant developments are to be made.

Often a change occurs continuously, that is, by infinitesimal steps, as when the earth moves through space, or a sunbather's skin darkens under exposure. The consideration of steps that are infinitesimal, however, raises a number of purely mathematical difficulties, so we shall avoid their consideration entirely. Instead, we shall assume in all cases that the changes occur by finite steps in time and that any difference is also finite. We shall assume that the change occurs by a measurable jump, as the money in a bank account changes by at least a penny. Though this supposition may seem artificial in a world in which continuity is common, it has great advantages in an Introduction and is not as artificial as it seems. When the differences are finite, all the important questions, as we shall see later, can be decided by simple counting, so that it is easy to be quite sure whether we are right or not. Were we to consider continuous changes we would often have to compare infinitesimal against infinitesimal, or to consider what we would have after adding together an infinite number of infinitesimals—questions by no means easy to answer.

As a simple trick, the discrete can often be carried over into the continuous, in a way suitable for practical purposes, by making a graph of the discrete, with the values shown as separate points. It is

9

then easy to see the form that the changes will take if the points were to become infinitely numerous and close together.

In fact, however, by keeping the discussion to the case of the finite difference we lose nothing. For having established with certainty what happens when the differences have a particular size we can consider the case when they are rather smaller. When this case is known with certainty we can consider what happens when they are smaller still. We can progress in this way, each step being well established, until we perceive the trend; then we can say what is the limit as the difference tends to zero. This, in fact, is the method that the mathematician always does use if he wants to be really sure of what happens when the changes are continuous.

Thus, consideration of the case in which all differences are finite loses nothing; it gives a clear and simple foundation; and it can always be converted to the continuous form if that is desired.

The subject is taken up again in S.3/3.

2/2. Next, a few words that will have to be used repeatedly. Consider the simple example in which, under the influence of sunshine, pale skin changes to dark skin. Something, the pale skin, is acted on by a factor, the sunshine, and is changed to dark skin. That which is acted on, the pale skin, will be called the **operand,** the factor will be called the **operator,** and what the operand is changed to will be called the **transform.** The change that occurs, which we can represent unambiguously by

$$\text{pale skin} \rightarrow \text{dark skin}$$

is the **transition.**

The transition is specified by the two states and the indication of which changed to which.

TRANSFORMATION

2/3. The single transition is, however, too simple. Experience has shown that if the concept of "change" is to be useful it must be enlarged to the case in which the operator can act on more than one operand, inducing a characteristic transition in each. Thus the operator "exposure to sunshine" will induce a number of transitions, among which are:

$$\text{cold soil} \rightarrow \text{warm soil}$$
$$\text{unexposed photographic plate} \rightarrow \text{exposed plate}$$
$$\text{coloured pigment} \rightarrow \text{bleached pigment}$$

Such a set of transitions, on a set of operands, is a **transformation.**

Another example of a transformation is given by the simple coding that turns each letter of a message to the one that follows it in the alphabet, Z being turned to A; so CAT would become DBU. The transformation is defined by the table:

$$A \to B$$
$$B \to C$$
$$\cdots$$
$$Y \to Z$$
$$Z \to A$$

Notice that the transformation is defined, not by any reference to what it "really" is, nor by reference to any physical cause of the change, but by the giving of a set of operands and a statement of what each is changed to. The transformation is concerned with *what* happens, not with *why* it happens. Similarly, though we may sometimes know something of the operator as a thing in itself (as we know something of sunlight), this knowledge is often not essential; what we *must* know is how it acts on the operands; that is, we must know the transformation that it effects.

For convenience of printing, such a transformation can also be expressed thus:

$$\downarrow \quad \begin{matrix} A & B & \cdots & Y & Z \\ B & C & \cdots & Z & A \end{matrix}$$

We shall use this form as standard.

2/4. *Closure.* When an operator acts on a set of operands it may happen that the set of transforms obtained contains no element that is not already present in the set of operands, i.e. the transformation creates no new element. Thus, in the transformation

$$\downarrow \quad \begin{matrix} A & B & \cdots & Y & Z \\ B & C & \cdots & Z & A \end{matrix}$$

every element in the lower line occurs also in the upper. When this occurs, the set of operands is **closed** under the transformation. The property of "closure" is a relation between a transformation and a particular set of operands; if either is altered the closure may alter.

It will be noticed that the test for closure is made, not by reference to whatever may be the cause of the transformation but by reference to the details of the transformation itself. It can therefore be applied even when we know nothing of the cause responsible for the changes.

11

Ex. 1: If the operands are the positive integers 1, 2, 3, and 4, and the operator is "add three to it", the transformation is:

$$\downarrow \begin{array}{cccc} 1 & 2 & 3 & 4 \\ 4 & 5 & 6 & 7 \end{array}$$

Is it closed?

Ex. 2: The operands are those English letters that have Greek equivalents (i.e. excluding *j*, *q*, etc.), and the operator is "turn each English letter to its Greek equivalent". Is the transformation closed?

Ex. 3: Are the following transformations closed or not:

$$A: \downarrow \begin{array}{cccc} a & b & c & d \\ a & a & a & a \end{array} \qquad B: \downarrow \begin{array}{cccc} f & g & p & q \\ g & f & q & p \end{array}$$

$$C: \downarrow \begin{array}{ccc} f & g & p \\ g & f & q \end{array} \qquad D: \downarrow \begin{array}{cc} f & g \\ g & f \end{array}$$

Ex. 4: Write down, in the form of Ex. 3, a transformation that has only one operand and is closed.

Ex. 5: Mr. C, of the Eccentrics' Chess Club, has a system of play that rigidly prescribes, for every possible position, both for White and Black (except for those positions in which the player is already mated) what is the player's best next move. The theory thus defines a transformation from position to position. On being assured that the transformation was a closed one, and that C always plays by this system, Mr. D. at once offered to play C for a large stake. Was D wise?

2/5. A transformation may have an infinite number of discrete operands; such would be the transformation

$$\downarrow \begin{array}{ccccc} 1 & 2 & 3 & 4 & \cdots \\ 4 & 5 & 6 & 7 & \cdots \end{array}$$

where the dots simply mean that the list goes on similarly without end. Infinite sets can lead to difficulties, but in this book we shall consider only the simple and clear. Whether such a transformation is closed or not is determined by whether one cannot, or can (respectively) find some particular, namable, transform that does not occur among the operands. In the example given above, each particular transform, 142857 for instance, will obviously be found among the operands. So that particular infinite transformation is closed.

Ex. 1: In *A* the operands are the even numbers from 2 onwards, and the transforms are their squares:

$$A: \downarrow \begin{array}{ccc} 2 & 4 & 6 \cdots \\ 4 & 16 & 36 \cdots \end{array}$$

Is *A* closed?

Ex. 2: In transformation *B* the operands are all the positive integers 1, 2, 3, ... and each one's transform is its right-hand digit, so that, for instance, $127 \rightarrow 7$, and $6493 \rightarrow 3$. Is *B* closed?

2/6. *Notation.* Many transformations become inconveniently lengthy if written out *in extenso*. Already, in S.2/3, we have been forced to use dots ... to represent operands that were not given individually. For merely practical reasons we shall have to develop a more compact method for writing down our transformations, though it is to be understood that, whatever abbreviation is used, the transformation is basically specified as in S.2/3. Several abbreviations will now be described. It is to be understood that they are a mere shorthand, and that they imply nothing more than has already been stated explicitly in the last few sections.

Often the specification of a transformation is made simple by some simple relation that links all the operands to their respective transforms. Thus the transformation of Ex. 2/4/1 can be replaced by the single line

Operand → operand plus three.

The whole transformation can thus be specified by the general rule, written more compactly,

$$Op. \rightarrow Op. + 3,$$

together with a statement that the operands are the numbers 1, 2, 3 and 4. And commonly the representation can be made even briefer, the two letters being reduced to one:

$$n \rightarrow n + 3 \quad (n = 1, 2, 3, 4)$$

The word "operand" above, or the letter n (which means *exactly* the same thing), may seem somewhat ambiguous. If we are thinking of how, say, 2 is transformed, then "n" means the number 2 and nothing else, and the expression tells us that it will change to 5. The same expression, however, can also be used with n not given any particular value. It then represents the whole transformation. It will be found that this ambiguity leads to no confusion in practice, for the context will always indicate which meaning is intended.

Ex. 1: Condense into one line the transformation

$$\downarrow \begin{matrix} 1 & 2 & 3 \\ 11 & 12 & 13 \end{matrix}$$

Ex. 2: Condense similarly the transformations:

a: $\downarrow \begin{matrix} 1 & 2 & 3 \\ 7 & 14 & 21 \end{matrix}$ b: $\downarrow \begin{matrix} 1 & 2 & 3 \\ 1 & 4 & 9 \end{matrix}$ c: $\downarrow \begin{matrix} 1 & 2 & 3 \\ 1 & \frac{1}{2} & \frac{1}{3} \end{matrix}$

d: $\downarrow \begin{matrix} 1 & 2 & 3 \\ 10 & 9 & 8 \end{matrix}$ e: $\downarrow \begin{matrix} 1 & 2 & 3 \\ 1 & 1 & 1 \end{matrix}$ f: $\downarrow \begin{matrix} 1 & 2 & 3 \\ 1 & 2 & 3 \end{matrix}$

We shall often require a symbol to represent the transform of such a symbol as n. It can be obtained conveniently by adding a prime to the operand, so that, whatever n may be, $n \rightarrow n'$. Thus, if the operands of Ex. 1 are n, then the transformation can be written as $n' = n + 10$ $(n = 1, 2, 3)$.

Ex. 3: Write out in full the transformation in which the operands are the three numbers 5, 6 and 7, and in which $n' = n - 3$. Is it closed?

Ex. 4: Write out in full the transformations in which:

(i) $n' = 5n$ $(n = 5, 6, 7)$;
(ii) $n' = 2n^2$ $(n = -1, 0, 1)$.

Ex. 5: If the operands are all the numbers (fractional included) between 0 and 1, and $n' = \frac{1}{2}n$, is the transformation closed? (Hint: try some representative values for n: $\frac{1}{2}, \frac{3}{4}, \frac{1}{4}, 0 \cdot 01, 0 \cdot 99$; try till you become sure of the answer.)

Ex. 6: (Continued) With the same operands, is the transformation closed if $n' = 1/(n + 1)$?

2/7.   The transformations mentioned so far have all been characterised by being "single-valued". A transformation is **single-valued** if it converts each operand to only one transform. (Other types are also possible and important, as will be seen in S.9/2 and 12/8.) Thus the transformation

$$\downarrow \begin{matrix} A & B & C & D \\ B & A & A & D \end{matrix}$$

is single-valued; but the transformation

$$\downarrow \begin{matrix} A & B & C & D \\ B \text{ or } D & A & B \text{ or } C & D \end{matrix}$$

is not single-valued.

2/8.   Of the single-valued transformations, a type of some importance in special cases is that which is **one-one**.   In this case the transforms are all different from one another.   Thus not only does each operand give a unique transform (from the single-valuedness) but each transform indicates (inversely) a unique operand.   Such a transformation is

$$\downarrow \begin{matrix} A & B & C & D & E & F & G & H \\ F & H & K & L & G & J & E & M \end{matrix}$$

This example is one-one but not closed.

On the other hand, the transformation of Ex. 2/6/2(e) is not one-one, for the transform "1" does not indicate a unique operand.   A transformation that is single-valued but not one-one will be referred to as **many-one**.

Ex. 1: The operands are the ten digits 0, 1, . . . 9; the transform is the third decimal digit of $\log_{10}(n+4)$. (For instance, if the operand is 3, we find in succession, 7, $\log_{10}7$, 0·8451, and 5; so $3 \to 5$.) Is the transformation one-one or many-one? (Hint: find the transforms of 0, 1, and so on in succession; use four-figure tables.)

·**2/9.** *The identity.* An important transformation, apt to be dismissed by the beginner as a nullity, is the **identical** transformation, in which no change occurs, in which each transform is the same as its operand. If the operands are all different it is necessarily one-one. An example is f in Ex. 2/6/2. In condensed notation $n'=n$.

Ex. 1: At the opening of a shop's cash register, the transformation to be made on its contained money is, in some machines, shown by a flag. What flag shows at the identical transformation?

Ex. 2: In cricket, the runs made during an over transform the side's score from one value to another. Each distinct number of runs defines a distinct transformation: thus if eight runs are scored in the over, the transformation is specified by $n' = n + 8$. What is the cricketer's name for the identical transformation?

2/10. *Representation by matrix.* All these transformations can be represented in a single schema, which shows clearly their mutual relations. (The method will become particularly useful in Chapter 9 and subsequently.)

Write the operands in a horizontal row, and the possible transforms in a column below and to the left, so that they form two sides of a rectangle. Given a particular transformation, put a "+" at the intersection of a row and column if the operand at the head of the column *is* transformed to the element at the left-hand side; otherwise insert a zero. Thus the transformation

$$\begin{vmatrix} A & B & C \\ A & C & C \end{vmatrix}$$

would be shown as

$\downarrow$	A	B	C
A	+	0	0
B	0	0	0
C	0	+	+

The arrow at the top left corner serves to show the direction of the transitions. Thus *every transformation can be shown as a matrix.*

If the transformation is large, dots can be used in the matrix if their meaning is unambiguous. Thus the matrix of the transformation in which $n' = n + 2$, and in which the operands are the positive integers from 1 onwards, could be shown as

↓	1	2	3	4	5	...
1	**0**	0	0	0	0	...
2	0	**0**	0	0	0	...
3	+	0	**0**	0	0	...
4	0	+	0	**0**	0	...
5	0	0	+	0	**0**	...
...	...	...	...	...	...	...

(The symbols in the **main diagonal,** from the top left-hand corner, have been given in bold type to make clear the positional relations.)

Ex. 1: How are the +'s distributed in the matrix of an identical transformation?

Ex. 2: Of the three transformations, which is (a) one-one, (b) single-valued but not one-one, (c) not single-valued?

(i)

↓	A	B	C	D
A	+	0	0	+
B	0	0	+	0
C	+	0	0	0
D	0	+	0	+

(ii)

↓	A	B	C	D
A	0	+	0	0
B	0	0	0	+
C	+	0	0	0
D	0	0	+	0

(iii)

↓	A	B	C	D
A	0	0	0	0
B	+	0	0	+
C	0	+	0	0
D	0	0	+	0

Ex. 3: Can a closed transformation have a matrix with (a) a row entirely of zeros? (b) a column of zeros?

Ex. 4: Form the matrix of the transformation that has $n' = 2n$ and the integers as operands, making clear the distribution of the +'s. Do they lie on a straight line? Draw the graph of $y = 2x$; have the lines any resemblance?

Ex. 5: Take a pack of playing cards, shuffle them, and deal out sixteen cards face upwards in a four-by-four square. Into a four-by-four matrix write + if the card in the corresponding place is black and 0 if it is red. Try some examples and identify the type of each, as in Ex. 2.

Ex. 6: When there are two operands and the transformation is closed, how many different matrices are there?

Ex. 7: (Continued). How many are single-valued?

REPEATED CHANGE

2/11. *Power.* The basic properties of the closed single-valued transformation have now been examined in so far as its single action is concerned; but such a transformation may be applied more than once, generating a series of changes analogous to the series of changes that a dynamic system goes through when active.

16

The generation and properties of such a series must now be considered.

Suppose the second transformation of S.2/3 (call it *Alpha*) has been used to turn an English message into code. Suppose the coded message to be again so encoded by *Alpha*—what effect will this have? The effect can be traced letter by letter. Thus at the first coding *A* became *B*, which, at the second coding, becomes *C*; so over the double procedure *A* has become *C*, or in the usual notation $A \to C$. Similarly $B \to D$; and so on to $Y \to A$ and $Z \to B$. Thus the *double* application of *Alpha* causes changes that are exactly the same as those produced by a *single* application of the transformation

$$\downarrow \begin{matrix} A & B & \ldots & Y & Z \\ C & D & \ldots & A & B \end{matrix}$$

Thus, from each closed transformation we can obtain another closed transformation whose effect, if applied once, is identical with the first one's effect if applied twice. The second is said to be the "square" of the first, and to be one of its "powers" (S.2/14). If the first one was represented by *T*, the second will be represented by T^2; which is to be regarded for the moment as simply a clear and convenient label for the new transformation.

Ex. 1: If Z: $\downarrow \begin{matrix} a & b & c \\ c & c & a \end{matrix}$, what is Z^2?

Ex. 2: Write down some identity transformation; what is its square?

Ex. 3: (See Ex. 2/4/3.) What is A^2?

Ex. 4: What transformation is obtained when the transformation $n' = n + 1$ is applied twice to the positive integers? Write the answer in abbreviated form, as $n' = \ldots$ (Hint: try writing the transformation out in full as in S.2/4.)

Ex. 5: What transformation is obtained when the transformation $n' = 7n$ is applied twice to the positive integers?

Ex. 6: If *K* is the transformation

$\downarrow$	A	B	C
A	0	+	+
B	0	0	0
C	+	0	0

what is K^2? Give the result in matrix form. (Hint: try re-writing *K* in some other form and then convert back.)

Ex. 7: Try to apply the transformation *W* twice:

$$W: \downarrow \begin{matrix} f & g & h \\ g & h & k \end{matrix}$$

17

2/12. The trial in the previous exercise will make clear the importance of closure. An unclosed transformation such as W cannot be applied twice; for although it changes h to k, its effect on k is undefined, so it can go no further. The unclosed transformation is thus like a machine that takes one step and then jams.

2/13. *Elimination.* When a transformation is given in abbreviated form, such as $n' = n + 1$, the result of its double application must be found, if only the methods described so far are used, by re-writing the transformation to show every operand, performing the double application, and then re-abbreviating. There is, however, a quicker method. To demonstrate and explain it, let us write out in full the transformation $T: n' = n + 1$, on the positive integers, showing the results of its double application and, underneath, the general symbol for what lies above:

$$T: \downarrow \begin{array}{ccccc} 1 & 2 & 3 & \dots & n & \dots \\ 2 & 3 & 4 & \dots & n' & \dots \end{array}$$
$$T: \downarrow \begin{array}{ccccc} 3 & 4 & 5 & \dots & n'' & \dots \end{array}$$

n'' is used as a natural symbol for the transform of n', just as n' is the transform of n.

Now we are given that $n' = n + 1$. As we apply the same transformation again it follows that n'' must be 1 more than n'. Thus $n'' = n' + 1$.

To specify the single transformation T^2 we want an equation that will show directly what the transform n'' is in terms of the operand n. Finding the equation is simply a matter of algebraic elimination: from the two equations $n'' = n' + 1$ and $n' = n + 1$, eliminate n'. Substituting for n' in the first equation we get (with brackets to show the derivation) $n'' = (n + 1) + 1$, i.e. $n'' = n + 2$.

This equation gives correctly the relation between operand (n) and transform (n'') when T^2 is applied, and in that way T^2 is specified. For uniformity of notation the equation should now be re-written as $m' = m + 2$. This is the transformation, in standard notation, whose single application (hence the single prime on m) causes the same change as the double application of T. (The change from n to m is a mere change of name, made to avoid confusion.)

The rule is quite general. Thus, if the transformation is $n' = 2n - 3$, then a second application will give second transforms n'' that are related to the first by $n'' = 2n' - 3$. Substitute for n', using brackets freely:

$$n'' = 2(2n - 3) - 3$$
$$= 4n - 9.$$

So the double application causes the same change as a single application of the transformation $m' = 4m - 9$.

2/14. *Higher powers.* Higher powers are found simply by adding symbols for higher transforms, n''', etc., and eliminating the symbols for the intermediate transforms. Thus, find the transformation caused by three applications of $n' = 2n - 3$. Set up the equations relating step to step:

$$n' = 2n - 3$$
$$n'' = 2n' - 3$$
$$n''' = 2n'' - 3$$

Take the last equation and substitute for n'', getting

$$n''' = 2(2n' - 3) - 3$$
$$= 4n' - 9.$$

Now substitute for n':

$$n''' = 4(2n - 3) - 9$$
$$= 8n - 21.$$

So the triple application causes the same changes as would be caused by a single application of $m' = 8m - 21$. If the original was T, this is T^3.

Ex. 1: Eliminate n' from $n'' = 3n'$ and $n' = 3n$. Form the transformation corresponding to the result and verify that two applications of $n' = 3n$ gives the same result.

Ex. 2: Eliminate a' from $a'' = a' + 8$ and $a' = a + 8$.

Ex. 3: Eliminate a'' and a' from $a''' = 7a''$, $a'' = 7a'$, and $a' = 7a$.

Ex. 4: Eliminate k' from $k'' = -3k' + 2$, $k' = -3k + 2$. Verify as in Ex. 1.

Ex. 5: Eliminate m' from $m'' = \log m'$, $m' = \log m$.

Ex. 6: Eliminate p' from $p'' = (p')^2$, $p' = p^2$

Ex. 7: Find the transformations that are equivalent to double applications, on all the positive numbers greater than 1, of:

$$\text{(i) } n' = 2n + 3;$$
$$\text{(ii) } n' = n^2 + n;$$
$$\text{(iii) } n' = 1 + 2\log n.$$

Ex. 8: Find the transformation that is equivalent to a triple application of $n' = -3n - 1$ to the positive and negative integers and zero. Verify as in Ex. 1.

Ex. 9: Find the transformations equivalent to the second, third, and further applications of the transformation $n' = 1/(1 + n)$. (Note: the series discovered by Fibonacci in the 12th century, 1, 1, 2, 3, 5, 8, 13, . . . is extended by taking as next term the sum of the previous two; thus, $3 + 5 = 8$, $5 + 8 = 13$, $8 + 13 = \ldots$, etc.)

19

Ex. 10: What is the result of applying the transformation $n' = 1/n$ twice, when the operands are all the positive rational numbers (i.e. all the fractions)?

Ex. 11: Here is a geometrical transformation. Draw a straight line on paper and mark its ends A and B. This line, in its length and position, is the operand. Obtain its transform, with ends A' and B', by the transformation-rule R: A' is midway between A and B; B' is found by rotating the line $A'B$ about A' through a right angle anticlockwise. Draw such a line, apply R repeatedly, and satisfy yourself about how the system behaves.

*Ex. 12: (Continued). If familiar with analytical geometry, let A start at $(0,0)$ and B at $(1,0)$, and find the limiting position. (Hint: Build up A's final x-co-ordinate as a series, and sum; similarly for A's y-co-ordinate.)

2/15.   *Notation.* The notation that indicates the transform by the addition of a prime ($'$) is convenient if only one transformation is under consideration; but if several transformations might act on n, the symbol n' does not show which one has acted. For this reason, another symbol is sometimes used: if n is the operand, and transformation T is applied, the transform is represented by $T(n)$. The four pieces of type, two letters and two parentheses, represent *one* quantity, a fact that is apt to be confusing until one is used to it. $T(n)$, really n' in disguise, can be transformed again, and would be written $T(T(n))$ if the notation were consistent; actually the outer brackets are usually eliminated and the T's combined, so that n'' is written as $T^2(n)$. The exercises are intended to make this notation familiar, for the change is only one of notation.

Ex. 1: If f: $\downarrow$ $\begin{matrix} 1 & 2 & 3 \\ 3 & 1 & 2 \end{matrix}$

what is $f(3)$? $f(1)$? $f^2(3)$?

Ex. 2: Write out in full the transformation g on the operands, 6, 7, 8, if $g(6) = 8$, $g(7) = 7$, $g(8) = 8$.

Ex. 3: Write out in full the transformation h on the operands α, β, γ, δ, if $h(\alpha) = \gamma$, $h^2(\alpha) = \beta$, $h^3(\alpha) = \delta$, $h^4(\alpha) = \alpha$.

Ex. 4: If $A(n)$ is $n + 2$, what is $A(15)$?

Ex. 5: If $f(n)$ is $-n^2 + 4$, what is $f(2)$?

Ex. 6: If $T(n)$ is $3n$, what is $T^2(n)$? (Hint: if uncertain, write out T *in extenso*.)

Ex. 7: If I is an identity transformation, and t one of its operands, what is $I(t)$?

2/16.   *Product.* We have just seen that after a transformation T has been applied to an operand n, the transform $T(n)$ can be treated as an operand by T again, getting $T(T(n))$, which is written $T^2(n)$. In exactly the same way $T(n)$ may perhaps become operand to a transformation U, which will give a transform $U(T(n))$. Thus, if they are

$$T: \downarrow \begin{matrix} a & b & c & d \\ b & d & a & b \end{matrix} \quad \text{and} \quad U: \downarrow \begin{matrix} a & b & c & d \\ d & c & d & b \end{matrix}$$

then $T(b)$ is d, and $U(T(b))$ is $U(d)$, which is b. T and U applied in that order, thus define a new transformation, V, which is easily found to be

$$V: \downarrow \begin{matrix} a & b & c & d \\ c & b & d & c \end{matrix}$$

V is said to be the **product** or **composition** of T and U. It gives simply the result of T and U being applied in succession, in that order, one step each.

If U is applied first, then $U(b)$ is, in the example above, c, and $T(c)$ is a; so $T(U(b))$ is a, not the same as $U(T(b))$. The product, when U and T are applied in the other order is

$$W: \downarrow \begin{matrix} a & b & c & d \\ b & a & b & d \end{matrix}$$

For convenience, V can be written as UT, and W as TU. It must always be remembered that a change of the order in the product may change the transformation.

(It will be noticed that V may be impossible, i.e. not exist, if some of T's transforms are not operands for U.)

Ex. 1: Write out in full the transformation U^2T.

Ex. 2: Write out in full: UTU.

*Ex. 3: Represent T and U by matrices and then multiply these two matrices in the usual way (rows into columns), letting the product and sum of $+$'s be $+$; call the resulting matrix M_1. Represent V by a matrix; call it M_2. Compare M_1 and M_2.

2/17. *Kinematic graph.* So far we have studied each transformation chiefly by observing its effect, in a single action, on all its possible operands (e.g. S.2/3). Another method (applicable only when the transformation is closed) is to study its effect on a single operand over many, repeated, applications. The method corresponds, in the study of a dynamic system, to setting it at some initial state and then allowing it to go on, without further interference, through such a series of changes as its inner nature determines. Thus, in an automatic telephone system we might observe all the changes that follow the dialling of a number, or in an ants' colony

21

we might observe all the changes that follow the placing of a piece of meat near-by.

Suppose, for definiteness, we have the transformation

$$U: \downarrow \begin{array}{ccccc} A & B & C & D & E \\ D & A & E & D & D \end{array}$$

If U is applied to C, then to $U(C)$, then to $U^2(C)$, then to $U^3(C)$ and so on, there results the series: $C, E, D, D, D, \ldots$ and so on, with D continuing for ever. If U is applied similarly to A there results the series $A, D, D, D, \ldots$ with D continuing again.

These results can be shown graphically, thereby displaying to the glance results that otherwise can be apprehended only after detailed study. To form the **kinematic graph** of a transformation, the set of operands is written down, each in any convenient place, and the elements joined by arrows with the rule that an arrow goes from A to B if and only if A is transformed in one step to B. Thus U gives the kinematic graph

$$C \rightarrow E \rightarrow D \leftarrow A \leftarrow B$$

(Whether D has a re-entrant arrow attached to itself is optional if no misunderstanding is likely to occur.)

If the graph consisted of buttons (the operands) tied together with string (the transitions) it could, as a network, be pulled into different shapes:

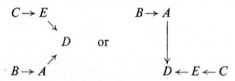

and so on. These different shapes are not regarded as different graphs, provided the internal connexions are identical.

The elements that occur when C is transformed cumulatively by U (the series $C, E, D, D, \ldots$) and the states encountered by a point in the kinematic graph that starts at C and moves over only one arrow at a step, always moving in the direction of the arrow, are obviously always in correspondence. Since we can often follow the movement of a point along a line very much more easily than we can compute $U(C)$, $U^2(C)$, etc., especially if the transformation is complicated, the graph is often a most convenient representation of the transformation in pictorial form. The moving point will be called the **representative** point.

When the transformation becomes more complex an important feature begins to show.   Thus suppose the transformation is

$$T: \downarrow \begin{array}{cccccccccccccccc} A & B & C & D & E & F & G & H & I & J & K & L & M & N & P & Q \\ D & H & D & I & Q & G & Q & H & A & E & E & N & B & A & N & E \end{array}$$

Its kinematic graph is:

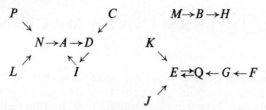

By starting at any state and following the chain of arrows we can verify that, under repeated transformation, the representative point always moves either to some state at which it stops, or to some cycle around which it circulates indefinitely.   Such a graph is like a map of a country's water drainage, showing, if a drop of water or a representative point starts at any place, to what region it will come eventually.   These separate regions are the graph's **basins**.   These matters obviously have some relation to what is meant by "stability", to which we shall come in Chapter 5.

Ex. 1: Draw the kinematic graphs of the transformations of A and B in Ex. 2/4/3.

Ex. 2: How can the graph of an identical transformation be recognised at a glance?

Ex. 3: Draw the graphs of some simple closed one-one transformations.   What is their characteristic feature?

Ex. 4: Draw the graph of the transformation V in which n' is the third decimal digit of $\log_{10}(n + 20)$ and the operands are the ten digits 0, 1, ..., 9.

Ex. 5: (Continued).   From the graph of V read off at once what is $V(8)$, $V^2(4)$, $V^4(6)$, $V^{84}(5)$.

Ex. 6: If the transformation is one-one, can two arrows come to a single point?

Ex. 7: If the transformation is many-one, can two arrows come to a single point?

Ex. 8: Form some closed single-valued transformations like T, draw their kinematic graphs, and notice their characteristic features.

Ex. 9: If the transformation is single-valued, can one basin contain two cycles?

23

Chapter 3

THE DETERMINATE MACHINE

3/1. Having now established a clear set of ideas about transformations, we can turn to their first application: the establishment of an exact parallelism between the properties of transformations, as developed here, and the properties of machines and dynamic systems, as found in the real world.

About the best definition of "machine" there could of course be much dispute. A **determinate machine** is defined as that which behaves in the same way as does a closed single-valued transformation. The justification is simply that the definition works—that it gives us what we want, and nowhere runs grossly counter to what we feel intuitively to be reasonable. The real justification does not consist of what is said in this section, but of what follows in the remainder of the book, and, perhaps, in further developments.

It should be noticed that the definition refers to a way of behaving, not to a material thing. We are concerned in this book with those aspects of systems that are determinate—that follow regular and reproducible courses. It is the determinateness that we shall study, not the material substance. (The matter has been referred to before in Chapter 1.)

Throughout Part I, we shall consider determinate machines, and the transformations to be related to them will all be single-valued. Not until S.9/2 shall we consider the more general type that is determinate only in a statistical sense.

As a second restriction, this Chapter will deal only with the machine in isolation—the machine to which nothing actively is being done.

As a simple and typical example of a determinate machine, consider a heavy iron frame that contains a number of heavy beads joined to each other and to the frame by springs. If the circumstances are constant, and the beads are repeatedly forced to some defined position and then released, the beads' movements will on each occasion be the same, i.e. follow the same path. The whole

24

system, started at a given "state", will thus repeatedly pass through the same succession of states.

By a **state** of a system is meant any well-defined condition or property that can be recognised if it occurs again. Every system will naturally have many possible states.

When the beads are released, their positions (P) undergo a series of changes, P_0, P_1, P_2 ...; this point of view at once relates the system to a transformation:

$$\downarrow \begin{matrix} P_0 & P_1 & P_2 & P_3 & \ldots \\ P_1 & P_2 & P_3 & P_4 & \ldots \end{matrix}$$

Clearly, the *operands* of the transformation correspond to the *states* of the system.

The series of positions taken by the system *in time* clearly corresponds to the series of elements generated by the successive *powers* of the transformation (S.2/14). Such a sequence of states defines a **trajectory** or **line of behaviour.**

Next, the fact that a determinate machine, from one state, cannot proceed to both of two different states corresponds, in the transformation, to the restriction that each transform is single-valued.

Let us now, merely to get started, take some further examples, taking the complications as they come.

A bacteriological culture that has just been inoculated will increase in "number of organisms present" from hour to hour. If at first the numbers double in each hour, the number in the culture will change in the same way hour by hour as n is changed in successive powers of the transformation $n' = 2n$.

If the organism is somewhat capricious in its growth, the system's behaviour, i.e. what state will follow a given state, becomes somewhat indeterminate. So "determinateness" in the real system evidently corresponds, in the transformation, to the transform of a given operand being single-valued.

Next consider a clock, in good order and wound, whose hands, pointing now to a certain place on the dial, will point to some determinate place after the lapse of a given time. The positions of its hands correspond to the transformation's elements. A single transformation corresponds to the progress over a unit interval of time; it will obviously be of the form $n' = n + k$.

In this case, the "operator" at work is essentially undefinable, for it has no clear or natural bounds. It includes everything that makes the clock go: the mainspring (or gravity), the stiffness of the brass in the wheels, the oil on the pivots, the properties of steel, the interactions between atoms of iron, and so on with no definite limit. As we said in S.2/3, the "operator" is often poorly defined and somewhat arbitrary—a concept of little scientific use. The *transformation*, however, is perfectly well defined, for it refers only to the *facts* of the changes, not to more or less hypothetical reasons for them.

A series of changes as regular as those of the clock are not readily found in the biological world, but the regular courses of some diseases show something of the same features. Thus in the days before the sulphonamides, the lung in lobar pneumonia passed typically through the series of states: Infection → consolidation → red hepatisation → grey hepatisation → resolution → health. Such a series of states corresponds to a transformation that is well defined, though not numerical.

Next consider an iron casting that has been heated so that its various parts are at various but determinate temperatures. If its circumstances are fixed, these temperatures will change in a determinate way with time. The casting's state at any one moment will be a set of temperatures (a vector, S.3/5), and the passage from state to state, $S_0 \rightarrow S_1 \rightarrow S_2 \rightarrow \ldots$, will correspond to the operation of a transformation, converting operand S_0 successively to $T(S_0)$, $T^2(S_0)$, $T^3(S_0)$, . . ., etc.

A more complex example, emphasising that transformations do not have to be numerical to be well defined, is given by certain forms of reflex animal behaviour. Thus the male and female three-spined stickleback form, with certain parts of their environment, a determinate dynamic system. Tinbergen (in his *Study of Instinct*) describes the system's successive states as follows: "Each reaction of either male or female is released by the preceding reaction of the partner. Each arrow (in the diagram below) represents a causal relation that by means of dummy tests has actually been proved to exist. The male's first reaction, the zigzag dance, is dependent on a visual stimulus from the female, in which the sign stimuli "swollen abdomen" and the special movements play a part. The female reacts to the red colour of the male and to his zigzag dance by swimming right towards him. This movement induces the male to turn round and to swim rapidly to the nest. This, in turn, entices the female to follow him, thereby stimulating the male to point its head into the entrance. His behaviour now releases the female's next reaction: she enters the nest. . . . This again releases the quivering reaction in the male which induces spawning. The presence of fresh eggs in the nest makes the male fertilise them." Tinbergen summarises the succession of states as follows:

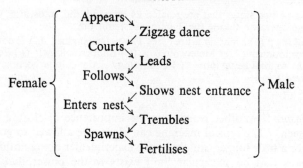

He thus describes a typical trajectory.

Further examples are hardly necessary, for the various branches of science to which cybernetics is applied will provide an abundance, and each reader should supply examples to suit his own speciality.

By relating machine and transformation we enter the discipline that relates the behaviours of real physical systems to the properties of symbolic expressions, written with pen on paper. The whole subject of "mathematical physics" is a part of this discipline. The methods used in this book are however somewhat broader in scope, for mathematical physics tends to treat chiefly systems that are continuous and linear (S.3/7). The restriction makes its methods hardly applicable to biological subjects, for in biology the systems are almost always non-linear, often non-continuous, and in many cases not even metrical, i.e. expressible in number. The exercises below (S.3/4) are arranged as a sequence, to show the gradation from the very general methods used in this book to those commonly used in mathematical physics. The exercises are also important as illustrations of the correspondences between transformations and real systems.

To summarise: Every machine or dynamic system has many distinguishable states. If it is a determinate machine, fixing its circumstances and the state it is at will determine, i.e. make unique, the state it next moves to. These transitions of state correspond to those of a transformation on operands, each state corresponding to a particular operand. Each state that the machine next moves to corresponds to that operand's transform. The successive powers of the transformation correspond, in the machine, to allowing double, treble, etc., the unit time-interval to elapse before recording the next state. And since a determinate machine cannot go to two states at once, the corresponding transformation must be single-valued.

Ex. : Name two states that are related as operand and transform, with time as the operator, taking the dynamic system from :

(a) Cooking; (b) Lighting a fire; (c) The petrol engine; (d) Embryological development; (e) Meteorology; (f) Endocrinology; (g) Economics; (h) Animal behaviour; (i) Cosmology. (Meticulous accuracy is not required.)

3/2. Closure. Another reason for the importance of closure can now be seen. The typical machine can always be allowed to go on in time for a little longer, simply by the experimenter doing nothing! This means that no particular limit exists to the power that the transformation can be raised to. Only the closed transformations allow, in general, this raising to *any* power. Thus the transformation T

$$T: \downarrow \begin{matrix} a & b & c & d & e & f & g \\ e & b & m & f & g & c & f \end{matrix}$$

is not closed. $T^4(a)$ is c and $T^5(a)$ is m. But $T(m)$ is not defined, so $T^6(a)$ is not defined. With a as initial state, this transformation does not define what happens after five steps. Thus *the transformation that represents a machine must be closed.* The full significance of this fact will appear in S.10/4.

3/3. The discrete machine. At this point it may be objected that most machines, whether man-made or natural, are smooth-working, while the transformations that have been discussed so far change by discrete jumps. These discrete transformations are, however, the best introduction to the subject. Their great advantage is their absolute freedom from subtlety and vagueness, for every one of their properties is unambiguously either present or absent. This simplicity makes possible a security of deduction that is essential if further developments are to be reliable. The subject was touched on in S.2/1.

In any case the discrepancy is of no real importance. The discrete change has only to become small enough in its jump to approximate as closely as is desired to the continuous change. It must further be remembered that in natural phenomena the observations are almost invariably made at discrete intervals; the "continuity" ascribed to natural events has often been put there by the observer's imagination, not by actual observation at each of an infinite number of points. Thus the real truth is that *the natural system is observed at discrete points*, and our transformation represents it at discrete points. There can, therefore, be no real incompatibility.

3/4. *Machine and transformation.* The parallelism between machine and transformation is shown most obviously when we compare the machine's behaviour, as state succeeds state, with the kinematic graph (S.2/17), as the arrows lead from element to element. If a particular machine and a particular graph show full correspondence it will be found that:

(1) Each possible state of the machine corresponds uniquely to a particular element in the graph, and vice versa. The correspondence is one-one.

(2) Each succession of states that the machine passes through because of its inner dynamic nature corresponds to an unbroken chain of arrows through the corresponding elements.

(3) If the machine goes to a state and remains there (a state of equilibrium, S.5/3) the element that corresponds to the state will have no arrow leaving it (or a re-entrant one, S.2/17).

(4) If the machine passes into a regularly recurring cycle of states, the graph will show a circuit of arrows passing through the corresponding elements.

(5) The stopping of a machine by the experimenter, and its restarting from some new, arbitrarily selected, state corresponds, in the graph, to a movement of the representative point from one element to another when the movement is due to the arbitrary action of the mathematician and not to an arrow.

When a real machine and a transformation are so related, the transformation is the **canonical representation** of the machine, and the machine is said to **embody** the transformation.

Ex. 1: A culture medium is inoculated with a thousand bacteria; their number doubles in each half-hour. Write down the corresponding transformation.

Ex. 2: (Continued.) Find *n* after the 1st, 2nd, 3rd, . . ., 6th steps.

Ex. 3: (Continued.) (i) Draw the ordinary graph, with two axes, showing the culture's changes in number with time. (ii) Draw the kinematic graph of the system's changes of state.

Ex. 4: 10^9 bacteria are being subjected to a disinfectant that, in each minute, kills 20 per cent of the survivors. Express the change in the number of survivors as a transformation.

Ex. 5: (Continued.) (i) Find the numbers of survivors after 1, 2, 3, 4, 5 minutes. (ii) To what limit does the number tend as time goes on indefinitely?

Ex. 6: Draw the kinematic graph of the transformation in which n' is, in a table of four-figure logarithms, the rounded-off right-hand digit of $\log_{10}(n + 70)$. What would be the behaviour of a corresponding machine?

Ex. 7: (Continued, but with 70 changed to 90.)

Ex. 8: (Continued, but with 70 changed to 10.) How many basins has this graph?

2*   29

Ex. 9: In each decade a country's population diminishes by 10 per cent, but in the same interval a million immigrants are added. Express the change from decade to decade as a transformation, assuming that the changes occur in finite steps.

Ex. 10: (Continued.) If the country at one moment has twenty million inhabitants, find what the population will be at the next three decades.

Ex. 11: (Continued.) Find, in any way you can, at what number the population will remain stationary. (Hint: when the population is "stationary" what relation exists between the numbers at the beginning and at the end of the decade?—what relation between operand and transform?)

Ex. 12: A growing tadpole increases in length each day by 1·2 mm. Express this as a transformation.

Ex. 13: Bacteria are growing in a culture by an assumed simple conversion of food to bacterium; so if there was initially enough food for 10^8 bacteria and the bacteria now number n, then the remaining food is proportional to $10^8 - n$. If the law of mass action holds, the bacteria will increase in each interval by a number proportional to the product: (number of bacteria) × (amount of remaining food). In this particular culture the bacteria are increasing, in each hour, by $10^{-8}n$ ($10^8 - n$). Express the changes from hour to hour by a transformation.

Ex. 14: (Continued.) If the culture now has 10,000,000 bacteria, find what the number will be after 1, 2, . . ., 5 hours.

Ex. 15: (Continued.) Draw an ordinary graph with two axes showing how the number of bacteria will change with time.

VECTORS

3/5. In the previous sections a machine's "state" has been regarded as something that is known as a whole, not requiring more detailed specification. States of this type are particularly common in biological systems where, for instance, characteristic postures or expressions or patterns can be recognised with confidence though no analysis of their components has been made. The states described by Tinbergen in S.3/1 are of this type. So are the types of cloud recognised by the meteorologist. The earlier sections of this chapter will have made clear that *a theory of such unanalysed states can be rigorous.*

Nevertheless, systems often have states whose specification demands (for whatever reason) further analysis. Thus suppose a news item over the radio were to give us the "state", at a certain hour, of a Marathon race now being run; it would proceed to give, for each runner, his position on the road at that hour. These positions, as a set, specify the "state" of the race. So the "state" of the race as a whole is given by the various states (positions) of the various runners, taken simultaneously. Such "compound" states are extremely common, and the rest of the book will be much concerned with them. It should be noticed that we are now beginning to consider the relation, most important in machinery, that exists between the whole and the parts. Thus, it often happens that the state of the whole is given by a list of the states taken, at that moment, by each of the parts.

Such a quantity is a **vector**, which is defined as a compound entity, having a definite number of **components**. It is conveniently written thus: $(a_1, a_2, \ldots, a_n)$, which means that the first component has the particular value a_1, the second the value a_2, and so on.

A vector is essentially a sort of variable, but more complex than the ordinary numerical variable met with in elementary mathematics. It is a natural generalisation of "variable", and is of extreme importance, especially in the subjects considered in this book. The reader is advised to make himself as familiar as possible with it, applying it incessantly in his everyday life, until it has become as ordinary and well understood as the idea of a variable. It is not too much to say that his familiarity with vectors will largely determine his success with the rest of the book.

Here are some well-known examples.

(1) A ship's "position" at any moment cannot be described by a single number; two numbers are necessary: its latitude and its longitude. "Position" is thus a vector with two components. One ship's position might, for instance, be given by the vector (58°N, 17°W). In 24 hours, this position might undergo the transition (58°N, 17°W) → (59°N, 20°W).

(2) "The weather at Kew" cannot be specified by a single number, but can be specified to any desired completeness by our taking sufficient components. An approximation would be the vector: (height of barometer, temperature, cloudiness, humidity), and a particular state might be (998 mbars, 56·2°F, 8, 72%). A weather prophet is accurate if he can predict correctly what state this present state will change to.

(3) Most of the administrative "forms" that have to be filled in are really intended to define some vector. Thus the form that the motorist has to fill in:

> Age of car: ....
> Horse-power: ....
> Colour: ....

is merely a vector written vertically.

Two vectors are considered **equal** only if each component of the one is equal to the corresponding component of the other. Thus if there is a vector (w,x,y,z), in which each component is some number, and if two particular vectors are (4,3,8,2) and (4,3,8,1), then these two particular vectors are unequal; for, in the fourth component, 2 is not equal to 1. (If they have different components, e.g. (4,3,8,2) and (H,T), then they are simply not comparable.)

When such a vector is transformed, the operation is in no way different from any other transformation, provided we remember that *the* operand is the vector as a whole, not the individual components (though how they are to change is, of course, an essential part of the transformation's definition). Suppose, for instance, the "system" consists of two coins, each of which may show either Head or Tail. The system has four states, which are

$$(H,H) \quad (H,T) \quad (T,H) \quad \text{and} \quad (T,T).$$

Suppose now my small niece does not like seeing two heads up, but always alters that to (T,H), and has various other preferences. It might be found that she always acted as the transformation

$$N: \downarrow \begin{array}{cccc} (H,H) & (H,T) & (T,H) & (T,T) \\ (T,H) & (T,T) & (T,H) & (H,H) \end{array}$$

As a transformation on four elements, N differs in no way from those considered in the earlier sections.

There is no reason why a transformation on a set of vectors should not be wholly arbitrary, but often in natural science the transformation has some simplicity. Often the components change in some way that is describable by a more or less simple rule. Thus if M were:

$$M: \downarrow \begin{array}{cccc} (H,H) & (H,T) & (T,H) & (T,T) \\ (T,H) & (T,T) & (H,H) & (H,T) \end{array}$$

it could be described by saying that the first component always changes while the second always remains unchanged.

Finally, nothing said so far excludes the possibility that some or all of the components may themselves be vectors! (E.g. S.6/3.) But we shall avoid such complications if possible.

Ex. 1: Using ABC as first operand, find the transformation generated by repeated application of the operator "move the left-hand letter to the right" (e.g. $ABC \rightarrow BCA$).

Ex. 2: (Continued.) Express the transformation as a kinematic graph.

Ex. 3: Using $(1,-1)$ as first operand, find the other elements generated by repeated application of the operator "interchange the two numbers and then multiply the new left-hand number by minus one".

Ex. 4: (Continued.)　Express the transformation as a kinematic graph.

Ex. 5: The first operand, x, is the vector $(0,1,1)$; the operator F is defined thus:

　　(i) the left-hand number of the transform is the same as the middle number of the operand;

　　(ii) the middle number of the transform is the same as the right-hand number of the operand;

　　(iii) the right-hand number of the transform is the sum of the operand's middle and right-hand numbers.

Thus, $F(x)$ is $(1,1,2)$, and $F^2(x)$ is $(1,2,3)$.　Find $F^3(x)$, $F^4(x)$, $F^5(x)$.　(Hint: compare Ex. 2/14/9.)

3/6.　*Notation.*　The last exercise will have shown the clumsiness of trying to persist in verbal descriptions.　The transformation F is in fact made up of three sub-transformations that are applied simultaneously, i.e. always in step.　Thus one sub-transformation acts on the left-hand number, changing it successively through $0 \rightarrow 1 \rightarrow 1 \rightarrow 2 \rightarrow 3 \rightarrow 5$, etc.　If we call the three components a, b, and c, then F, operating on the vector (a, b, c), is equivalent to the simultaneous action of the three sub-transformations, each acting on one component only:

$$F: \begin{cases} a' = b \\ b' = c \\ c' = b + c \end{cases}$$

Thus, $a' = b$ says that the new value of a, the left-hand number in the transform, is the same as the middle number in the operand; and so on.　Let us try some illustrations of this new method; no new idea is involved, only a new manipulation of symbols.　(The reader is advised to work through all the exercises, since many important features appear, and they are not referred to elsewhere.)

Ex. 1: If the operands are of the form (a,b), and one of them is $(\frac{1}{2},2)$, find the vectors produced by repeated application to it of the transformation T:

$$T: \begin{cases} a' = b \\ b' = -a \end{cases}$$

(Hint: find $T(\frac{1}{2},2)$, $T^2(\frac{1}{2},2)$, etc.)

Ex. 2: If the operands are vectors of the form (v,w,x,y,z) and U is

$$U: \begin{cases} v' = w \\ w' = v \\ x' = x \\ y' = z \\ z' = y \end{cases}$$

find $U(a)$, where $a = (2,1,0,2,2)$.

Ex. 3: (Continued.)　Draw the kinematic graph of U if its only operands are a, $U(a)$, $U^2(a)$, etc.

Ex. 4: (Continued.) How would the graph alter if further operands were added?

Ex. 5: Find the transform of $(3,-2,1)$ by A if the general form is (g,h,j) and the transformation is

$$A: \begin{cases} g' = 2g - h \\ h' = h - j \\ j' = g + h \end{cases}$$

Ex. 6: Arthur and Bill agree to have a gamble. Each is to divide his money into two equal parts, and at the umpire's signal each is to pass one part over to the other player. Each is then again to divide his new wealth into two equal parts and at a signal to pass a half to the other; and so on. Arthur started with 8/- and Bill with 4/-. Represent the initial operand by the vector $(8,4)$. Find, in any way you can, all its subsequent transforms.

Ex. 7: (Continued.) Express the transformation by equations as in Ex. 5 above.

Ex. 8: (Continued.) Charles and David decide to play a similar game except that each will hand over a sum equal to a half of what *the other* possesses. If they start with 30/- and 34/- respectively, what will happen to these quantities?

Ex. 9: (Continued.) Express the transformation by equations as in Ex. 5.

Ex. 10: If, in Ex. 8, other sums of money had been started with, who in general would be the winner?

Ex. 11: In an aquarium two species of animalcule are prey and predator. In each day, each predator destroys one prey, and also divides to become two predators. If today the aquarium has m prey and n predators, express their changes as a transformation.

Ex. 12: (Continued.) What is the operand of this transformation?

Ex. 13: (Continued.) If the state was initially $(150,10)$, find how it changed over the first four days.

Ex. 14: A certain pendulum swings approximately in accordance with the transformation $x' = \frac{1}{2}(x - y)$, $y' = \frac{1}{2}(x + y)$, where x is its angular deviation from the vertical and y is its angular velocity; x' and y' are their values one second later. It starts from the state $(10,10)$; find how its angular deviation changes from second to second over the first eight seconds. (Hint: find x', x'', x''', etc.; can they be found without calculating y', y'', etc?)

Ex. 15: (Continued.) Draw an ordinary graph (with axes for x and t) showing how x's value changed with time. Is the pendulum frictionless?

Ex. 16: In a certain economic system a new law enacts that at each yearly readjustment the wages shall be raised by as many shillings as the price index exceeds 100 in points. The economic effect of wages on the price index is such that at the end of any year the price index has become equal to the wage rate at the beginning of the year. Express the changes of wage-level and price-index over the year as a transformation.

Ex. 17: (Continued.) If this year starts with the wages at 110 and the price index at 110, find what their values will be over the next ten years.

Ex. 18: (Continued.) Draw an ordinary graph to show how prices and wages will change. Is the law satisfactory?

Ex. 19: (Continued.) The system is next changed so that its transformation becomes $x' = \frac{1}{2}(x + y)$, $y' = \frac{1}{2}(x - y) + 100$. It starts with wages and prices both at 110. Calculate what will happen over the next ten years.

Ex. 20: (Continued.) Draw an ordinary graph to show how prices and wages will change.

Ex. 21: Compare the graphs of Exs. 18 and 20. How would the distinction be described in the vocabulary of economics?

Ex. 22: If the system of Ex. 19 were suddenly disturbed so that wages fell to 80 and prices rose to 120, and then left undisturbed, what would happen over the next ten years? (Hint: use (80,120) as operand.)

Ex. 23: (Continued.) Draw an ordinary graph to show how wages and prices would change after the disturbance.

Ex. 24: Is transformation T one-one between the vectors (x_1, x_2) and the vectors (x_1', x_2')?

$$T: \begin{cases} x_1' = 2x_1 + x_2 \\ x_2' = x_1 + x_2 \end{cases}$$

(Hint: If (x_1, x_2) is given, is (x_1', x_2') uniquely determined? And vice versa?)

*Ex. 25: Draw the kinematic graph of the 9-state system whose components are residues:

$$\left. \begin{array}{l} x' = x + y \\ y' = y + 2 \end{array} \right\} \text{ (Mod 3)}$$

How many basins has it?

3/7. (This section may be omitted.) The previous section is of fundamental importance, for it is an introduction to the methods of mathematical physics, as they are applied to dynamic systems. The reader is therefore strongly advised to work through *all* the exercises, for only in this way can a real grasp of the principles be obtained. If he has done this, he will be better equipped to appreciate the meaning of this section, which summarises the method.

The physicist starts by naming his variables—x_1, x_2, ... x_n. The basic equations of the transformation can then always be obtained by the following fundamental method:—

(1) Take the first variable, x_1, and consider what state it will change to next. If it changes by finite steps the next state will be x_1', if continuously the next state will be $x_1 + dx_1$. (In the latter case he may, equivalently, consider the value of dx_1/dt.)

(2) Use what is known about the system, and the laws of physics, to express the value of x_1', or dx_1/dt (i.e. what x_1 *will be*) in terms of the values that x_1, ..., x_n (and any other necessary factors) have *now*. In this way some equation such as

$$x_1' = 2\alpha x_1 - x_3 \quad \text{or} \quad dx_1/dt = 4k \sin x_3$$

is obtained.

(3) Repeat the process for each variable in turn until the whole transformation is written down.

The set of equations so obtained—giving, for each variable in the system, what it will be as a function of the present values of the variables and of any other necessary factors—is the **canonical representation** of the system. *It is a standard form to which all descriptions of a determinate dynamic system may be brought.*

If the functions in the canonical representation are all linear, the system is said to be **linear.**

Given an initial state, the trajectory or line of behaviour may now be computed by finding the powers of the transformation, as in S.3/9.

*Ex. 1: Convert the transformation (now in canonical form)

$$dx/dt = y$$
$$dy/dt = z$$
$$dz/dt = z + 2xy - x^2$$

to a differential equation of the third order in one variable, x. (Hint: Eliminate y and z and their derivatives.)

*Ex. 2: The equation of the simple harmonic oscillator is often written

$$\frac{d^2x}{dt^2} + ax = 0$$

Convert this to canonical form in two independent variables. (Hint: Invert the process used in Ex. 1.)

*Ex. 3: Convert the equation

$$x\frac{d^2x}{dt^2} - (1 - x^2)\frac{dx}{dt} + \frac{2}{1 + x^2} = 0$$

to canonical form in two variables.

3/8. After this discussion of differential equations, the reader who is used to them may feel that he has now arrived at the "proper" way of representing the effects of time, the arbitrary and discrete tabular form of S.2/3 looking somewhat improper at first sight. He should notice, however, that the algebraic way is a restricted way, applicable only when the phenomena show the special property of continuity (S.7/20). The tabular form, on the other hand, can be used *always*; for *the tabular form includes the algebraic.* This is of some importance to the biologist, who often has to deal with phenomena that will not fit naturally into the algebraic form. When this happens, he should remember that the tabular form can always provide the generality, and the rigour, that he needs. The rest of this book will illustrate in many ways how naturally and easily the tabular form can be used to represent biological systems.

3/9. *"Unsolvable" equations.* The exercises to S.3/6 will have shown beyond question that if a closed and single-valued transformation is given, and also an initial state, then the trajectory from that state is both determined (i.e. single-valued) and can be found by computation. For if the initial state is x and the transformation T, then the successive values (the trajectory) of x is the series

$$x, T(x), T^2(x), T^3(x), T^4(x), \text{ and so on.}$$

This process, of deducing a trajectory when given a transformation and an initial state, is, mathematically, called "integrating" the transformation. (The word is used especially when the transformation is a set of differential equations, as in S.3/7; the process is then also called "solving" the equations.)

If the reader has worked all through S.3/6, he is probably already satisfied that, given a transformation and an initial state, he can *always* obtain the trajectory. He will not therefore be discouraged if he hears certain differential equations referred to as "non-integrable" or "unsolvable". These words have a purely technical meaning, and mean only that the trajectory cannot be obtained if one is restricted to certain defined mathematical operations. Tustin's *Mechanism of Economic Systems* shows clearly how the economist may want to study systems and equations that are of the type called "unsolvable"; and he shows how the economist can, in practice, get what he wants.

3/10. *Phase space.* When the components of a vector are numerical variables, the transformation can be shown in geometric form; and this form sometimes shows certain properties far more clearly and obviously than the algebraic forms that have been considered so far.

As example of the method, consider the transformation

$$x' = \tfrac{1}{2}x + \tfrac{1}{2}y$$
$$y' = \tfrac{1}{2}x + \tfrac{1}{2}y$$

of Ex. 3/6/7. If we take axes x and y, we can represent each particular vector, such as (8,4), by the point whose x-co-ordinate is 8 and whose y-co-ordinate is 4. The state of the system is thus represented initially by the point P in Fig. 3/10/1 (I).

The transformation changes the vector to (6,6), and thus changes the system's state to P'. The movement is, of course, none other than the change drawn in the kinematic graph of S.2/17, now drawn in a plane with rectangular axes which contain numerical scales. This two-dimensional space, in which the operands and transforms can be represented by points, is called the **phase-space** of the system. (The "button and string" freedom of S.2/17 is no longer possible.)

In II of the same figure are shown enough arrows to specify generally what happens when *any* point is transformed. Here the arrows show the other changes that would have occurred had other states been taken as the operands. It is easy to see, and to prove geometrically, that all the arrows in this case are given by one rule: with any given point as operand, run the arrow at 45° up and to the left (or down and to the right) till it meets the diagonal represented by the line $y = x$.

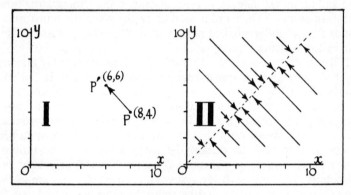

Fig. 3/10/1

The usefulness of the phase-space (II) can now be seen, for the whole range of trajectories in the system can be seen at a glance, frozen, as it were, into a single display. In this way it often happens that some property may be displayed, or some thesis proved, with the greatest ease, where the algebraic form would have been obscure.

Such a representation in a plane is possible only when the vector has two components. When it has three, a representation by a three-dimensional model, or a perspective drawing, is often still useful. When the number of components exceeds three, actual representation is no longer possible, but the principle remains, and a sketch representing such a higher-dimensional structure may still be most useful, especially when what is significant are the general topological, rather than the detailed, properties.

(The words "phase space" are sometimes used to refer to the empty space before the arrows have been inserted, i.e. the space into which *any* set of arrows may be inserted, or the diagram, such as II above, containing the set of arrows appropriate to a particular transformation. The context usually makes obvious which is intended.)

Ex.: Sketch the phase-spaces, with detail merely sufficient to show the main features, of some of the systems in S.3/4 and 6.

3/11.   What is a "*system*"?   In S.3/1 it was stated that every real determinate machine or dynamic system corresponds to a closed, single-valued transformation; and the intervening sections have illustrated the thesis with many examples. It does not, however, follow that the correspondence is always obvious; on the contrary, any attempt to apply the thesis generally will soon encounter certain difficulties, which must now be considered.

Suppose we have before us a particular real dynamic system—a swinging pendulum, or a growing culture of bacteria, or an automatic pilot, or a native village, or a heart-lung preparation—and we want to discover the corresponding transformation, starting from the beginning and working from first principles. Suppose it is actually a simple pendulum, 40 cm long. We provide a suitable recorder, draw the pendulum through 30° to one side, let it go, and record its position every quarter-second. We find the successive deviations to be 30° (initially), 10°, and −24° (on the other side). So our first estimate of the transformation, under the given conditions, is

$$\downarrow \begin{array}{cc} 30° & 10° \\ 10° & -24° \end{array}$$

Next, as good scientists, we check that transition from 10°: we draw the pendulum aside to 10°, let it go, and find that, a quarter-second later, it is at +3°! Evidently the change from 10° is not single-valued—the system is contradicting itself. What are we to do now?

Our difficulty is typical in scientific investigation and is fundamental: we want the transformation to be single-valued but it will not come so. We cannot give up the demand for singleness, for to do so would be to give up the hope of making single-valued predictions. Fortunately, experience has long since shown what is to be done: the system must be re-defined.

At this point we must be clear about how a "system" is to be defined. Our first impulse is to point at the pendulum and to say "the system is that thing there". This method, however, has a fundamental disadvantage: *every material object contains no less than an infinity of variables and therefore of possible systems.* The real pendulum, for instance, has not only length and position; it has also mass, temperature, electric conductivity, crystalline structure, chemical impurities, some radio-activity, velocity, reflecting power, tensile strength, a surface film of moisture, bacterial contamination, an optical absorption, elasticity, shape, specific gravity, and so on and on. Any suggestion that we should study "all" the facts is unrealistic, and actually the attempt is never made. What is necessary is that we should pick out and study the facts that are relevant to some main interest that is already given.

The truth is that in the world around us only certain sets of facts are capable of yielding transformations that are closed and single-valued. The discovery of these sets is sometimes easy, sometimes difficult. The history of science, and even of any single investigation, abounds in examples. Usually the discovery involves the other method for the defining of a system, that of *listing the variables that are to be taken into account*. The **system** now means, not a thing, but a list of variables. This list can be varied, and the experimenter's commonest task is that of varying the list ("taking other variables into account") until he finds a set of variables that gives the required singleness. Thus we first considered the pendulum as if it consisted solely of the variable "angular deviation from the vertical"; we found that the system so defined did not give singleness. If we were to go on we would next try other definitions, for instance the vector:

(angular deviation, mass of bob),

which would also be found to fail. Eventually we would try the vector:

(angular deviation, angular velocity)

and then we would find that *these* states, defined in this way, would give the desired singleness (cf. Ex. 3/6/14).

Some of these discoveries, of the missing variables, have been of major scientific importance, as when Newton discovered the importance of momentum, or when Gowland Hopkins discovered the importance of vitamins (the behaviour of rats on diets was not single-valued until they were identified). Sometimes the discovery is scientifically trivial, as when single-valued results are obtained only after an impurity has been removed from the water-supply, or a loose screw tightened; but the singleness is always essential.

(Sometimes what is wanted is that certain *probabilities* shall be single-valued. This more subtle aim is referred to in S.7/4 and 9/2. It is not incompatible with what has just been said: it merely means that it is the *probability* that is the important variable, not the variable that is giving the probability. Thus, if I study a roulette-wheel scientifically I may be interested in the variable "*probability* of the next throw being Red", which is a variable that has numerical values in the range between 0 and 1, rather than in the variable "*colour* of the next throw", which is a variable that has only two values: Red and Black. A system that includes the latter variable is almost certainly not predictable, whereas one that includes the former (the probability) may well be predictable, for the probability has a *constant* value, of about a half.)

The "absolute" system described and used in *Design for a Brain* is just such a set of variables.

It is now clear why it can be said that *every* determinate dynamic system corresponds to a single-valued transformation (in spite of the fact that we dare not dogmatise about what the real world contains, for it is full of surprises). We can make the statement simply because science refuses to study the other types, such as the one-variable pendulum above, dismissing them as "chaotic" or "non-sensical". It is *we* who decide, ultimately, what we will accept as "machine-like" and what we will reject. (The subject is resumed in S.6/3.)

Chapter 4

THE MACHINE WITH INPUT

4/1. In the previous chapter we studied the relation between transformation and machine, regarding the latter simply as a unit. We now proceed to find, in the world of transformations, what corresponds to the fact that every ordinary machine can be acted on by various conditions, and thereby made to change its behaviour, as a crane can be controlled by a driver or a muscle controlled by a nerve. For this study to be made, a proper understanding must be had of what is meant by a "parameter"

So far, each transformation has been considered by itself; we must now extend our view so as to consider the relation between one transformation and another. Experience has shown that just the same methods (as S.2/3) applied again will suffice; for the change from transformation A to transformation B is nothing but the transition $A \rightarrow B$. (In S.2/3 it was implied that the elements of a transformation may be anything that can be clearly defined: there is therefore no reason why the elements should not themselves be transformations.) Thus, if T_1, T_2, and T_3 are three transformations, there is no reason why we should not define the transformation U:

$$U: \downarrow \begin{array}{ccc} T_1 & T_2 & T_3 \\ T_2 & T_2 & T_1 \end{array}$$

All that is necessary for the avoidance of confusion is that the changes induced by the transformation T_1 should not be allowed to become confused with those induced by U; by whatever method is appropriate in the particular case the two sets of changes must be kept conceptually distinct.

An actual example of a transformation such as U occurs when a boy has a toy-machine T_1, built of interchangeable parts, and then dismantles it to form a new toy-machine T_2. (In this case the changes that occur when T_1 goes from one of its states to the next (i.e. when T_1 "works") are clearly distinguishable from the change that occurs when T_1 changes to T_2.)

Changes from transformation to transformation may, in general, be wholly arbitrary. We shall, however, be more concerned with

formation must tell what they are to be changed to. So all quantities that appear on the right, but not on the left, must be parameters. The examples below will clarify the facts.

Ex. 1: What are the three transformations obtained by giving parameter a the values -1, 0, or $+1$ in T_a:

$$T_a: \begin{cases} g' = (1-a)g + (a-1)h \\ h' = \quad 2g + \quad 2ah. \end{cases}$$

Ex. 2: What are the two transformations given when the parameter α takes the value 0 or 1 in S?:

$$S: \begin{cases} h' = (1-\alpha)j + \log(1+\alpha+\sin \alpha h) \\ j' = (1+\sin \alpha j)e^{(a-1)h}. \end{cases}$$

Ex. 3: The transducer $n' = n + a^2$, in which a and n can take only positive integral values, is started at $n = 10$. (i) At what value should a be kept if, in spite of repeated transformations, n is to remain at 10? (ii) At what value should a be kept if n is to advance in steps of 4 at a time (i.e. 10, 14, 18, . . .)? (iii) What values of a, chosen anew at each step, will make n follow the series 10, 11, 15, 16, 20, 21, 25, 26, . . ., in which the differences are alternately 1 and 4? (iv) What values of a will make n advance by unit steps to 100 and then jump directly to 200?

Ex. 4: If a transducer has n operands and also a parameter that can take n values, the set shows a **triunique** correspondence between the values of operand, transform, and parameter if (1) for given parameter value the transformation is one-one, and (2) for given operand the correspondence between parameter-value and transform is one-one. Such a set is

↓	a	b	c	d
R_1	c	d	a	b
R_2	b	a	c	d
R_3	d	c	b	a
R_4	a	b	d	c

Show that the transforms must form a Latin square, i.e. one in which each row (and each column) contains each transform once and once only.

Ex. 5: A certain system of one variable V behaves as

$$V' = \frac{1}{10}\left(V + \frac{90}{P}\right),$$

where P is a parameter. Set P at some value P_1, e.g. 10, and find the limit that V tends to as the transformation is repeated indefinitely often; call this limit V_1. Then set P at another value P_2, e.g. 3, and find the corresponding limit V_2. After several such pairs of values (of P and limit-V) have been found, examine them to see if any law holds between them. Does V behave like the volume of a gas when subjected to a pressure P?

Ex. 6: What transformation, with a parameter a, will give the three series of values to n?:

$$a = 1: \quad 0, \rightarrow 1, \rightarrow \; 2, \rightarrow \; 3, \rightarrow \; 4, \ldots$$
$$a = 2: \quad 0, \rightarrow 4, \rightarrow \; 8, \rightarrow 12, \rightarrow 16, \ldots$$
$$a = 3: \quad 0, \rightarrow 9, \rightarrow 18, \rightarrow 27, \rightarrow 36, \ldots$$

(Hint: Try some plausible expressions such as $n' = n + a$, $n' = a^2n$, etc.)

Ex. 7: If $n' = n + 3a$, does the value given to a determine how large is n's jump at each step?

45

4/3. When the expression for a transducer contains more than one parameter, the number of distinct transformations may be as large as the number of combinations of values possible to the parameters (for each combination may define a distinct transformation), but can never exceed it.

Ex. 1: Find all the transformations in the transducer U_{ab} when a can take the values 0, 1, or 2, and b the values 0 or 1.

$$U_{ab}: \begin{cases} s' = (1 - a)s + abt \\ t' = (1 + b)t + (b - 1)a. \end{cases}$$

How many transformations does the set contain?

Ex. 2: (Continued.) If the vector (a,b) could take only the values (0,1), (1,1), and (2,0), how many transformations would the transducer contain?

Ex. 3: The transducer T_{ab}, with variables p and q:

$$T_{ab}: \begin{cases} p' = ap + bq \\ q' = bp + aq \end{cases}$$

is started at (3,5). What values should be given to the parameters a and b if (p,q) is to move, at one step, to (4,6)? (Hint: the expression for T_{ab} can be regarded as a simultaneous equation.)

Ex. 4: (Continued.) Next find a value for (a,b) that will make the system move, in one step, back from (4,6) to (3,5).

Ex. 5: The transducer $n' = abn$ has parameters a and b, each of which can take any of the values 0, 1, and 2. How many distinct transformations are there? (Such indistinguishable cases are said tc be "degenerate"; the rule given at the beginning of this section refers to the maximal number of transformations that are possible; the maximal number need not always be achieved).

4/4. *Input and output.* The word "transducer" is used by the physicist, and especially by the electrical engineer, to describe any determinate physical system that has certain defined places of input, at which the experimenter may enforce changes that affect its behaviour, and certain defined places of output, at which he observes the changes of certain variables, either directly or through suitable instruments. It will now be clear that the mathematical system described in S.4/1 is the natural representation of such a material system. It will also be clear that the machine's "input" corresponds to the set of states provided by its parameters; for as the parameters or input are altered so is the machine's or transducer's behaviour affected.

With an electrical system, the input is usually obvious and restricted to a few terminals. In biological systems, however, the number of parameters is commonly very large and the whole set of them is by no means obvious. It is, in fact, co-extensive with the set of "all variables whose change directly affects the organism". The parameters thus include the conditions in which the organism lives. In the chapters that follow, the reader must therefore be prepared to interpret the word "input" to mean either the few parameters appropriate to a simple mechanism or the many parameters appropriate to the free-living organism in a complex environment. (The increase in the number of parameters does not necessarily imply any diminution in the rigour of the argument, for all the quantities concerned can be measured with an accuracy that is bounded only by the experimenter's resources of time and money.)

Ex. 1: An electrical machine that receives potentials on its two input-terminals is altered by having the two terminals joined permanently by a wire. To what alteration in T_{ab} would this correspond if the machine were represented as in Ex. 4/3/3?

Ex. 2: "When an organism interacts with its environment, its muscles are the environment's input and its sensory organs are the environment's output." Do you agree?

4/5. *Transient.* The electrical engineer and the biologist tend to test their systems by rather different methods. The engineer often investigates the nature of some unknown system by submitting it to an incessant regular change at its input while observing its output. Thus, in Fourier analysis, he submits it to prolonged stimulation by a regular sinusoidal potential of a selected frequency, and he observes certain characteristics in the output; then he repeats the test with another frequency, and so on; eventually he deduces something of the system's properties from the relations between the input-frequencies and the corresponding output-characteristics. During this testing, the machine is being disturbed incessantly.

The biologist often uses a method that disturbs the system not at all, after the initial establishment of the conditions. Thus he may put a piece of meat near an ants' colony and then make no further change whatever—keeping the conditions, the parameters, constant —while watching the whole evolution of the complex patterns of behaviour, individual and social, that develop subsequently.

Contrary to what is observed in living systems, the behaviour of mechanical and electrical systems often settles to some uniformity fairly quickly from the moment when incessant change at the input stops. The response shown by the machine after some disturbance, the input being subsequently held constant, is called a transient. It is important to appreciate that, to the engineer, the complex sequence of events at the ants' nest is a transient. It may be defined in more general terms as the sequence of states produced by a transducer in constant conditions before the sequence starts repeating itself.

To talk about the transient, as distinct from the repetitive part that follows, it is convenient to be able to mark, unambiguously, its end. If the transformation is discrete, the following method gives its length rigorously: Let the sequence of states go on till repetition becomes evident, thus

A B C D C D C D C D C... or H E F G G G G G G G...

Then, coming in from the right, make the mark "1" as soon as the sequence departs from the cycle, thus

A B^1 C D C D C D C D C... or H E F^1 G G G G G G G...

Next add the mark "2", to the right of 1, to include one complete cycle, thus

A B^1 C D^2 C D C D C D C... or H E F^1 G^2 G G G G G G G...

Then the **transient** is defined as the sequence of states from the initial state to the mark 2: A B C D, or H E F G.

Rigorous form can now be given to the intuitive impression that complex systems can produce, in constant conditions, more complex forms of behaviour than can the simple. By drawing an arbitrary kinematic graph on N states it is easy to satisfy oneself that if a closed single-valued transformation with N operands is applied repeatedly, then *the length of transient cannot exceed N states.*

Ex. 1: What property must the graph have if the onset of a recurrence is to be postponed as long as possible?

Ex. 2: What is the transient of the system of Ex. 3/6/6, started from the state (8,5)?

COUPLING SYSTEMS

4/6. A fundamental property of machines is that they can be coupled. Two or more whole machines can be coupled to form one machine; and any one machine can be regarded as formed by the coupling of its parts, which can themselves be thought of as small, sub-, machines. The coupling is of profound importance in science, for when the experimenter runs an experiment he is coupling himself temporarily to the system that he is studying. To what does this process, the joining of machine to machine or of part to part, correspond in the symbolic form of transformations? Of what does the *operation* of "coupling" consist?

Before proceeding to the answer we must notice that there is more than one answer. One way is to force them roughly together, so that they become "coupled" as two automobiles may be locked together after an accident. This form, however, is of little interest to us, for the automobiles are too much changed by the process. What we want is a way of coupling that does no violence to each machine's inner working, so that after the coupling each machine is still the same machine that it was before.

For this to be so, the coupling must be arranged so that, in principle, each machine affects the other only by affecting its *conditions*, i.e. by affecting its input. Thus, if the machines are to retain their individual natures after being coupled to form a whole, the coupling must be between the (given) inputs and outputs, other parts being left alone no matter how readily accessible they may be.

4/7. Now trace the operation in detail. Suppose a machine (transducer) P is to be joined to another, R. For simplicity, assume that P is going to affect R, without R affecting P, as when a microphone is joined to an amplifier, or a motor nerve grows down to supply an embryonic muscle. We must couple P's output to R's input. Evidently R's behaviour, or more precisely the transformation that describes R's changes of state, will depend on, and change with, the state of P. It follows that R must have parameters, for input, and the values of these parameters must be at each moment some function of the state of P. Suppose for definiteness that the machine or transducer R has the three transformations shown in S.4/1, i.e.

$\downarrow$	a	b	c	d
R_1	c	d	d	b
R_2	b	a	d	c
R_3	d	c	d	b

and that P has the transformation, on the three states i, j, k:

$$P: \downarrow \begin{matrix} i & j & k \\ k & i & i \end{matrix}$$

P and R are now to be joined by our specifying what value R's parameter, call it α, is to take when P has any one of its states. Suppose we decide on the relation Z (a transformation, single-valued but not closed):

$$Z: \begin{cases} \text{state of } P: & \downarrow \begin{matrix} i & j & k \end{matrix} \\ \text{value of } \alpha: & \begin{matrix} 2 & 3 & 2 \end{matrix} \end{cases}$$

(The relation between P and α has been made somewhat irregular to emphasise that the details are quite arbitrary and are completely

49

under the control of whoever arranges the coupling.) Let us further suppose—this is essential to the orderliness of the coupling—that the two machines P and R work on a common time-scale, so that their changes keep in step.

It will now be found that the two machines form *a new machine of completely determined behaviour*. Thus, suppose the whole is started with R at a and P at i. Because P is at i, the R-transformation will be R_2 (by Z). This will turn a to b; P's i will turn to k; so the states a and i have changed determinately to b and k. The argument can now be repeated. With P at k, the R-transformation will again (by Z) be R_2; so b will turn (under R_2) to a, and k will turn (under P) to i. This happens to bring the whole system back to the initial state of (a,i), so the whole will evidently go on indefinitely round this cycle.

The behaviour of the whole machine becomes more obvious if we use the method of S.3/5 and recognise that the state of the whole machine is simply a vector with two components (x,y), where x is one of a, b, c, d and y is one of i, j, k. The whole machine thus has twelve states, and it was shown above that the state (a,i) undergoes the transitions

$$(a,i) \rightarrow (b,k) \rightarrow (a,i) \rightarrow \text{etc.}$$

Ex. 1: If Q is the transformation of the whole machine, of the twelve states (x,y), complete Q.

Ex. 2: Draw Q's kinematic graph. How many basins has it?

Ex. 3: Join P and R by using the transformation Y

$$Y: \begin{cases} \text{state of } P: & i \quad j \quad k \\ \text{value of } \alpha: & \downarrow\ 1 \quad 2 \quad 3 \end{cases}$$

What happens when this machine is started from (a,i)?

Ex. 4: If two machines are joined to form a whole, does the behaviour of the whole depend on the manner of coupling? (Hint: use the previous Ex.)

Ex. 5: If two machines of n_1 and n_2 states respectively are joined together, what is the maximal length of transient that the whole can produce?

Ex. 6: If machine M has a maximal length of transient of n states, what will be the maximal length of transient if a machine is formed by joining three M's together?

Ex. 7: Take many parts $(A, B, C, \ldots)$ each with transformation

$\downarrow$	0	1	2
α	0	2	0
β	1	1	1
γ	2	2	2

and join them into a single long chain

$$\text{input} \rightarrow \boxed{A} \rightarrow \quad \rightarrow \boxed{C} \rightarrow \text{etc.,}$$

so that A affects B, B affects C, and so on, by Z:

$$Z: \downarrow \begin{array}{ccc} 0 & 1 & 2 \\ \alpha & \beta & \gamma \end{array}$$

If the input to A is kept at α, what happens to the states down the chain?

Ex. 8: (Continued.) What happens if the input is now changed for one step to β and then returned to α, where it is held?

4/8. *Coupling with feedback.* In the previous section, P was coupled to R so that P's changes affected, or determined in some way, what R's changes would be, but P's changes did not depend on what state R was at. Two machines can, however, be coupled so that each affects the other.

For this to be possible, each must have an input, i.e. parameters. P had no parameters, so this double coupling cannot be made directly on the machines of the previous section. Suppose, then, that we are going to couple R (as before) to S, given below:

$\downarrow$	a	b	c	d
R_1	c	d	d	b
R_2	b	a	d	c
R_3	d	c	d	b

$\downarrow$	e	f
S_1	f	f
S_2	e	f
S_3	f	f
S_4	f	e

S could be coupled to affect R by Y (if R's parameter is α):

$$Y: \begin{cases} \text{state of } S: & e \quad f \\ \text{value of } \alpha: & \downarrow 3 \quad 1 \end{cases}$$

and R to affect S by X (if S's parameter is β):

$$X: \begin{cases} \text{state of } R: & a \quad b \quad c \quad d \\ \text{value of } \beta: & \downarrow 3 \quad 1 \quad 1 \quad 2 \end{cases}$$

To trace the changes that this new whole machine (call it T) will undergo, suppose it starts at the vector state (a,e). By Y and X, the transformations to be used at the first step are R_3 and S_3. They, acting on a and e respectively, will give d and f; so the new state of the whole machine is (d,f). The next two transformations will be R_1 and S_2, and the next state therefore (b,f); and so on.

Ex. 1: Construct T's kinematic graph.

Ex. 2: Couple S and R in some other way.

Ex. 3: Couple S and R so that S affects R but R does not affect S. (Hint: Consider the effect in X of putting all the values of β the same.)

4/9. *Algebraic coupling.* The process of the previous sections, by treating the changes that each state and parameter undergo individually, shows the relations that are involved in "coupling" with perfect clarity and generality. Various modifications can be developed without any loss of this clarity.

Thus suppose the machines are specified, as is common, in terms of vectors with numerical components; then the rule for coupling remains unaltered: each machine must have one or more parameters, and the coupling is done by specifying *what function these parameters are to be of the other machine's variables.* Thus the machines M and N

$$M: \begin{cases} a' = a^2 + pb \\ b' = -qa \end{cases} \qquad N: \begin{cases} c' = rsc + ud^2 \\ d' = 2tue \\ e' = uce \end{cases}$$

might be joined by the transformations U and V:

$$U: \begin{cases} p = 2c \\ q = de^2 \end{cases} \qquad V: \begin{cases} r = a + b \\ s = a - b \\ t = -a \\ u = b^2 \end{cases}$$

U is a shorthand way of writing a whole set of transitions from a value of (c,d,e) to a value of (p,q), e.g.

$$U: \downarrow \quad \begin{matrix} (0,0,0) & (0,0,1) & (1,3,5) & (2,2,4) \\ (0,0) & (0,0) & (2,75) & (4,32) \end{matrix}$$

Similarly for V, a transformation from (a,b) to (r,s,t,u), which includes, e.g. $(5,7) \rightarrow (12,-2,-5,49)$ (and compare P of S.6/9).

The result of the coupling is the five-variable system with representation:

$$a' = a^2 + 2bc$$
$$b' = -ade^2$$
$$c' = (a^2 - b^2)c + b^2d^2$$
$$d' = -2ab^2e$$
$$e' = b^2ce$$

(Illustrations of the same process with differential equations have been given in *Design for a Brain*, S.21/6.)

Ex. 1.: Which are the parameters in M? Which in N?

Ex. 2.: Join M and N by W and X, and find what state $(1, 0, 0, 1, 0)$, a value of (a, b, c, d, e), will change to:

$$W: \begin{cases} p = d \\ q = c \end{cases} \qquad X: \begin{cases} r = a \\ s = ab \\ t = a \\ u = a \end{cases}$$

4/10. Ex. 4/7/1 has already shown that parts can, in general, be coupled in different ways to form a whole. *The defining of the component parts does not determine the way of coupling.*

From this follows an important corollary. That a whole machine should be built of parts of given behaviour is not sufficient to determine its behaviour as a whole: only when the details of coupling are added does the whole's behaviour become determinate.

FEEDBACK

4/11. In S.4/7, *P* and *R* were joined so that *P* affected *R* while *R* had no effect on *P*. *P* is said to **dominate** *R*, and (to anticipate S.4/12) we may represent the relation between the parts by

$$\boxed{P} \to \boxed{R}$$

(The arrow cannot be confused with that used to represent a transition (S.2/2), for the latter always relates two states, whereas the arrow above relates two parts. In the diagrams to come, parts will always be shown boxed.)

Cybernetics is, however, specially interested in the case of S.4/8, where each affects the other, a relation that may be represented by

$$\boxed{P} \leftrightarrows \boxed{R}$$

When this circularity of action exists between the parts of a dynamic system, **feedback** may be said to be present.

The definition of feedback just given is that most in accord with the spirit of this book, which is concerned essentially with principles.

Other definitions, however, are possible, and there has been some dispute as to the best; so a few words in explanation may be useful. There are two main points of view that have to be considered.

On the one side stand those who are following the path taken by this book—those whose aim is to get an understanding of the *principles* behind the multitudinous special mechanisms that exhibit them. To such workers, "feedback" exists between two parts when each affects the other, as for instance, in

$$x' = 2xy$$
$$y' = x - y^2;$$

for *y*'s value affects how *x* will change and so does *x*'s value affect *y*. By contrast, feedback would not be said to be present in

$$x' = 2x$$
$$y' = x - y^2$$

for x's change does not now depend on y's value; x dominates y, and the action is one way only.

On the other side stand the practical experimenters and constructors, who want to use the word to refer, when some forward effect from P to R can be taken for granted, to the deliberate conduction of some effect back from R to P by some connexion that is physically or materially evident.   They object to the mathematician's definition, pointing out that this would force them to say that feedback was present in the ordinary pendulum (see Ex. 3/6/14) between its position and its momentum—a "feedback" that, from the practical point of view, is somewhat mystical.   To this the mathematician retorts that if feedback is to be considered present only when there is an actual wire or nerve to represent it, then the theory becomes chaotic and riddled with irrelevancies.

In fact, there need be no dispute, for the exact definition of "feedback" is nowhere important.   The fact is that the concept of "feedback", so simple and natural in certain elementary cases, becomes artificial and of little use when the interconnexions between the parts become more complex.   When there are only two parts joined so that each affects the other, the properties of the feedback give important and useful information about the properties of the whole.   But when the parts rise to even as few as four, if every one affects the other three, then twenty circuits can be traced through them; and knowing the properties of all the twenty circuits does *not* give complete information about the system.   Such complex systems cannot be treated as an interlaced set of more or less independent feedback circuits, but only as a whole.

For understanding the general principles of dynamic systems, therefore, the concept of feedback is inadequate in itself.   What is important is that complex systems, richly cross-connected internally, have complex behaviours, and that these behaviours can be goal-seeking in complex patterns.

Ex. 1: Trace twenty circuits in the diagram of Fig. 4/11/1:

Fig. 4/11/1

Ex. 2: A machine with input α, has the transformation

$$T: \begin{cases} x' = y - \alpha z \\ y' = 2z \\ z' = x + \alpha \end{cases}$$

What machine (as transformation) results if its input α is coupled to its output z, by $\alpha = -z$?

Ex. 3: (Continued.) Will this second machine behave differently from the first one when the first has α held permanently at -1?

Ex. 4: A machine has, among its inputs, a photoelectric cell; among its outputs a lamp of variable brightness. In Condition 1 there is no connexion from lamp to cell, either electrical or optical. In Condition 2 a mirror is placed so that variations in the lamp's brightness cause variations in the cell's potential (i.e. so that the machine can "see itself"). Would you expect the behaviours in Conditions 1 and 2 to differ? (Hint: compare with Ex. 3.)

INDEPENDENCE WITHIN A WHOLE

4/12. In the last few sections the concept of one machine or part or variable "having an effect on" another machine or part or variable has been used repeatedly. It must now be made precise, for it is of profound importance. What does it mean in terms of actual operations on a given machine? The process is as follows.

Suppose we are testing whether part or variable i has an immediate effect on part or variable j. Roughly, we let the system show its behaviour, and we notice whether the behaviour of part j is changed when part i's value is changed. If part j's behaviour is just the same, whatever i's value, then we say, in general, that i has no effect on j.

To be more precise, we pick on some one state S (of the whole system) first. With i at some value we notice the transition that occurs in part j (ignoring those of other variables). We compare this transition with those that occur when states S_1, S_2, etc.—other than S—are used, in which S_1, S_2, etc. differ from S *only in the value of the i-th component.* If S_1, S_2, etc., give the same transition in part j as S, then we say that *i has no immediate effect on j,* and vice versa. ("Immediate" effect because we are considering j's values over only one step of time.)

Next consider what the concept means in a transformation. Suppose its elements are vectors with four components (u,x,y,z), and that the third line of the canonical equations reads

$$y' = 2uy - z.$$

This tells us that if y is at some value now, the particular value it will be at at the next step will depend on what values u and z have, but will not depend on what value x has. The variables u and z are said to have an **immediate effect** on y.

It should be noticed, if the rigour is to be maintained, that the presence or absence of an immediate effect, of u on y say, can be stated primarily only for *two given states*, which must have the same values in their x, y, and z-components and must differ in their u-components. For an immediate effect at one pair of states does not, in general, restrict the possibilities at another pair of states. Thus, the transformation mentioned above gives the transitions:

$$(0,0,0,0) \rightarrow (\ , \ ,0, \ )$$
$$(1,0,0,0) \rightarrow (\ , \ ,0, \ )$$
$$(0,0,1,0) \rightarrow (\ , \ ,0, \ )$$
$$(1,0,1,0) \rightarrow (\ , \ ,2, \ )$$

(where irrelevant values have been omitted). The first two show that in one region of space u does *not* have an immediate effect on y, and the second two show that in another region it does. Strictly, therefore, the question "what is the immediate effect of u on y?" can be answered only for a given pair of states. Often, in simple systems, the same answer is given over the whole phase space; if this should happen we can then describe the immediate effect of u on y unconditionally. Thus in the example above, u *has* an immediate effect on y at all points but a particular few.

This test, for u's immediate effect on y, simply does in symbols what the experimenter does when he wishes to test whether one variable has an immediate effect on another: he fixes all variables except this pair, and compares how one behaves when the other has a value u_1 with how it behaves when the other has the value u_2.

The same method is, in fact, used generally in everyday life. Thus, if we go into a strange room and wish to turn on the light, and find there are three switches, our problem is to find which switches are and which are not having an effect on the light's behaviour. We *change* one of the switches and observe whether this is followed by a *change* in the light's behaviour. In this way we discover on which switch the light is dependent.

The test thus accords with common sense and has the advantage of being applicable and interpretable even when we know nothing of the real physical or other factors at work. It should be noticed that the test requires no knowledge of extraneous factors: the result is deduced directly from the system's observed behaviour, and depends only on *what* the system does, not on *why* it does it.

It was noticed above that a transducer may show any degree of arbitrariness in the distribution of the immediate effects over the phase space. Often, however, the distribution shows continuity, so that over some appreciable region, the variable u, say, has an immediate effect on y while over the same region x has none. When this occurs, a diagram can often usefully be drawn showing these relations as they hold over the region (which may sometimes be the whole phase-space). An arrow is drawn from u to y if and only if u has an immediate effect on y. Such a diagram will be called the **diagram of immediate effects.**

Such diagrams are already of common occurrence. They are often used in physiology to show how a related set of variables (such as blood pressure, pulse rate, secretion of adrenaline, and activity at the carotid sinus) act on one another. In the design of computing machines and servomechanisms they are known as "control-flow charts". They are also used in some large businesses to show the relations of control and information existing between the various departments.

The arrow used in such a diagram is, of course, profoundly different in meaning from the arrow used to show change in a transition (S.2/2). In the latter case it means simply that one state changes to another; but the arrow in the diagram of immediate effects has a much more complex meaning. In this case, an arrow from A to B says that if, over a series of tests, A has a variety of different values—B and all other conditions starting with the same value throughout—then the values that B changes to over the series will also be found to show variety. We shall see later (S.8/11) that this is simply to say that a *channel of communication* goes from A to B.

When a transducer is given, either in algebraic or real material form, we can examine the immediate effects within the system and thus deduce something of its internal organisation and structure. In this study we must distinguish carefully between "immediate" and "ultimate" effects. In the test given above, the effect of x on y was considered over a single step only, and this restriction is necessary in the basic theory. x was found to have no immediate effect on y; it may however happen that x has an immediate effect on u and that u has an immediate effect on y; then x does have some effect on y, shown after a delay of one extra step. Such an effect, and those that work through even longer chains of variables and with longer delay, will be referred to as **ultimate** effects. A **diagram of ultimate effects** can be constructed by drawing an arrow from A to B if and only if A has an ultimate effect on B. The two diagrams are simply related, for the diagram of immediate effects, if altered by the addition of another arrow wherever there are two joined head to tail, turning

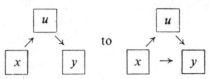

and continuing this process until no further additions are possible, gives the diagram of ultimate effects.

If a variable or part has no ultimate effect on another, then the second is said to be **independent** of the first.

Both the diagrams, as later examples will show, have features corresponding to important and well-known features of the system they represent.

Ex. 1: Draw the diagrams of immediate effects of the following absolute systems; and notice the peculiarity of each:

    (i) $x' = xy, y' = 2y$.
    (ii) $x' = y, y' = z + 3, z' = x^2$.
    (iii) $u' = 2 + ux, v' = v - y, x' = u + x, y' = y + v^2$.
    (iv) $u' = 4u - 1, x' = ux, y' = xy + 1, z' = yz$.
    (v) $u' = u + y, x' = 1 - y, y' = \log y, z' = z + yz$.
    (vi) $u' = \sin 2u, x' = x^2, y' = y + 1, z' = xy + u$.

Ex. 2: If $y' = 2uy - z$, under what conditions does u have no immediate effect on y?

Ex. 3: Find examples of real machines whose parts are related as in the diagrams of immediate effects of Ex. 1.

Ex. 4: (Continued.) Similarly find examples in social and economic systems.

Ex. 5: Draw up a table to show all possible ways in which the kinematic graph and the diagram of immediate effects are different.

4/13. In the discussion of the previous section, the system was given by algebraic representation; when described in this form, the deduction of the diagram of immediate effects is easy. It should be noticed, however, that the diagram can also be deduced directly from the transformation, even when this is given simply as a set of transitions.

Suppose, for instance that a system has two variables, x and y, each of which can take the values 0, 1 or 2, and that its (x,y)-states behave as follows (parentheses being omitted for brevity):

$$\begin{array}{c c c c c c c c c}
\downarrow & 00 & 01 & 02 & 10 & 11 & 12 & 20 & 21 & 22 \\
& 01 & 00 & 11 & 11 & 00 & 21 & 11 & 20 & 11
\end{array}$$

What of y's transitions? We can re-classify them, with x as parameter, by representing, e.g. "00 → 01" as "when $x = 0$, y goes from 0 to 1". This gives the table

$$y$$

↓	0	1	2
0	1	0	1
x 1	1	0	1
2	1	0	1

It shows at once that y's transitions do not depend on the value of x. So x has no immediate effect on y.

Now classify x's transitions similarly. We get:

$$x$$

↓	0	1	2
0	1	1	1
y 1	0	0	2
2	1	2	1

What x will do (i.e. x's transition) *does* depend on y's value, so y has an immediate effect on x.

Thus, the diagram of immediate effects can be deduced from a statement of the primary transitions. It is, in fact,

$$\boxed{y} \rightarrow \boxed{x}$$

and y has been *proved* to dominate x.

> *Ex.*: A system has three variables—x, y, z—each of which can take only the values 0 or 1. If the transformation is
>
> | ↓ | 000 | 001 | 010 | 011 | 100 | 101 | 110 | 111 |
> |---|-----|-----|-----|-----|-----|-----|-----|-----|
> | | 110 | 111 | 100 | 101 | 110 | 011 | 100 | 001 |
>
> what is the diagram of immediate effects? (Hint: First find how z's transitions depend on the values of the others.)

4/14. *Reducibility.* In S.4/11 we noticed that a whole system may consist of two parts each of which has an immediate effect on the other:

$$\boxed{P} \rightleftarrows \boxed{Q}$$

We also saw that the action may be only one way, in which case one part dominates the other:

$$\boxed{P} \rightarrow \boxed{Q}$$

In this case the whole is less richly connected internally, for one of the actions, or channels, is now missing.

The lessening can continue. We may find that the diagram of immediate effects is simply

P		Q

so that the whole consists really of two parts that are functionally independent. In this case the whole is said to be **reducible.** The importance of this concept will be referred to later (S.13/21).

Ex.: Of the systems in Ex. 4/12/1, which are reducible?

4/15. *Materiality.* The reader may now like to test the methods of this chapter as an aid to solving the problem set by the following letter. It justifies the statement made in S.1/2 that cybernetics is not bound to the properties found in terrestrial matter, nor does it draw its laws from them. What is important in cybernetics is the extent to which the observed behaviour is regular and reproducible.

"Graveside"
Wit's End
Haunts.

Dear Friend,

Some time ago I bought this old house, but found it to be haunted by two ghostly noises—a ribald Singing and a sardonic Laughter. As a result it is hardly habitable. There is hope, however, for by actual testing I have found that their behaviour is subject to certain laws, obscure but infallible, and that they can be affected by my playing the organ or burning incense.

In each minute, each noise is either sounding or silent— they show no degrees. What each will do during the ensuing minute depends, in the following exact way, on what has been happening during the preceding minute:

The Singing, in the succeeding minute, will go on as it was during the preceding minute (sounding or silent) unless there was organ-playing with no Laughter, in which case it will change to the opposite (sounding to silent, or vice versa).

As for the Laughter, if there was incense burning, then it will sound or not according as the Singing was sounding or not (so that the Laughter copies the Singing a minute later). If however there was no incense burning, the Laughter will do the opposite of what the Singing did.

At this minute of writing, the Laughter and Singing are both sounding. Please tell me what manipulations of incense and organ I should make to get the house quiet, and to keep it so.

(Hint: Compare Ex. 4/1/4.)

Ex. 2: (Continued.) Does the Singing have an immediate effect on the Laughter?
Ex. 3: (Continued.) Does the incense have an immediate effect on the Singing?
Ex. 4: (Continued.) Deduce the diagram of immediate effects of this machine with input (with two parameters and two variables).

THE VERY LARGE SYSTEM

4/16. Up till now, the systems considered have all seemed fairly simple, and it has been assumed that at all times we have understood them in all detail.   Cybernetics, however, looks forward to being able to handle systems of vastly greater complexity—computing machines, nervous systems, societies.   Let us, then, consider how the methods developed so far are to be used or modified when the system is very large.

4/17. What is meant by its "size" needs clarification, for we are not here concerned with mere mass.   The sun and the earth form only a "small" system to us, for astronomically they have only twelve degrees of freedom.   Rather, we refer to the system's complexity. But what does that mean here?   If our dynamic system were a native family of five persons, would we regard it as made of 5 parts, and therefore simple, or as of 10^{25} atoms, and therefore very complex?

In the concepts of cybernetics, a system's "largeness" must refer to the number of *distinctions* made: either to the number of states available or, if its states are defined by a vector, to the number of components in the vector (i.e. to the number of its variables or of its degrees of freedom, S.7/13).   The two measures are correlated, for if other things are equal, the addition of extra variables will make possible extra states.   A system may also be made larger from our functional point of view if, the number of variables being fixed, each is measured more precisely, so as to make it show more distinguishable states.   We shall not, however, be much interested in any exact measure of largeness on some particular definition; rather we shall refer to a relation between the system and some definite, given, observer who is going to try to study or control it.   In this book I shall use the words "very large" to imply that some definite observer is given, with definite resources and techniques, and that the system is, in some practical way, too large for him; so that he cannot observe it completely, or control it completely, or carry out the calculations for prediction completely. In other words, he says the system is "very large" if in some way it beats *him* by its richness and complexity.

Such systems are common enough. A classic case occurred when the theoretical physicist of the nineteenth century tried to use Newtonian mechanics to calculate how a gas would behave. The number of particles in an ordinary volume of gas is so vast that no practical observation could record the system's state, and no practical calculation could predict its future. Such a system was "very large" in relation to the nineteenth century physicist.

The stock-breeder faces a "very large" system in the genes he is trying to mould to a new pattern. Their number and the complexities of their interactions makes a *detailed* control of them by him impossible in practice.

Such systems, in relation to our present resources for observation and control, are very common in the biological world, and in its social and economic relatives. They are certainly common in the brain, though for many years the essential complexity was given only grudging recognition. It is now coming to be recognised, however, that this complexity is something that can be ignored no longer. "Even the simplest bit of behavior", says Lashley, "requires the integrated action of millions of neurons. . . . I have come to believe that almost every nerve cell in the cerebral cortex may be excited in every activity. . . . The same neurons which maintain the memory traces and participate in the revival of a memory are also involved, in different combinations, in thousands of other memories and acts." And von Neumann: "The number of neurons in the central nervous system is somewhere of the order of 10^{10}. We have absolutely no past experience with systems of this degree of complexity. All artificial automata made by man have numbers of parts which by any comparably schematic count are of the order 10^3 to 10^6." (*Cerebral Mechanisms in Behavior.*)

4/18. It should be noticed that largeness *per se* in no way invalidates the principles, arguments, and theorems of the previous chapters. Though the *examples* have been confined to systems with only a few states or a few variables, this restriction was solely for the author's and reader's convenience: the arguments remain valid without any restriction on the number of states or variables in the system. It is a peculiar advantage of the method of arguing about states, rather than the more usual variables, that it requires no explicit mention of the system's number of parts; and theorems once proved true are true for systems of all sizes (provided, of course, that the systems conform to the suppositions made in the argument).

What remains valid is, of course, the truth of the mathematical deductions about the *mathematically defined* things. What may change, as the system becomes very large, is the applicability of these theorems to some real material system. The applicability, however, can be discussed only in relation to particular cases. For the moment, therefore, we can notice that size by itself does not invalidate the reasonings that have been used so far.

4/19. *Random coupling.* Suppose now that the observer faces a system that, for him, is very large. How is he to proceed? Many questions arise, too many to be treated here in detail, so I shall select only a few topics, letting them serve as pattern for the rest. (See S.6/19 and Chapter 13.) First, how is the system to be specified?

By definition, the observer can specify it only incompletely. This is synonymous with saying that he must specify it "statistically", for statistics is the art of saying things that refer only to some aspect or portion of the whole, the whole truth being too bulky for direct use. If it has too many parts for their specification individually, they must be specified by a manageable number of rules, each of which applies to many parts. The parts specified by one rule need not be identical; generality can be retained by assuming that each rule specifies a set statistically. This means that the rule specifies a distribution of parts and a way in which it shall be sampled. The particular details of the individual outcome are thus determined not by the observer but by the process of sampling (as two people might leave a decision to the spin of a coin).

The same method must be used for specification of the coupling. If the specification for coupling is not complete it must in some way be supplemented, for ultimately some individual and single coupling must actually occur between the parts. Thus the coupling must contain a "random" element. What does this mean?

To make the discussion definite, suppose an experimenter has before him a large number of identical boxes, electrical in nature, each with three input and three output terminals. He wishes to form an extensive network, coupled "at random", to see what its properties will be. He takes up some connecting wires and then realises that to say "couple them at random" is quite insufficient as a definition of the way of coupling; all sorts of "couplings at random" are possible. Thus he might, if there are *n* boxes, label 6*n* cards with numbers from 1 to 6*n*, label the terminals similarly, shuffle the cards and then draw two cards to nominate the two terminals that shall be joined with the first wire. A second pair of cards will name the terminals joined by the second wire; and so on. A decision would have to be made whether the first two drawn cards were to be replaced or not before the next shuffling and drawing. The decision is important, for replacement allows some terminals to have no wire and others to have several, while non-replacement forces every terminal to have one wire and one only. This distinction would probably be significant in the characteristics of the network, and would therefore require specification. Again, the method just mentioned has the property of allowing output to be joined to output. If this were undesirable a new method would have to be defined; such might be: "Label the inputs 1 to 3*n* and also the outputs 1 to 3*n*; label 3*n* cards with numbers 1 to 3*n*; join a wire to input 1 and draw a card to find which output to connect it to; go on similarly through inputs 2, . . ., 3*n*". Here again replacement of the card means that one output may go to several inputs, or to none; non-replacement would give one output to each input.

Enough has probably been said to show how essential an accurate definition of the mode of sampling can be. Sometimes, as when the experimenter takes a sample of oxygen to study the gas laws in it, he need not specify how he obtained the sample, for almost all samples will have similar properties (though even here the possibility of exact definition may be important, as Rayleigh and Ramsay found when some specimens of nitrogen gave persistently different atomic weights from others).

This "statistical" method of specifying a system— by specification of distributions with sampling methods—should not be thought of as essentially different from other methods. It includes the case of the system that is *exactly* specified, for the exact specification is simply one in which each distribution has shrunk till its scatter is zero, and in which, therefore, "sampling" leads to one inevitable result. What *is* new about the statistical system is that the specification allows a number of machines, not identical, to qualify for inclusion. The statistical "machine" should therefore be thought of as a set of machines rather than as one machine. For this chapter, however, this aspect will be ignored (it is taken up fully in Chapter 7).

It will now be seen, therefore, that it is, in a sense, possible for an observer to specify a system that is too large for him to specify! The method is simple in principle: he must specify broadly, and must specify a *general* method by which the details shall be specified by some source other than himself. In the examples above, it was a pack of cards that made the final decision. A final, unique system can thus be arrived at provided his specification is *supplemented.* (The subject is developed more thoroughly in S.13/18.)

Ex. 1: Define a method (using dice, cards, random numbers, etc.) that will bring the closed single-valued transformation T:

$$T: \downarrow \begin{array}{cccccc} S_1 & S_2 & S_3 & S_4 & S_5 & S_6 \\ ? & ? & ? & ? & ? & ? \end{array}$$

to some particular form, so that the final particular form is selected by the method and not by the reader.

Ex. 2: (Continued.) Define a method so that the transformation shall be one-one, but not otherwise restricted.

Ex. 3: (Continued.) Define a method so that no even-numbered state shall transform to an odd-numbered state.

Ex. 4: (Continued.) Define a method so that any state shall transform only to a state adjacent to it in number.

Ex. 5: Define a method to imitate the network that would be obtained if parts were coupled by the following rule: In two dimensions, with the parts placed in a regular pattern thus:

$$\begin{array}{ccc} 0 & 0 & 0 \\ 0 & 0 & 0 \\ 0 & 0 & 0 \end{array}$$

extending indefinitely in all directions in the plane, each part either has an immediate effect on its neighbour directly above it or does not, with equal probability; and similarly for its three neighbours to right and left and below. Construct a sample network.

4/20. *Richness of connexion.* The simplest system of given largeness is one whose parts are all identical, mere replicates of one another, and between whose parts the couplings are of zero degree (e.g. Ex. 4/1/6). Such parts are in fact independent of each other, which makes the whole a "system" only in a nominal sense, for it is totally reducible. Nevertheless this type of system must be considered seriously, for it provides an important basic form from which modifications can be made in various ways. Approximate examples of this type of system are the gas whose atoms collide only rarely, the neurons in the deeply narcotised cortex (if they can be assumed to be approximately similar to one another) and a species of animals when the density of population is so low that they hardly ever meet or compete. In most cases the properties of this basic type of system are fairly easily deducible.

The first modification to be considered is obviously that by which a small amount of coupling is allowed between the parts, so that some coherence is introduced into the whole. Suppose then that into the system's diagram of immediate effects some actions, i.e. some arrows, are added, but only enough to give coherency to the set of parts. The least possible number of arrows, if there are n parts, is $n - 1$; but this gives only a simple long chain. A small amount of coupling would occur if the number of arrows were rather more than this but not so many as $n^2 - n$ (which would give every part an immediate effect on every other part).

Smallness of the amount of interaction may thus be due to smallness in the number of immediate effects. Another way, important because of its commonness, occurs when one part or variable affects another only under certain conditions, so that the immediate effect is present for much of the time only in a nominal sense. Such temporary and conditional couplings occur if the variable, for any reason, spends an appreciable proportion of its time not varying (the "part-function"). One common cause of this is the existence of a threshold, so that the variable shows no change except when the disturbance coming to it exceeds some definite value. Such are the voltage below which an arc will not jump across a given gap, and the damage that a citizen will sustain before he thinks it worth while going to law. In the nervous system the phenomenon of threshold is, of course, ubiquitous.

The existence of threshold induces a state of affairs that can be regarded as a cutting of the whole into temporarily isolated sub-systems; for a variable, so long as it stays constant, cannot, by S.4/12, have an effect on another; neither can it be affected by another. In the diagram of immediate effects it will lose both the arrows that go from it and those that come to it. The action is shown diagrammatically in Fig. 4/20/1.

The left square shows a basic network, a diagram of immediate effects, as it might have been produced by the method of Ex. 4/19/5. The middle square shows what remains if thirty per cent of the variables remain constant (by the disturbances that are coming to them being below threshold). The right square shows what remains if the proportion constant rises to fifty per cent. Such changes, from left to right, might be induced by a rising threshold. It will be seen that the reacting sub-systems tend to grow smaller and smaller, the rising threshold having the effect, functionally, of cutting the whole network into smaller and smaller parts.

Thus there exist factors, such as "height of threshold" or "proportion of variables constant", which can vary a large system continuously along the whole range that has at one end the totally-joined form, in which every variable has an immediate effect on every other

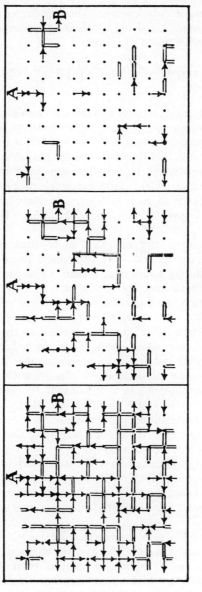

Fig. 4/20/1

variable, and at the other end the totally-unjoined form, in which every variable is independent of every other. Systems can thus show more or less of "wholeness". Thus the degree may be specifiable statistically even though the system is far too large for the details to be specified individually.

Ex.: Can a disturbance at A (Fig. 4/20/1) affect B in the left-hand system? In the other two?

4/21. *Local properties.* Large systems with much repetition in the parts, few immediate effects, and slight couplings, can commonly show some property in a *localised* form, so that it occurs in only a few variables, and so that its occurrence (or not) in the few variables does not determine whether or not the same property can occur in other sets of a few variables. Such localisable properties are usually of great importance in such systems, and the remainder of this chapter will be given to their consideration. Here are some examples.

In simple chemistry—the reaction of silver nitrate in solution with sodium chloride for instance—the component parts number about 10^{22}, thus constituting a very large system. The parts (atoms, ions, etc.) are largely repetitive, for they consist of only a dozen or so types. In addition, each part has an immediate effect on only a minute fraction of the totality of parts. So the coupling (or not) of one silver ion to a chloride ion has no effect on the great majority of other pairs of ions. As a result, the property "coupled to form AgCl" can exist over and over again in recognisable form throughout the system. Contrast this possibility of repetition with what happens in a well coupled system, in a thermostat for instance. In the thermostat, such a localised property can hardly exist, and can certainly not be repeated independently elsewhere in the system; for the existence of any property at one point is decisive in determining what shall happen at the other points.

The change from the chemistry of the solution in a test tube to that of protoplasm is probably of the same type, the protoplasm, as a chemically dynamic system, being too richly interconnected in its parts to allow much local independence in the occurrence of some property.

Another example is given by the biological world itself, regarded as a system of many parts. This system, composed ultimately of the atoms of the earth's surface, is made of parts that are largely repetitive, both at a low level in that all carbon atoms are chemically alike, and at a high level in that all members of a species are more or less alike. In this system various properties, if they exist in one place, can also exist in other places. It follows that the basic properties of the biological world will be of the types to be described in the following sections.

4/22. *Self-locking properties.* It is a general property of these systems that their behaviour in time is much affected by whether there can, or cannot, develop properties within them such that the property, once developed, becomes inaccessible to the factors that would "undevelop" it. Consider, for instance, a colony of oysters. Each oyster can freely receive signals of danger and can shut close; once shut, however, it cannot receive the signals of safety that would re-open it. Were these the only factors at work we could predict that in time the colony of oysters would pass entirely into the shut condition—an important fact in the colony's history!

In many other systems the same principle can be traced more seriously, and in almost all it is important. Consider, for instance, a solution of reacting molecules that can form various compounds, some of which can react again but one of which is insoluble, so that molecules in that form are unreactive. The property of "being the insoluble compound" is now one which can be taken by part after part but which, after the insolubility has taken the substance out of solution, cannot be reversed. The existence of this property is decisive in the history of the system, a fact well known in chemistry, where it has innumerable applications.

Too little is known about the dynamics of the cerebral cortex for us to be able to say much about what happens there. We can however see that if the nerve cells belong to only a few types, and if the immediate effects between them are sparse, then if any such "self-locking" property can exist among them it is almost certain to be important—to play a major part in determining the cortex's behaviour, especially when this continues over a long time. Such would occur, for instance, if the cells had some chance of getting into closed circuits that reverberated too strongly for suppression by inhibition. Other possibilities doubtless deserve consideration. Here we can only glance at them.

The same principle would also apply in an economic system if workers in some unpleasant industry became unemployed from time to time, and during their absence discovered that more pleasant forms of employment were available. The fact that they would pass readily from the unpleasant to the pleasant industry, but would refuse to go back, would clearly be a matter of high importance in the future of the industry.

In general, therefore, changes that are self-locking are usually of high importance in determining the eventual state of the system.

4/23. *Properties that breed.* It should be noticed that in the previous section we considered, in each example, two different systems. For though each example was based on only one material entity, it was used to provide two sets of variables, and these sets form, by S. 3/11, two systems. The first was the obvious set, very large in number, provided by the parts; the second was the system with one variable: "*number* of parts showing the property". The examples showed cases in which this variable could not diminish with time. In other words it behaved according to the transformation (if the number is n):

$$n' \geqslant n.$$

This transformation is one of the many that may be found when the changes of the second system (number of parts showing the property) is considered. It often happens that the existence of the property at some place in the system affects the probability that it will exist, one time-interval later, at another place. Thus, if the basic system consists of a trail of gunpowder along a line 12 inches long, the existence of the property "being on fire" now at the fourth inch makes it highly probable that, at an interval later, the same property will hold at the third and fifth inches. Again, if a car has an attractive appearance, its being sold to one house is likely to increase its chance of being sold to adjacent houses. And if a species is short of food, the existence of one member decreases the chance of the continued, later existence of another member.

Sometimes these effects are of great complexity; sometimes however the change of the variable "number having the property" can be expressed sufficiently well by the simple transformation $n' = kn$, where k is positive and independent of n.

When this is so, the history of the system is often acutely dependent on the value of k, particularly in its relation to $+1$. The equation has as solution, if t measures the number of time-intervals that have elapsed since $t = 0$, and if n_0 was the initial value:

$$n = n_0 e^{(k-1)t}$$

Three cases are distinguishable.

(1) $k < 1$. In this case the number showing the property falls steadily, and the density of parts having the property decreases. It

is shown, for instance, in a piece of pitchblende, by the number of atoms that are of radium. It is also shown by the number in a species when the species is tending to extinction.

(2) $k = 1$. In this case the number tends to stay constant. An example is given by the number of molecules dissociated when the percentage dissociated is at the equilibrial value for the conditions obtaining. (Since the slightest deviation of k from 1 will take the system into one of the other two cases it is of little interest.)

(3) $k > 1$. This case is of great interest and profound importance. The property is one whose presence increases the chance of its further occurrence elsewhere. The property "breeds", and the system is, in this respect, potentially explosive, either dramatically, as in an atom bomb, or insidiously, as in a growing epidemic. A well known example is autocatalysis. Thus if ethyl acetate has been mixed with water, the chance that a particular molecule of ethyl acetate will turn, in the next interval, to water and acetic acid depends on how many acetate molecules already have the property of being in the acid form. Other examples are commonly given by combustion, by the spread of a fashion, the growth of an avalanche, and the breeding of rabbits.

It is at this point that the majestic development of life by Darwinian evolution shows its relation to the theory developed here of dynamic systems. The biological world, as noticed in S.4/21, is a system with something like the homogeneity and the fewness of immediate effects considered in this chapter. In the early days of the world there were various properties with various k's. Some had k less than 1—they disappeared steadily. Some had k equal to 1—they would have remained. And there were some with k greater than 1—they developed like an avalanche, came into conflict with one another, commenced the interaction we call "competition", and generated a process that dominated all other events in the world and that still goes on.

Whether such properties, with k greater than 1, exist or can exist in the cerebral cortex is unknown. We can be sure, however, that if such do exist they will be of importance, imposing outstanding characteristics on the cortex's behaviour. It is important to notice that this prediction can be made without any reference to the particular details of what happens in the mammalian brain, for it is true of all systems of the type described.

4/24. The remarks made in the last few sections can only illustrate, in the briefest way, the main properties of the very large system. Enough has been said, however, to show that the very large system is not wholly different from the systems considered in the earlier chapters, and to show that the construction of a really adequate theory of systems in general is more a question of time and labour than of any profound or peculiar difficulty.

The subject of the very large system is taken up again in S.6/14.

Chapter 5

STABILITY

5/1. The word "stability" is apt to occur frequent in discussions of machines, but is not always used with precision. Bellman refers to it as ". . . stability, that much overburdened word with an unstabilised definition". Since the ideas behind the word are of great practical importance, we shall examine the subject with some care, distinguishing the various types that occur.

Today's terminology is unsatisfactory and confused; I shall not attempt to establish a better. Rather I shall focus attention on the actual facts to which the various words apply, so that the reader will tend to think of the facts rather than the words. So far as the words used are concerned, I shall try only to do no violence to established usages, and to be consistent within the book. Each word used will be carefully defined, and the defined meaning will be adhered to.

5/2. *Invariant.* Through all the meanings runs the basic idea of an "invariant": that although the system is passing through a series of changes, there is some aspect that is unchanging; so some statement can be made that, in spite of the incessant changing, is true unchangingly. Thus, if we take a cube that is resting on one face and tilt it by 5 degrees and let it go, a whole series of changes of position follow. A statement such as "its tilt is 1°" may be true at one moment but it is false at the next. On the other hand, the statement "its tilt does not exceed 6°" remains true permanently. This truth is invariant for the system. Next consider a cone stood on its point and released, like the cube, from a tilt of 5°. The statement "its tilt does not exceed 6°" is soon falsified, and (if we exclude reference to other subjects) so are the statements with wider limits. This inability to put a bound to the system's states along some trajectory corresponds to "instability".

These are the basic ideas. To make them incapable of ambiguity we must go back to first principles.

5/3. *State of equilibrium.* The simplest case occurs when a state and a transformation are so related that the transformation does

73

not cause the state to change.   Algebraically it occurs when $T(x) = x$. Thus if T is

$$T: \downarrow \begin{matrix} a & b & c & d & e & f & g & h \\ d & b & h & a & e & f & b & e \end{matrix}$$

then since $T(b) = b$, the state b is a **state of equilibrium** under T. So also are e and f.

If the states are defined by vectors, then, for a vector to be unchanged, each component must be unchanged (by S.3/5).   Thus if the state is a vector (x,y), and the transformation is

$$U: \begin{cases} x' = 2x - y + 2 \\ y' = x + y + 3 \end{cases}$$

then, at a state of equilibrium (x',y') must equal (x,y), and values for x and y must satisfy the equations

$$\begin{cases} x = 2x - y + 2 \\ y = x + y + 3 \end{cases}$$

i.e.
$$\begin{cases} x - y = -2 \\ x = -3 \end{cases}$$

So this system has only one state of equilibrium, at $(-3, -1)$. Had the equations not been linear there might have been more.

Exactly the same state, of course, is obtained by using the fact that at a state of equilibrium each component's change must be zero, giving $x' - x = 0$, $y' - y = 0$; which leads to the same equations as before.

If the equations are in differential form, then the statement that x is to be unchanged with time is equivalent to saying that dx/dt must be zero.   So in the system

$$dx/dt = 2x - y^2$$
$$dy/dt = xy - \tfrac{1}{2}$$

the state $(\tfrac{1}{2},1)$ is one of equilibrium, because when x and y have these values all the derivatives become zero, i.e. the system stops moving.

Ex. 1: Verify that U transforms $(-3,-1)$ to $(-3,-1)$.

Ex. 2: Has the system (of the last paragraph) any state of equilibrium other than $(\tfrac{1}{2},1)$?

Ex. 3: Find all the states of equilibrium of the transformation:
$$x' = e^{-y} \sin x, \qquad y' = x^2.$$

Ex. 4: Find all the states of equilibrium of the transformation:

$$dx/dt = e^- \sin x, \qquad dy/dt = x^2.$$

Ex. 5: If $x' = 2x - y + j$, $y' = x + y + k$, find values for j and k that will give a state of equilibrium at $(1,1)$. (Hint: First modify the equations to represent the state of equilibrium.)

Ex. 6: If $T(b) = b$, must $T^2(b)$, $T^3(b)$, etc., all also equal b?

Ex. 7: Can an absolute system have more states of equilibrium than it has basins?

Ex. 8: What is the characteristic appearance of the kinematic graph of a transformation whose states are all equilibrial?

Ex. 9: (Continued.) What special name was such a transformation given in an earlier chapter?

Ex. 10: If the transformation is changed (the set of operands remaining the same) are the states of equilibrium changed?

Ex. 11: If a machine's input is changed, do its states of equilibrium change? (Hint: See Ex.5.)

5/4. Cycle. Related to the states of equilibrium is the **cycle**, a sequence of states such that repeated application of the transformation takes the representative point repeatedly round the sequence. Thus if T is

$$T: \downarrow \begin{array}{cccccccc} a & b & c & d & e & f & g & h \\ c & h & b & h & a & c & c & g \end{array}$$

then, from a, T generates the trajectory

$$a \quad c \quad b \quad h \quad g \quad c \quad b \quad h \quad g \quad c \quad b \ldots$$

and the representative point repeatedly traverses the cycle

$$\begin{array}{ccc} c & \rightarrow & b \\ \uparrow & & \downarrow \\ g & \leftarrow & h \end{array}$$

Ex. 1: Write down a transformation that contains two distinct cycles and three states of equilibrium.

Ex. 2: (Continued.) Draw its kinematic graph.

Ex. 3: Can a state of equilibrium occur in a cycle?

Ex. 4: Can an absolute system have more cycles than it has basins?

Ex. 5: Can one basin contain two cycles?

*Ex. 6: Has the system $dx/dt = y$, $dy/dt = -x$ a cycle?

*Ex. 7: If the transformation has a finite number of states and is closed and single-valued, can a trajectory end in any way other than at a state of equilibrium or in a cycle?

5/5. *Stable region.* If *a* is a state of equilibrium, *T*(*a*) is, as we saw in S.5/3, simply *a*. Thus the operation of *T* on *a* has generated no *new* state.

The same phenomenon may occur with a *set* of states. Thus, suppose *T* is the (unclosed) transformation

$$T: \downarrow \begin{matrix} a & b & c & d & e & f & g & h \\ p & g & b & f & a & a & b & m \end{matrix}$$

It has no state of equilibrium; but the set composed of *b* and *g* has the peculiarity that it transforms thus

$$T: \downarrow \begin{matrix} b & g \\ g & b \end{matrix}$$

i.e. the operation of *T* on this set has generated no *new* state. Such a set is **stable** with respect to *T*.

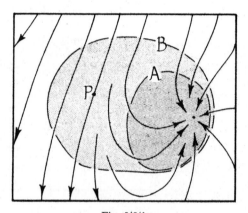

Fig. 5/5/1

This relation between a set of states and a transformation is, of course, identical with that described earlier (S.2/4) as "closure". (The words "stable set" could have been used from there onwards, but they might have been confusing before the concept of stability was made clear; and this could not be done until other matters had been explained first.)

If the transformation is continuous, the set of states may lie in a connected region. Thus in Fig. 5/5/1, the region within the boundary *A* is stable; but that within *B* is not, for there are points within the region, such as *P*, which are taken outside the region.

The concept of closure, of a stable set of states, is of fundamental importance in our studies. Some reasons were given in S.3/2, where it was pointed out that only when the set is stable can the transformation proceed to all its higher powers unrestrictedly.

Another reason is discussed more fully in S.10/4, where it is shown that such stability is intimately related to the idea of some entity "surviving" some operation.

Ex. 1: What other sets are stable with respect to *T*?

Ex. 2: Is the set of states in a basin always stable?

Ex. 3: Is the set of states in a cycle always stable?

Ex. 4: If a set of states is stable under *T*, and also under *U*, is it necessarily stable under *UT*?

DISTURBANCE

5/6. In the cases considered so far, the equilibrium or stability has been examined only at the particular state or states concerned. Nothing has been said, or implied, about the behaviour at *neighbouring* states.

The elementary examples of equilibrium—a cube resting on its face, a billiard ball on a table, and a cone exactly balanced on its point—all show a state that is one of equilibrium. Yet the cone is obviously different, and in an important way, from the cube. The difference is shown as soon as the two systems are *displaced* by disturbance from their states of equilibrium to a neighbouring state. How is this displacement, and its outcome, to be represented generally?

A "disturbance" is simply that which displaces, that which moves a system from one state to another. So, if defined accurately, it will be represented by a transformation having the system's states as operands. Suppose now that our dynamic system has transformation *T*, that *a* is a state of equilibrium under *T*, and that *D* is a given displacement-operator. In plain English we say: "Displace the system from its state of equilibrium and then let the system follow its own laws for some time and see whether the system does or does not come back to the same state". In algebraic form, we start with a state of equilibrium *a*, displace the system to state $D(a)$, and then find $TD(a)$, $T^2D(a)$, $T^3D(a)$, and so on; and we notice whether this succession of states does or does not finish as *a*, *a*, *a*, ... More compactly: the state of equilibrium *a* in the system with transformation *T* is **stable under displacement D** if and only if

$$\lim_{n \to \infty} T^n D(a) = a.$$

Try this formulation with the three standard examples. With the cube, *a* is the state with angle of tilt $= 0°$. *D* displaces this to, say, $5°$; and T eventually will bring this back to $0°$. With the cone (having transformation U, say) D can be the same displacement, but the limit, whatever it is, of $U^n D(a)$ is certainly not a tilt of $0°$; the equilibrium is **unstable**. With the billiard ball, at position a, the dynamic laws will not bring it back to a after displacement, so it is not stable by the definition given here. It has the peculiarity, however, that the limit is $D(a)$; i.e. it retains the displacement, neither annulling it nor exaggerating it. This is the case of **neutral** equilibrium.

(It will be noticed that this study of what happens after the system has been displaced from a is worth making only if a is a state of equilibrium.)

Ex. 1: Is the state of equilibrium c stable to T under the displacement D if T and D are given by:

$$
\begin{array}{c|ccccc}
 & a & b & c & d & e \\
T \downarrow & c & d & c & a & e \\
D & b & a & d & e & d \\
\end{array}
$$

Ex. 2: (Continued.)   What if the state of equilibrium is e?

Ex. 3: The region composed of the set of states b, c and d is stable under U:

$$
\begin{array}{c|cccccc}
\downarrow & a & b & c & d & e & f \\
U & d & c & b & b & c & a \\
E & b & e & f & f & f & d \\
\end{array}
$$

What is the effect of displacement E, followed by repeated action of U? (Hint: Consider all three possibilities.)

5/7. When the dynamic system can vary continuously, small disturbances are, in practice, usually acting on it incessantly. Electronic systems are disturbed by thermal agitation, mechanical systems by vibration, and biological systems by a host of minor disturbances. For this reason the only states of equilibrium that can stay occupied are those that are stable in the sense of the previous section. States of unstable equilibrium are of small practical importance in the continuous system (though they may be of importance in the system that can change only by a discrete jump).

The concept of unstable equilibrium is, however, of some theoretical importance. For if we are working with the *theory* of some mechanism, the algebraic manipulations (S.5/3) will give us *all* the states of equilibrium—stable, neutral, and unstable—and a good deal of elimination may be necessary if this set is to be reduced to the set of those states that have a real chance of persistence.

Ex.: Make up a transformation with two states of equilibrium, a and b, and two disturbances, D and E, so that a is stable to D but not to E, and b is stable to E but not to D.

5/8. In general, the results of repeated application of a transformation to a state depend on what that state is. The outcome of the test of finding what is

$$\lim_{n \to \infty} T^n(x)$$

will thus depend in general on which state is x. Thus if there are two disturbances available, D and E, and D takes a to b, while E takes a to c (no order being implied between a, b and c) the limits of $T^n D(a)$ and $T^n E(a)$ may be different.

Thus the result of a test for stability, carried out in the manner of S.5/6, may give different results according to whether the displacement is D or E. The distinction is by no means physically unreasonable. Thus a pencil, balanced on its square-cut base, may be stable to D, if D is a displacement of 1° from the vertical, but may be unstable to E, if E is a displacement of 5°.

The representation given in S.5/6 thus accords with common practice. A system can be said to be in stable equilibrium only if some sufficiently definite set of displacements D is specified. If the specification is explicit, then D is fully defined. Often D is not given explicitly but is understood; thus if a radio circuit is said to be "stable", one understands that D means any of the commonly occurring voltage fluctuations, but it would usually be understood to exclude the stroke of lightning. Often the system is understood to be stable provided the disturbance lies within a certain range. What is important here is that in unusual cases, in biological systems for instance, precise specification of the disturbances D, and of the state of equilibrium under discussion a, may be necessary if the discussion is to have exactness.

5/9. *The continuous system.* In the previous sections, the states considered were usually arbitrary. Real systems, however, often show some continuity, so that the states have the natural relationship amongst themselves (quite apart from any transformation imposed by their belonging to a transducer) that two states can be "near" or "far from" one another.

With such systems, and a state of equilibrium a, D is usually defined to be a displacement, from a, to one of the states "near" a. If the states are defined by vectors with numerical components, i.e. based on measurements, then D often has the effect of adding small numerical quantities δ_1, δ_2, $\ldots$, δ_n, to the components, so that the vector $(x_1, \ldots, x_n)$ becomes the vector $(x_1 + \delta_1, \ldots, x_n + \delta_n)$.

In this form, more specialised tests for stability become possible. An introduction to the subject has been given in *Design* .... The

79

subject soon becomes somewhat mathematical; here it is sufficient to notice that these questions are *always* capable of being answered, at least in principle, by the process of actually tracing the changes as the system moves successively through the states $D(a)$, $TD(a)$, $T^2D(a)$, etc. (Compare S.3/9.) The sole objection to this simple, fundamental, and reliable method is that it is apt to become exceedingly laborious in the complicated cases. It is, however, capable of giving an answer in cases to which the more specialised methods are inapplicable. In biological material, the methods described in this chapter are likely to prove more useful than the more specialised; for the latter often are applicable only when the system is continuous and linear, whereas the methods of this chapter are applicable always.

A specially simple and well known case occurs when the system consists of parts between which there is feedback, and when this has the very simple form of a single loop. A simple test for stability (from a state of equilibrium assumed) is to consider the sequence of changes that follow a small displacement, as it travels round the loop. If the displacement ultimately arrives back at its place of origin with size and sign so that, when added algebraically to the initial displacement, the initial displacement is diminished, i.e. brought nearer the state of equilibrium, then the system, around that state of equilibrium, is (commonly) stable. The feedback, in this case, is said to be "negative" (for it causes an eventual *subtraction* from the initial displacement).

The test is simple and convenient, and can often be carried out mentally; but in the presence of any complications it is unreliable if carried out in the simple form described above. The next section gives an example of one way in which the rule may break down if applied crudely.

Ex. 1: Identify a, D and T in Ex. 3/6/17. Is this system stable to this displacement?

Ex. 2: (Continued.) Contrast Ex. 3/6/19.

Ex. 3: Identify a and T in Ex. 2/14/11. Is it stable if D is any displacement from a?

Ex. 4: Take a child's train (one that runs on the floor, not on rails) and put the line of carriages slightly out of straight. Let M be the set of states in which the deviations from straightness nowhere exceed $5°$. Let T be the operation of drawing it along by the locomotive. Is M stable under T?

Ex. 5: (Continued.) Let U be the operation of pushing it backwards by the locomotive. Is M stable under U?

Ex. 6: Why do trains have their locomotives in front?

Ex. 7: A bus service starts with its buses equally spaced along the route. If a bus is delayed, extra passengers collect at the stopping points, so it has to take up, and set down, more passengers than usual. The bus that follows it, being closer than usual, has fewer passengers to handle and is delayed less than usual. Are irregularities of spacing self-correcting or self-aggravating?

Ex. 8: What would happen if an increase of carbon dioxide in the blood made the respiratory centre *less* active?

Ex. 9: Is the system $x' = \frac{1}{2}y$, $y' = \frac{1}{2}x$ stable around (0,0)?

5/10. *Positive feedback.* The system described in the last exercise deserves closer attention.

From (10,10) it goes to (5,5)
  „ (10,12) „ „ „ (6,5);

so an increase in y (from 10 to 12) leads to an increase in x (from 5 to 6). (Compare S.4/13.) Similarly,

from (10,10) it goes to (5,5)
  „ (12,10) „ „ „ (5,6)

so an increase in x (from 10 to 12) leads to an increase in y (from 5 to 6). Each variable is thus having a *positive* effect on the other and if the system were discussed in plain words these facts might be used to "prove" that it is unstable, for a vicious circle seems to be acting.

The system's behaviour, by converging back to (0,0), declares indisputably that the system is stable around this state of equilibrium. It shows clearly that arguments based on some short cut, e.g. by showing that the feedback is positive, may not be reliable. (It shows also that feedback can be positive and yet leave the system stable; yet another example of how unsuitable is the concept of feedback outside its particular range of applicability.)

5/11. *Undesirable stability.* Stability is commonly thought of as desirable, for its presence enables the system to combine something of flexibility and activity in performance with something of permanence. Behaviour that is goal-seeking is an example of behaviour that is stable around a state of equilibrium. Nevertheless, stability is not always good, for a system may persist in returning to some state that, for other reasons, is considered undesirable. Once petrol is lit it stays in the lit state, returning to it after disturbance has changed it to "half-lit"—a highly undesirable stability to a fireman.

Another example is given by the suggestion that as the more intelligent members of the community are not reproducing their kind as freely as are the less intelligent, the Intelligence Quotient of the community will fall. Clearly it cannot fall very low, because the feebleminded can reproduce better than the idiot. So if these were the only factors in the situation, the I.Q. would be stable at about 90. Stability at this figure would be regarded by most people as undesirable.

An interesting example of stability occurs in the condition known as "causalgia", in which severe pain, without visible cause, occurs in a nerve which has previously been partly divided. Granit has shown that it is almost certainly due to conduction, at the site of injury, of impulses from the motor (outgoing) to the sensory (incoming) nerves, allowing the formation of a regenerative circuit via the reflex centres in the spinal cord. Such a circuit has two states of equilibrium, each stable: conducting few impulses or conducting the maximal number. It is like a top-heavy see-saw, that will rest in either of two extreme conditions but will not rest in between. The patient is well aware that "stability" can be either good or bad, for of the two stable states one is comfortable and the other extremely painful.

EQUILIBRIUM IN PART AND WHOLE

5/12. We can now notice a relation between coupling and equilibrium that will be wanted later (S.12/14 and 13/19), for it has important applications.

Suppose some whole system is composed of two parts A and B, which have been coupled together:

$$\boxed{A} \rightleftarrows \boxed{B}$$

and suppose the whole is at a state of equilibrium.

This means that the whole's state is unchanging in time. But the whole's state is a vector with two components: that of A's state and that of B's. It follows that A, regarded as a sub-system, is also unchanging; and so is B.

Not only is A's state unchanging but so is the value of A's input; for this value is determined by B's state (S.4/7), which is unchanging. Thus A is at a state of equilibrium in the conditions provided by B. (Cf. Ex. 5/3/11.) The similar property holds for B. Thus, *if the whole is at a state of equilibrium, each part must be in a state of equilibrium in the conditions provided by the other.*

The argument can also be reversed. Suppose A and B are at states of equilibrium, and that each state provides, for the other system, an input-value that makes the other's state to be one of equilibrium. Then neither can change, and the whole cannot change; and thus the whole must be at a state of equilibrium. Thus each implies the other. Formally: *the whole is at a state of equilibrium if and only if each part is at a state of equilibrium in the conditions provided by the other part.* (If there are several parts the last word is merely changed to "parts".)

5/13. Power of veto. The same thesis can be stated more vividly, making it more useful conceptually. Suppose A and B are coupled and suppose we are interested only in the occurrence of a state of equilibrium (not of cycles). When the whole is started from some initial state, and goes along some trajectory, A and B will pass through various states. Suppose it happens that at some moment B's state provides conditions that make A's present state one of equilibrium. A will not change during the next step. If B is not itself at a state of equilibrium in the conditions provided by A, it will move to a new state. A's conditions will thereby be changed, its states of equilibrium will probably be changed, and the state it is at will probably no longer be one of equilibrium. So A will start moving again.

Picturesquely, we can say that A proposed a state of equilibrium (for A was willing to stop), but B refused to accept the proposal, or vetoed the state. We can thus regard each part as having, as it were, a power of veto over the states of equilibrium of the whole. *No state (of the whole) can be a state of equilibrium unless it is acceptable to every one of the component parts,* each acting in the conditions given by the others.

Ex.: Three one-variable systems, with Greek-letter parameters, are:
$$x' = -x + \alpha, \qquad y' = 2\beta y + 3, \qquad z' = -\gamma z + \delta.$$
Can they be coupled so as to have a state of equilibrium at (0,0,0)? (Hint: What value would β have to have?)

5/14. The homeostat. This principle provides a simple way of looking at the homeostat and of understanding its working. It can be regarded as a part A coupled to a part B (Fig. 5/14/1).

Part A consists essentially of the four needles (with ancillary coils, potentiometers, etc.) acting on one another to form a four-variable system to which B's values are input. A's state is specified by the positions of the four needles. Depending on the conditions and input, A may have states of equilibrium with the needles either central or at the extreme deviation.

Part B consists essentially of a relay, which can be energised or not, and four stepping-switches, each of which can be in any one of 25 positions (not shown accurately in the Figure). Each position carries a resistor of some value. So *B* has 2 × 25 × 25 × 25 × 25, i.e. 781250, states. To this system *A* is input. *B* has been built so that, with the relay energised, *none* of *B*'s states is equilibrial (i.e. the switches keep moving), while, with the relay not energised, *all* are equilibrial (i.e. all switches stay where they are).

Finally, *B* has been coupled to *A* so that the relay is non-energised when and only when *A* is stable at the *central* positions.

When a problem is set (by a change of value at some input to *A* not shown formally in the Figure), *A* has a variety of possible states of equilibrium, some with the needles at the central positions, some with the needles fully diverged. The whole will go to some state of equilibrium. An equilibrium of the whole implies that *B* must be

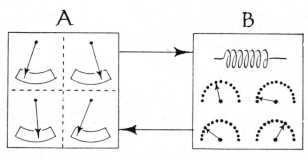

Fig. 5/14/1

in equilibrium, by the principle of the previous section. But *B* has been made so that this occurs only when the relay is non-energised. And *B* has been coupled to *A* so that the relay is non-energised only when *A*'s needles are at or near the centres. Thus the attachment of *B* vetoes all of *A*'s equilibria except such as have the needles at the centre.

It will now be seen that every graph shown in *Design* . . . could have been summed up by one description: "trajectory of a system running to a state of equilibrium". The homeostat, in a sense, does nothing more than run to a state of equilibrium. What *Design* . . . showed was that this simple phrase may cover many intricate and interesting ways of behaving, many of them of high interest in physiology and psychology.

(The subject of "stability" recurs frequently, especially in S.9/6, 10/4, 12/11; that of the homeostat is taken up again in S.12/15.)

5/15. The complex of ideas involved in "stability" can now be *summarised.*

First there is the state of equilibrium—the state that is unchanged by the transformation. Then the state may become multiple, and we get the stable set of states, of which the cycle and basin are examples.

Given such a state or set of states and some particular disturbance we can ask whether, after a disturbance, the system will return to its initial region. And if the system is continuous, we can ask whether it is stable against all disturbances within a certain range of values.

Clearly, the concept of stability is essentially a compound one. Only when every aspect of it has been specified can it be applied unambiguously to a particular case. Then if its use calls for so much care, why should it be used at all? Its advantage is that, in the suitable case, it can sum up various more or less intricate possibilities *briefly.* As shorthand, when the phenomena are suitably simple, words such as equilibrium and stability are of great value and convenience. Nevertheless, it should be always borne in mind that they are mere shorthand, and that the phenomena will not always have the simplicity that these words presuppose. At all times the user should be prepared to delete them and to substitute the actual facts, in terms of states and transformations and trajectories, to which they refer.

It is of interest to notice, to anticipate S.6/19, that the attempt to say what is significant about a system by a reference to its stability is an example of the "topological" method for describing a large system. The question "what will this system do?", applied to, say, an economic system, *may* require a full description of every detail of its future behaviour, but it *may* be adequately answered by the much simpler statement "It will return to its usual state" (or perhaps "it will show ever increasing divergence"). Thus our treatment in this chapter has been of the type required when dealing with the very large system.

Chapter 6

THE BLACK BOX

6/1. The methods developed in the previous chapters now enable us to undertake a study of the Problem of the Black Box; and the study will provide an excellent example of the use of the methods.

The Problem of the Black Box arose in electrical engineering. The engineer is given a sealed box that has terminals for input, to which he may bring any voltages, shocks, or other disturbances he pleases, and terminals for output, from which he may observe what he can. He is to deduce what he can of its contents.

Sometimes the problem arose literally, when a secret and sealed bomb-sight became defective and a decision had to be made, without opening the box, whether it was worth returning for repair or whether it should be scrapped. Sometimes the problem arose practically, as when a telephone engineer considered a complicated set of relations between tests applied and results observed, in the middle of a mass of functioning machinery that was not to be dismantled for insufficient reason.

Though the problem arose in purely electrical form, its range of application is far wider. The clinician studying a patient with brain damage and aphasia may be trying, by means of tests given and speech observed, to deduce something of the mechanisms that are involved. And the psychologist who is studying a rat in a maze may act on the rat with various stimuli and may observe the rat's various behaviours; and by putting the facts together he may try to deduce something about the neuronic mechanism that he cannot observe. I need not give further examples as they are to be found everywhere (S.6/17).

Black Box theory is, however, even wider in application than these professional studies. The child who tries to open a door has to manipulate the handle (the input) so as to produce the desired movement at the latch (the output); and he has to learn how to control the one by the other without being able to see the internal mechanism that links them. In our daily lives we are confronted at every turn with systems whose internal mechanisms are not fully open to inspection, and which must be treated by the methods appropriate to the Black Box.

86

The experimenter who is not interested in Black Box theory usually regards any casing as merely a nuisance, for it delays his answering the question "what is in *this* Box?" We, however, shall be considering such larger questions as

"How should an experimenter proceed when faced with a Black Box?"

"What properties of the Box's contents are discoverable and what are fundamentally not discoverable?"

"What methods should be used if the Box is to be investigated efficiently?"

Proper attention can be given to these questions only by our accepting the existence, at least temporarily, of a casing, and proceeding accordingly. Then, and only then, can we develop a scientific epistemology.

6/2. To start with, let us make no assumptions at all about the nature of the Box and its contents, which might be something, say, that has just fallen from a Flying Saucer. We assume, though, that the experimenter has certain given resources for acting on it (e.g. prodding it, shining a light on it) and certain given resources for observing its behaviour (e.g. photographing it, recording its temperature). By thus acting on the Box, and by allowing the Box to affect him and his recording apparatus, the experimenter is *coupling* himself to the Box, so that the two together form a system with feedback:

$$\boxed{\text{Box}} \rightleftarrows \boxed{\text{Experimenter}}$$

For the coupling to be made in some defined and reproducible way, the Box's "input" must be specified, if only arbitrarily and provisionally. Every real system has an indefinitely large number of possible inputs—of possible means by which the experimenter may exert some action on the Box. Equally, it has an indefinitely large number of possible outputs—of ways by which it may affect the experimenter, perhaps through recording instruments. If the investigation is to be orderly, the set of inputs to be used and of outputs to be observed must be decided on, at least provisionally. Let us assume, then, that this has been done.

The situation that we (author and reader) are considering can be made clearer by the introduction of two harmless conventions. Let it be assumed that the inputs, whatever their real nature, are replaced by, or represented by, a set of levers or pointers—like the controls to a domestic cooking oven. We can then be quite clear as to what is meant by the input "being in a certain state"—it is the state that would be shown on a snapshot of the controls. Also let us assume that the output consists of a set of dials, attached to the Box and affected by the mechanism inside, so that the pointers on the dials show, by their positions at any particular moment, the state of the output.

We now see the experimenter much like the engineer in a ship, who sits before a set of levers and telegraphs by which he may act on the engines, and who can observe the results on a row of dials. The representation, though it may seem unnatural, is in fact, of course, capable of representing the great majority of natural systems, even if biological or economic.

6/3. *The Investigation.* A man cannot step twice into the same river; neither can he twice conduct the same experiment. What he can do is to perform another experiment which differs from the first only in some way that is agreed to be negligible.

The same fact applies to an examination of the Black Box. The basic data will always be of the form:

Time	States of input and output
↓ · · ·	· · · · · ·
· · ·	· · · · · ·

in which, at each of a sequence of times, the states of the Box's various parts, input and output, are recorded. Thus, the Box that fell from the Flying Saucer might lead to the protocol:

Time	State
11.18 a.m.	I did nothing—the Box emitted a steady hum at 240 c/s.
11.19	I pushed over the switch marked K: the note rose to 480 c/s and remained steady.
11.20	Accidentally I pushed the button marked "!"—the Box increased in temperature by 20°C.
· · ·	Etc.

(The word **protocol** will be reserved for such a form and sequence.)

Thus every system, fundamentally, is investigated by the collection of a long protocol, drawn out in time, showing the sequence of input and output states. Thus if one system had possible input states α and β, and possible output states f, g, h and j, a typical protocol might read (and be yet another transformation!):

Time:　 1　2　3　4　5　6　7　8　9　10　11　12　13　14　15　16　17
State:　 αg　αj　αf　αf　αf　βf　βh　βh　αh　αj　βf　αh　βj　βf　αh　βj　αf

(Parentheses have been omitted for brevity.)

This form, though it may seem artificial and unnatural, is in fact typical and general. It will represent anything from the investigation of an electrical network by putting in a sinusoidal voltage and observing the output, to a psychiatric interview at which questions α, β were put and answers g, f, h, j elicited.

Thus, the primary data of any investigation of a Black Box consists of a sequence of values of the vector with two components:

(input state, output state).

(The possibility is not excluded that each component may itself be a vector (S.3/5).)

From this there follows the fundamental deduction that *all knowledge obtainable from a Black Box* (*of given input and output*) *is such as can be obtained by re-coding the protocol*; all that, and nothing more.

Ex.: Tabulate the transitions observed in the system that started at αg. Find some regularities in them.

6/4. It will be noticed that nothing has been said about the skill of the experimenter in manipulating the input. The omission was deliberate, for no skill is called for! We are assuming, remember, that *nothing* is known about the Box, and when this is so the method of making merely random variations (e.g. guided by throws of a die) on the input-switches is as defensible as any other method; for no facts yet exist that could be appealed to as justification for preferring any particular method. With terrestrial machinery—industrial, biological, neuronic—the experimenter has often had previous experiences with Boxes of the same class. When this is so he may be able to use a method that explores what he does *not* know about the present Box more efficiently than some other method. (These matters, of exploring a partly known system, lead into questions of altogether more advanced type, and their consideration must be postponed; a little is said on the subject in S.13/5 and onwards.)

6/5. *Absoluteness.* When a generous length of record has been obtained, the experimenter will look for regularities, for *repetiveness* in the behaviour (S.7/19). He may notice, for instance, in

Ex. 6/3/1, that αj is always followed by either αf or βf—that although the α's transition is not single-valued, that of the j *is*.

So he examines the record. Usually his first concern is to see whether the Box is absolute if the input state is given. He does this by collecting:

(i) all the transitions that followed the input state α, sorting them into what g went to, what h went to, and so on through all the output states;
(ii) the same for input β;
(iii) and so on through all the observed input states.

What he tries, in other words, is to fill in a set of transformations like those of S.4/1, and he examines what he gets to see if they are single-valued.

Thus, if the given protocol is tested, and if every one of the 16 transforms is recorded, there results:

$\downarrow$	f	g	h	j
α	*fff*	*j*	*jjj*	*ff*
β	*hhh*	.	*hh*	*ff*

(No transition was observed from g with input at β.) Within each cell the letters are all equal, so the table can be simplified to:

$\downarrow$	f	g	h	j
α	f	j	j	f
β	h	.	h	f

with a statement that throughout the protocol this closed single-valued transformation was observed.

Thus by direct re-coding of the protocol the experimenter can demonstrate that the behaviour is machine-like, and *he can deduce its canonical representation.*

It should be noticed that he has deduced it from direct observation of the Box's actual behaviour. He has relied on no "borrowed" knowledge. Whatever he may have expected, and regardless of the confidence of his expectation, the final deduction depends only on what actually happened. Thus, in any conflict between what he, or others, expected and what was found, these empirical results are final as a statement of the Box's nature.

Should the system not be determinate, i.e. the transformation not single-valued, he can proceed in either of two ways.

One way is to alter the set of inputs and outputs—to take more variables into account—and then to see if the *new* system (equivalent to a new Box, S.3/11) is determinate. Thus a chemist may find that a system's behaviour is at first not determinate, but that when the presence of traces of chloride is taken into account it becomes determinate. A great deal of research consists of such searches for a suitable set of variables.

A second way is to abandon the attempt to find strict determinacy and to look for *statistical* determinacy, i.e. determinacy in averages, etc. The experimenter, with extensive records available, then studies them in long sections, to see whether, if the details are not predictable from step to step, the *averages* (or similar statistics) are predictable from section to section. He may find that the records show the statistical determinateness of the Markov chain; (but discussion of this will be left to Chapter 9, for until then we shall be concerned only with machines that are determinate from step to step).

To summarise: once the protocol has been obtained, the system's determinateness can be tested, and (if found determinate) its canonical representation can be deduced.

Ex. 1: Deduce the kinematic graph for input at α directly from the protocol of the system of S.6/3.

Ex. 2: (Continued.) and for input at β.

Ex. 3: A system with only one input state gave the following sequence of states as output:

$$D \quad G \quad A \quad H \quad C \quad L \quad H \quad C \quad L \quad H \quad C \quad F \quad C \dots$$

Is it absolute?

Ex. 4: A system has two variables, x and y, each of which can take the values 0, 1 or 2. The input can take two values, α or β. The protocol gave:

Time:	1	2	3	4	5	6	7	8	9	10	11	12	13
Input:	α	α	α	α	α	β	α	α	α	α	α	α	α
x:	1	0	0	0	0	0	1	2	2	1	0	0	0
y:	1	0	1	0	1	0	2	1	0	1	0	1	0

Time:	14	15	16	17	18	19	20	21	22	23	24	25
Input:	β	α	α	β	β	β	α	β	β	β	α	β
x:	0	0	1	0	1	1	1	1	1	2	2	1
y:	1	2	1	0	2	1	0	1	0	0	2	1

Is it a machine with input?

Ex. 5: (Continued.) What is its transformation if the input is held at α?

Ex. 6: If a machine has m input-states and n output-states, what is the least number of steps of observation sufficient for its complete study?

91

Ex. 7: Two Black Boxes are of identical external appearance, and each has a single input α and a single output x, each a numerical variable. They were labelled I and II, and their canonical representations were found to be

$$\text{I}: x' = x + 1 - \alpha$$
$$\text{II}: x' = (1 + \alpha)x - 2 + \alpha.$$

Unfortunately the labels "I" and "II" have since become detached and it is now not known which is which. Suggest a simple test that will re-identify them.

6/6. *Inaccessible states.* Examination of the transformations

$\downarrow$	f	g	h	j
α	f	j	j	f
β	h	f	h	f

shows that the state g, once past in the protocol, cannot be made to re-appear by any manipulations of the input. The transitions from g thus cannot be explored further or tested repeatedly. This fact, that certain states of the Box cannot be returned to at will, is very common in practice. Such states will be called **inaccessible.**

In its most dramatic form it occurs when the investigation of a new type of enemy mine leads to an explosion—which can be described more abstractly by saying that the system has passed from a state to which no manipulation at the input can make the system return. Essentially the same phenomenon occurs when experiments are conducted on an organism that learns; for as time goes on it leaves its "unsophisticated" initial state, and no simple manipulation can get it back to this state. In such experiments, however, the psychologist is usually investigating not the particular individual but the particular species, so he *can* restore the initial state by the simple operation of taking a new individual.

Thus the experimenter, if the system is determinate, must either restrict himself to the investigation of a set of states that is both closed and accessible, such as f, h, j in the example, or he must add more states to his input so that more transformations become available and thus, perhaps, give a transition to g.

6/7. *Deducing connexions.* It is now clear that something of the connexions within a Black Box can be obtained by deduction. For direct manipulation and observation gives the protocol, this (if the system is determinate) gives the canonical representation, and this gives the diagram of immediate effects (one for each input state) (S.4/13). But we must go cautiously.

It must be noticed that in a real system the "diagram of internal

connexions" is *not unique*. The radio set, for instance, has one
diagram of connexions if considered electrically and another if
considered mechanically. An insulator, in fact, is just such a
component as will give firm mechanical connexion while giving no
electrical connexion. *Which pattern of connexions will be found
depends on which set of inputs and outputs is used.*

Even if the diagram of immediate effects is unique, it does not
indicate a unique pattern of connexions within the Box. Thus
suppose a Black Box has an output of two dials, x and y; and
suppose it has been found that x dominates y. The diagram of
immediate effects is thus

$$\boxed{x} \rightarrow \boxed{y}$$

(in which the two boxes are parts of the whole Box). This relationship can be given by an infinity of possible internal mechanisms. A
particular example occurs in the case in which relays open or close
switches in order to give a particular network of connexions. It
has been shown by Shannon that any given behaviour can be pro-

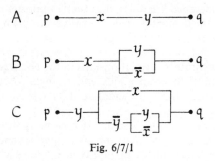

Fig. 6/7/1

duced by an indefinitely large number of possible networks. Thus,
let x represent a contact that will be closed when the relay X is
energised, and let $\bar{x}$ represent one that will be opened. Suppose
similarly that another relay Y has similar contacts y and $\bar{y}$. Suppose
that the network is to conduct from p to q when and only when
both X and Y are energised. The network A of Fig. 6/7/1, in
which x and y are connected in series, will show the required behaviour. So also will B, and C, and an indefinitely large number
of other networks.

The behaviour does not specify the connexions uniquely.

Ex.: (Ex. 6/5/4 continued.) Deduce the diagram of immediate effects when the
input is fixed at α. (Hint: S.4/13.)

4*

ISOMORPHIC MACHINES

6/8. Study of a Black Box can thus give the experimenter information up to a certain amount; and, if the inputs and outputs are given, cannot possibly be made to give more. How much information will be discussed in S.13/15 (especially its last Ex.). Here it is sufficient if we notice that the canonical representation specifies or identifies the mechanism "up to an isomorphism".

"Isomorphic" means, roughly, "similar in pattern". It is a concept of the widest range and of the utmost importance to all who would treat accurately of matters in which "pattern" plays a part. Let us consider first a few examples merely to illustrate the basic ideas.

A photographic negative and the print from it are, so far as the pattern of the picture is concerned, isomorphic. Squares in the negative appear as squares in the print; circles appear as circles; parallel lines in the one stay as parallel lines in the other. Thus certain *relations* between the parts within the negative appear as the same *relations* in the print, though the appearances so far as brightness is concerned are different, exactly opposite in fact. Thus the operation of changing from negative to print leaves these relations unaltered (compare S.5/2).

A map and the countryside that it represents are isomorphic (if the map is accurate!). Relationships in the country, such as that towns *A*, *B* and *C* form an equilateral triangle, occur unchanged on the map, where the representative dots for *A*, *B* and *C* also form an equilateral triangle.

The patterns need not be visual. If a stone is thrown vertically upwards with an initial velocity of 50 ft. per second, there is an isomorphism between the set of points in the air such that at time *t* the stone was *h* feet up and the set of those points on a graph that satisfy the equation

$$y = 50x - 16x^2.$$

The lines along which air flows (at sub-sonic speeds) past an aerofoil form a pattern that is identical with the lines along which electric current flows in a conducting liquid past a non-conductor of the same shape as the aerofoil. The two patterns are the same, though the physical bases are different.

Another isomorphism is worth consideration in more detail. Fig. 6/8/1 shows two dynamic systems, each with an input and an output. In the upper one, the left-hand axle *I* is the input; it can be rotated to any position, shown on the dial *u*. It is connected

through a spring S to a heavy wheel M, which is rigidly connected
to the output shaft O. O's degree of rotation is shown on the dial
v, which is its output.   The wheel dips into a trough with liquid F,
which applies a frictional force to the wheel, proportional to the
wheel's velocity.   If now, starting from given conditions, the input
u is taken through some sequence of values, so will the output v
pass through some determinate sequence of values, the particular
sequence depending on v's initial value, on v's rate of change at
that moment, and on the sequence used for the input at u.

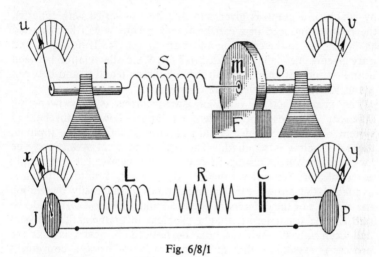

Fig. 6/8/1

The lower system is electrical.   Its input is a potentiometer, or
other device, J, that emits the voltage shown on the scale x.   In
series are an inductance L, a resistance R, and a capacitance C.
P is a current meter (such as is used in domestic supplies) recording
the sum of the currents that have passed through it.   The sum is
shown on the scale y, which is its output.

If now the values of L, R and C are adjusted to match the stiffness
of the spring, inertia of the wheel, and friction at F (though not
respectively), then the two systems can show a remarkable functional
identity.   Let them both start from rest.   Apply any input-sequence
of values at u, however long and arbitrary, and get an output-
sequence at v, of equal length: if the same sequence of values is
given at x, the output at y will be identical, along its whole length,
with that at v.   Try another input sequence to u and record what
appears at v: the same input given to x will result in an output at

95

y that copies that at *v*. Cover the central parts of the mechanism and the two machines are indistinguishable throughout an infinite number of tests applied. Machines can thus show the profoundest similarities in behaviour while being, from other points of view, utterly dissimilar.

Nor is this all. Well known to mathematicians are equations of the type

$$a\frac{d^2z}{dt^2} + b\frac{dz}{dt} + cz = w$$

by which, if a graph is given showing how *w* varied with time (*t*), the changes induced in *z* can be found. Thus *w* can be regarded as an "input" to the equation and *z* an "output". If now *a*, *b*, and *c* are given values suitably related to *L*, *R*, *S*, etc., the relation between *w* and *z* becomes identical with those between *u* and *v*, and between *x* and *y*. *All three systems are isomorphic.*

The great practical value of isomorphisms is now becoming apparent. Suppose the problem has arisen how the mechanical system will behave under certain conditions. Given the input *u*, the behaviour *v* is required. The real mechanical system may be awkward for direct testing: it may be too massive, or not readily accessible, or even not yet made! If, however, a mathematician is available, the answer can be found quickly and easily by finding the output *z* of the differential equation under input *w*. It would be said, in the usual terms, that a problem in mathematical physics had been solved. What should be noticed, however, is that the process is essentially that of using a map—of using a convenient isomorphic representation rather than the inconvenient reality.

It may happen that no mathematician is available but that an electrician is. In that case, the same principle can be used again. The electrical system is assembled, the input given to *x*, and the answer read off at *y*. This is more commonly described as "building an electrical model".

Clearly no one of the three systems has priority; any can substitute for the others. Thus if an engineer wants to solve the differential equation, he may find the answer more quickly by building the electrical system and reading the solutions at *y*. He is then usually said to have "built an analogue computer". The mechanical system might, in other circumstances, be found a more convenient form for the computer. The big general-purpose digital computer is remarkable precisely because it can be programmed to become isomorphic with any dynamic system whatever.

The use of isomorphic systems is thus common and important.

It is important because most systems have both difficult and easy patches in their properties. When an experimenter comes to a difficult patch in the particular system he is investigating he may, if an isomorphic form exists, find that the corresponding patch in the other form is much easier to understand or control or investigate. And experience has shown that the ability to change to an isomorphic form, though it does not give absolutely trustworthy evidence (for an isomorphism may hold only over a certain range), is nevertheless a most useful and practical help to the experimenter. In science it is used ubiquitously.

6/9. It must now be shown that this concept of isomorphism, vast though its range of applicability, is capable of exact and objective

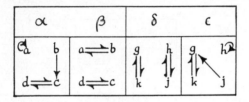

Fig. 6/9/1

definition. The most fundamental definition has been given by Bourbaki; here we need only the form suitable for dynamic systems. It applies quite straightforwardly once two machines have been reduced to their canonical representations.

Consider, for instance, the two simple machines M and N, with canonical representations

$$M:\begin{array}{c|cccc} \downarrow & a & b & c & d \\ \hline \alpha & a & c & d & c \\ \beta & b & a & d & c \end{array} \qquad N:\begin{array}{c|cccc} \downarrow & g & h & j & k \\ \hline \delta & k & j & h & g \\ \epsilon & k & h & g & g \end{array}$$

They show no obvious relation. If, however, their kinematic graphs are drawn, they are found to be as in Fig. 6/9/1. Inspection shows that there is a deep resemblance. In fact, by merely rearranging the *points* in N without disrupting any arrow (S.2/17) we can get the form shown in Fig. 6/9/2. These graphs are identical with M's graphs, apart from the labelling.

More precisely: the canonical representations of two machines are **isomorphic** if a one-one transformation of the states (input and output) of the one machine into those of the other can convert the one representation to the other.

Thus, in the example given, apply the one-one transformation P

$$P: \downarrow \begin{array}{cccccc} \delta & \epsilon & g & h & j & k \\ \beta & \alpha & c & a & b & d \end{array}$$

to N's table, applying it to the borders as well as to the body. The result is

$\downarrow$	c	a	b	d
β	d	b	a	c
α	d	a	c	c

This is essentially the same as M.   Thus, c and β in the border

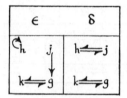

Fig. 6/9/2

give d in both.   The isomorphism thus corresponds to the definition. (The isomorphism can be seen more clearly if first the rows are interchanged, to

$\downarrow$	c	a	b	d
α	d	a	c	c
β	d	b	a	c

and then the columns interchanged, to

$\downarrow$	a	b	c	d
α	a	c	d	c
β	b	a	d	c

but this re-arrangement is merely for visual convenience.)

When the states are defined by vectors the process is essentially unchanged.   Suppose R and S are two absolute systems:

$$R: \begin{cases} x' = x + y \\ y' = x - y \end{cases} \qquad S: \begin{cases} u' = -u - v \\ v' = -u + v \end{cases}$$

The transformation P:

$$P: \downarrow \begin{matrix} u & v \\ y & -x \end{matrix}$$

is a shorthand way of describing the one-one transformation that pairs off states in S and R thus:

in S,	(2,3)	against	(−3,2)	in R
,, ,,	(1,0)	,,	(0,1)	,, ,,
,, ,,	(4,5)	,,	(−5,4)	,, ,,
,, ,,	(−3,0)	,,	(0,−3)	,, ,,
i.e. ,, ,,	(u,v)	,,	$(−v,u)$	,, ,,

(Compare U of S.4/9.) Apply P to all the description of S; the result is

$$\begin{cases} y' = -y + x \\ -x' = -y - x \end{cases}$$

which is algebraically identical with R. So R and S are isomorphic.

Ex. 1: What one-one transformation will show these absolute systems to be isomorphic?

$$Y: \downarrow \begin{matrix} a & b & c & d & e \\ c & c & d & d & b \end{matrix} \qquad Z: \downarrow \begin{matrix} p & q & r & s & t \\ r & q & q & p & r \end{matrix}$$

(Hint: Try to identify some characteristic feature, such as a state of equilibrium.)

Ex. 2: How many one-one transformations are there that will show these absolute systems to be isomorphic?

$$A: \downarrow \begin{matrix} a & b & c \\ b & c & a \end{matrix} \qquad B: \downarrow \begin{matrix} p & q & r \\ r & p & q \end{matrix}$$

Ex. 3: Write the canonical equations of the two systems of Fig. 6/8/1 and show that they are isomorphic. (Hint: How many variables are necessary if the system is to be a machine with input?)

Ex. 4: Find a re-labelling of variables that will show the absolute systems A and B to be isomorphic.

$$A: \begin{cases} x' = -x^2 + y \\ y' = -x^2 - y \\ z' = y^2 + z \end{cases} \qquad B: \begin{cases} u' = w^2 + u \\ v' = -v^2 + w \\ w' = -v^2 - w \end{cases}$$

(Hint: On the right side of A one variable is mentioned only once; the same is true of B. Also, in A, only one of the variables depends on itself quadratically, i.e. if of the form $a' = \pm a^2 \ldots$; the same is true of B.)

6/10. The previous section showed that two machines are isomorphic if one can be made identical to the other by simple re-labelling. The "re-labelling", however, can have various degrees of complexity, as we will now see.

The system that is specified only by states, as in the previous section, contains no direct reference either to parts or to variables. In such a case, "re-labelling" can mean only "re-labelling the states". A system with parts or variables, however, can also be re-labelled at its variables—by no means the same thing. Re-labelling the variables, in effect, re-labels the states but in a way subject to considerable constraint (S.7/8), whereas the re-labelling of states can be as arbitrary as we please. So a re-labelling of the states is more general than a re-labelling of the variables.

Thus suppose a system has nine states; an arbitrary re-labelling of eight of the states does not restrict what label shall be given to the ninth. Now suppose that the system has two variables, x and y, and that each can take three values: x_1, x_2, x_3 and y_1, y_2, y_3. Nine states are possible, of which two are (x_2,y_3) and (x_3,y_1). Suppose this system is re-labelled in its *variables*, thus

$$\downarrow \begin{matrix} x & y \\ \xi & \eta \end{matrix}$$

If now (x_2,y_3) is transformed to some state (α,β), and (x_3,y_1) is transformed to (γ,δ), then, for consistency, the state (x_2,y_1) *must* transform to (α,δ). (Draw the phase spaces and identify the values on the ξ and η axes.) Thus the nine states now cannot be transformed arbitrarily and independently. *A re-labelling of the variables offers less scope for change than a re-labelling of states.*

As a result, certain features that are destroyed by a re-labelling of states are preserved by a re-labelling of variables. Among them is the diagram of immediate effects.

The system described by its states has, of course, no such diagram, for it has in effect only one variable. A system with variables, however, has a diagram of immediate effects. The phase-space now has axes; and it is easily seen, after a few trials, that a one-one transformation that re-labels the variables, changes the diagram of immediate effects only to the extent of a "button and string" change; turning, say, A into B:

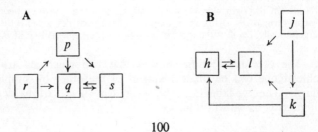

Ex. 1: (Ex. 6/9/4 continued.)   Compare the diagram of immediate effects of *A* and *B*.

Ex. 2: Mark the following properties of an absolute system as changed or unchanged by a re-labelling of its states: (i) The number of basins in its phase-space; (ii) whether it is reducible; (iii) its number of states of equilibrium; (iv) whether feedback is present; (v) the number of cycles in its phase-space.

Ex. 3: (Continued.)   How would they be affected by a re-labelling of variables?

6/11.   The subject of isomorphism is extensive, and only an introduction to the subject can be given here.   Before we leave it, however, we should notice that transformations more complex than a simple re-labelling of variables can change the diagram of immediate effects.   Thus the systems

$$A: \begin{cases} x' = \tfrac{1}{2}(x^2 + y^2) + xy + y \\ y' = \tfrac{1}{2}(x^2 + y^2) + xy + x \end{cases} \qquad B: \begin{cases} u' = -u \\ v' = v + v^2 \end{cases}$$

are isomorphic under the one-one transformation

$$P: \begin{cases} u = x - y \\ v = x + y \end{cases}$$

Yet *A*'s diagram is

$$\boxed{x} \rightleftarrows \boxed{y}$$

while *B*'s diagram is

$$\boxed{u} \quad \boxed{v},$$

i.e. two unconnected variables.

The "method of normal co-ordinates", widely used in mathematical physics, consists in applying just such a transformation as will treat the system not in its obvious form but in an isomorphic form that has all its variables independent.   In this transformation the diagram of immediate effects is altered grossly; what is retained is the set of normal modes, i.e. its characteristic way of behaving.

Such a transformation (as *P* above), that forms some function of the variables (i.e. $x - y$) represents, to the experimenter, more than a mere re-labelling of the x-, y-output dials.   It means that the Box's output of x and y must be put through some physical apparatus that will take x and y as input and will emit $x - y$ and $x + y$ as new outputs.   This combining corresponds to a more complex operation than was considered in S.6/10.

Ex.: Show that *A* and *B* are isomorphic.   (Hint: $(x - y)' = x' - y'$: why?)

HOMOMORPHIC MACHINES

6/12. The definition given for isomorphism defines "equality" in the strictest sense—it allows that two machines (or two Black Boxes) are "equal" only when they are so alike that an accidental interchange of them would be subsequently indetectable, at least by any test applied to their behaviours.

There are, however, lesser degrees of resemblance. Thus two pendulums, one beating seconds and the other half-seconds, are obviously similar, yet they are not isomorphic in the strict sense. There is, however, some similarity, which is shown by the fact that they become isomorphic if they are measured on separate time-scales, the one having half the values of the other.

Two machines may also be related by a "homomorphism." This occurs when a many-one transformation, applied to the more complex, can reduce it to a form that is isomorphic with the simpler. Thus the two machines M and N

$$
M: \begin{array}{c|ccccc}
\downarrow & a & b & c & d & e \\
\hline
i & b & a & b & c & a \\
j & a & b & c & b & c \\
k & a & b & b & e & d \\
l & b & c & a & e & e \\
\end{array}
\qquad
N: \begin{array}{c|cc}
\downarrow & g & h \\
\hline
\alpha & g & h \\
\beta & h & h \\
\end{array}
$$

may seem at first sight to have little resemblance. There is, however, a deep similarity. (The reader will gain much if he reads no further until he has discovered, if only vaguely, where the similarity lies; notice the peculiarity of N's table, with three elements alike and one different—can anything like that be seen in the table of M?—if cut into quadrants?)

Transform M by the many-one transformation T:

$$
T: \downarrow \begin{array}{cccccccc}
a & b & c & d & e & i & j & k & l \\
h & h & h & g & g & \beta & \beta & \alpha & \alpha \\
\end{array}
$$

(which is single-valued but not one-one as in S.6/9) and we get

$$
\begin{array}{c|ccccc}
\downarrow & h & h & h & g & g \\
\hline
\beta & h & h & h & h & h \\
\beta & h & h & h & h & h \\
\alpha & h & h & h & g & g \\
\alpha & h & h & h & g & g \\
\end{array}
$$

It will be found that the repetitions do not contradict one another, and that the table can equally well be given as

↓	h	g
β	h	h
α	h	g

which is isomorphic with N.

Examination of M shows now where the resemblance to N lies. Within M the transitions occur in blocks; thus a, b and c always go to some one of a, b or c. And the *blocks* in M undergo transitions in the same way as the *states* in N. *N is thus equivalent to a simplified version of M.*

The relation can be displayed in another way. Suppose first the two machines are viewed by some one who can distinguish all the five states of M; he will report simply that M is different from N (i.e. not isomorphic) and more complex. Suppose next that they are viewed by some observer with less power of discrimination, one who cannot discriminate between a, b, and c, but lumps them all together as, say, A; and who also lumps d and e together as B, i and j as Γ, and k and l as Δ. This new observer, seeing this simplified version of M, will report that it is isomorphic with N. Thus two machines are homomorphic when they become alike if one is merely simplified, i.e. observed with less than full discrimination.

Formally, if two machines are so related that a many-one transformation can be found that, applied to one of the machines, gives a machine that is isomorphic with the other, then the other (the simpler of the two) is a **homomorphism** of the first.

Ex.: Is isomorphism simply an extreme case of homomorphism?

Problem: What other types of homomorphism are there between machine and machine?

6/13. If the methods of this book are to be applied to biological systems, not only must the methods become sufficiently complex to match the systems but the systems must be considerably simplified if their study is ever to be practical. No biological system has yet been studied in its full complexity, nor is likely to be for a very long time. In practice the biologist always imposes a tremendous simplification before he starts work: if he watches a bird building its nest he does not see all the intricate pattern of detailed neuronic activities in the bird's brain; if he studies how a lizard escapes from its enemies he does not observe the particular molecular and ionic changes in its muscles; if he studies a tribe at its council meeting he does not observe all the many detailed processes going on in the individual members. The biologist thus usually studies only a small fraction of the system that faces him. Any statement he makes is only a half-truth, a simplification. To what extent can systems justifiably be simplified? Can a scientist work properly with half-truths?

The practical man, of course, has never doubted it. Let us see whether we can make the position clear and exact.

Knowledge can certainly be partial and yet complete in itself. Perhaps the most clear-cut example occurs in connexion with ordinary multiplication. The complete truth about multiplication is, of course, very extensive, for it includes the facts about all possible pairs, including such items as that

$$14792 \times 4{,}183584 = 61883{,}574528.$$

There is, however, a much smaller portion of the whole which consists simply in the facts that

$$\text{Even} \times \text{Even} = \text{Even}$$
$$\text{Even} \times \text{Odd} = \text{Even}$$
$$\text{Odd} \times \text{Even} = \text{Even}$$
$$\text{Odd} \times \text{Odd} = \text{Odd}$$

What is important here is that though this knowledge is only an infinitesimal fraction of the whole it is complete *within itself*. (It was, in fact, the first homomorphism considered in mathematics.) Contrast this completeness, in respect of Even and Odd, with the incompleteness shown by

$$2 \times 2 = 4$$
$$2 \times 4 = 8$$
$$4 \times 2 = 8$$
$$4 \times 4 = 16$$

which leaves unmentioned what is 4×8, etc. Thus it is perfectly possible for some knowledge, though partial in respect of some larger system, to be complete within itself, complete so far as it goes.

Homomorphisms may, as we have seen, exist between two different machines. They may also exist within one machine: between the various possible simplifications of it that *still retain the characteristic property of being machine-like* (S.3/1). Suppose, for instance, that the machine were A:

$$A: \downarrow \begin{array}{ccccc} a & b & c & d & e \\ e & b & a & b & e \end{array}$$

This is the machine as seen by the first observer (call him One). Suppose now that another observer (call him Two) was unable to distinguish states a and d, and also unable to distinguish b and e. Let us give the states new names for clarity:

$$\downarrow \begin{array}{ccccc} a & d & c & b & e \\ \underbrace{} & & \underbrace{} & & \\ K & L & M \end{array}$$

The second observer, seeing states K, L or M would find the machine's behaviour determinate. Thus when at K (really a or d) it would always go to M (either b or e), and so on. He would say that it behaved according to the closed transformation

$$\downarrow \begin{array}{ccc} K & L & M \\ M & K & M \end{array}$$

and that this was single-valued, and thus determinate.

The new system has been formed simply by grouping together certain states that were previously distinct, but it does not follow that any arbitrary grouping will give a homomorphism. Thus suppose yet another observer Three could distinguish only two states:

$$\downarrow \begin{array}{ccccc} a & b & c & d & e \\ \underbrace{} & & & \underbrace{} & \\ P & & & Q \end{array}$$

He would find that P changed sometimes to Q (when P was really at a) and sometimes to P (when P was really at b or c). The change from P is thus not single-valued, and Three would say that the machine (with states P and Q) was not determinate. He would be dissatisfied with the measurements that led to the distinction between P and Q and would try to become more discriminating, so as to remove the unpredictability.

A machine can thus be simplified to a new form when its states are compounded suitably. Scientific treatment of a complex system does *not* demand that every possible distinction be made.

Ex. 1: What homomorphism combines Odd and Even by the operation of addition?

Ex. 2: Find all possible simplifications of the four-state system

$$\downarrow \begin{array}{cccc} a & b & c & d \\ b & b & d & c \end{array}$$

which leaves the result still a determinate machine.

Ex. 3: What simplification is possible in

$$\begin{cases} x' = -y \\ y' = x^2 + y, \end{cases}$$

if the result is still to be a determinate machine?

6/14. The deliberate refusal to attempt all possible distinctions, and the deliberate restriction of the study of a dynamic system to some homomorphism of the whole, become justified, and in fact almost unavoidable, when the experimenter is confronted with the system of biological origin.

We usually assumed, in the earlier chapters, that the observer knew, at each moment, just what state the system was in. It was assumed, in other words, that at every moment his information about the system was complete. There comes a stage, however, as the system becomes larger and larger, when the reception of all the information is impossible by reason of its sheer bulk. Either the recording channels cannot carry all the information, or the observer, presented with it all, is overwhelmed. When this occurs, what is he to do? The answer is clear: he must give up any ambition to know the *whole* system. His aim must be to achieve a partial knowledge that, though partial over the whole, is none the less complete within itself, and is sufficient for his ultimate practical purpose.

These facts emphasise an important matter of principle in the study of the very large system. Faced with such a system, the observer must be cautious in referring to "the system", for the term will probably be ambiguous, perhaps highly so. "*The* system" may refer to the whole system quite apart from any observer to study it— the thing as it is in itself; or it may refer to the set of variables (or states) with which some given observer is concerned. Though the former sounds more imposing philosophically, the practical worker inevitably finds the second more important. Then the second meaning can itself be ambiguous if the particular observer is not specified, for the system may be any one of the many sub-machines provided by homomorphism. Why all these meanings should be distinguished is because different sub-machines can have different properties; so that although both sub-machines may be abstracted from the same real "thing", a statement that is true of one may be false of another.

It follows that there can be no such thing as *the* (unique) behaviour of a very large system, apart from a given observer. For there can legitimately be as many sub-machines as observers, and therefore as many behaviours, which may actually be so different as to be incompatible if they occurred in one system. Thus the 5-state system with kinematic graph

$$h \rightleftarrows k \qquad m \rightarrow l \rightleftarrows j$$

has two basins, and always ends in a cycle. The homomorphic

sub-machine (with states r and s) given by the transformation

$$
\begin{array}{c}
h \quad j \quad k \quad l \qquad m \\
\downarrow \underbrace{\hspace{3em}} \quad \underbrace{\hspace{1em}} \\
\quad r \qquad\qquad s
\end{array}
$$

has graph $s \rightarrow r$, with one basin and no cycle. Both statements are equally true, and are compatible because they refer to different systems (as defined in S.3/11).

The point of view taken here is that science (as represented by the observer's discoveries) is not immediately concerned with discovering what the system "really" is, but with co-ordinating the various observers' discoveries, each of which is only a portion, or an aspect, of the whole truth.

Were the engineer to treat bridgebuilding by a consideration of every atom he would find the task impossible by its very size. He therefore ignores the fact that his girders and blocks are really composite, made of atoms, and treats them as his units. As it happens, the nature of girders permits this simplification, and the engineer's work becomes a practical possibility. It will be seen therefore that the method of studying very large systems by studying only carefully selected aspects of them is simply what is always done in practice. Here we intend to follow the process more rigorously and consciously.

6/15. *The lattice.* The various simplifications of a machine have exact relations to one another   Thus, the six forms of the system of Ex. 6/13/2 are:

(1) a, b, c, d
(2) $a + b, c, d$
(3) $a, b, c + d$
(4) $a + b, c + d$
(5) $a, b + c + d$
(6) $a + b + c + d$

where, e.g. "$a + b$" means that a and b are no longer distinguished. Now (4) can be obtained from (3) by a merging of a and b. But (5) cannot be obtained from (4) by a simple merging; for (5) uses a distinction between a and b that has been lost in (4). Thus it is soon verified that simplification can give:

from (1): all the other five,
„ (2): (4) and (6),
„ (3): (4), (5) and (6),
„ (4): (6),
„ (5): (6),
„ (6): none.

The various simplifications are thus related as in the diagram, in which a descending line connects the simpler form (below) with the form from which it can be directly obtained (above):

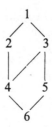

This diagram is of a type known as a lattice—a structure much studied in modern mathematics. What is of interest in this Introduction is that this ordering makes precise many ideas about systems, ideas that have hitherto been considered only intuitively.

Every lattice has a single element at the top (like 1) and a single element at the bottom (like 6). When the lattice represents the possible simplifications of a machine, the element at the top corresponds to the machine with every state distinguished; it corresponds to the knowledge of the experimenter who takes note of every distinction available in its states. The element at the bottom corresponds to a machine with every state merged; if this state is called Z the machine has as transformation only

This transformation is closed, so *something* persists (S.10/4), and the observer who sees only at this level of discrimination can say of the machine: "it persists", and can say no more. This persistance is, of course, the most rudimentary property of a machine, distinguishing it from the merely evanescent. (The importance of "closure", emphasised in the early chapters, can now be appreciated —it corresponds to the intuitive idea that, to be a machine, an entity must at least persist.)

Between these extremes lie the various simplifications, in their natural and exact order. Near the top lie those that differ from the full truth only in some trifling matter. Those that lie near the bottom are the simplifications of the grossest type. Near the bottom lies such a simplification as would reduce a whole economic system with a vast number of interacting parts, going through a trade cycle, to the simple form of two states:

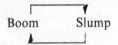

Boom   Slump

Thus, *the various simplifications of a dynamic system can be ordered and related.*

6/16. *Models.* We can now see much more clearly what is meant by a "model". The subject was touched on in S.6/8, where three systems were found to be isomorphic and therefore capable of being used as representations of each other. The subject is of some importance to those who work with biological systems, for in many cases the use of a model is helpful, either to help the worker think about the subject or to act as a form of analogue computer.

The model will seldom be *iso*morphic with the biological system: usually it will be a homomorphism of it. But the model itself is seldom regarded in all its practical detail: usually it is only some *aspect* of the model that is related to the biological system; thus the tin mouse may be a satisfactory model of a living mouse—provided one ignores the tinniness of the one and the proteinness of the other. Thus what usually happens is that the two systems, biological and model, are so related that a homomorphism of the one is isomorphic with a homomorphism of the other. (This relation is symmetric, so either may justifiably be said to be a "model" of the other.) The higher the homomorphisms are on their lattices, the better or more realistic will be the model.

At this point this Introduction must leave the subject of Homomorphisms. Enough has been said to show the foundations of the subject and to indicate the main lines for its development. But these developments belong to the future.

Ex. 1: What would be the case when it was the two top-most elements of the two lattices that were isomorphic?

Ex. 2: To what degree is the Rock of Gibraltar a model of the brain?

Ex. 3: To what extent can the machine

$$\downarrow \begin{matrix} p & q & r \\ q & r & r \end{matrix}$$

provide models for the system of Ex. 6/13/2?

THE VERY LARGE BOX

6/17. The previous sections have shown how the properties that are usually ascribed to machines can also be ascribed to Black

Boxes. We do in fact work, in our daily lives, much more with Black Boxes than we are apt to think. At first we are apt to think, for instance, that a bicycle is not a Black Box, for we can see every connecting link. We delude ourselves, however. The ultimate links between pedal and wheel are those interatomic forces that hold the particles of metal together; of these we see nothing, and the child who learns to ride can become competent merely with the knowledge that pressure on the pedals makes the wheels go round.

To emphasise that the theory of Black Boxes is practically co-extensive with that of everyday life, let us notice that if a set of Black Boxes has been studied by an observer, he is in a position to couple them together to form *designed* machinery. The method is straightforward: as the examination of each Box has given its canonical representation (S.6/5), so can they be coupled, inputs to outputs, to form new systems exactly as described in S.4/8.

What is being suggested now is not that Black Boxes behave somewhat like real objects but that the real objects are in fact all Black Boxes, and that we have in fact been operating with Black Boxes all our lives. The theory of the Black Box is merely the theory of real objects or systems, when close attention is given to the question, relating object and observer, about what information comes from the object, and how it is obtained. Thus the theory of the Black Box is simply the study of the relations between the experimenter and his environment, when special attention is given to the flow of information. "A study of the real world thus becomes a study of transducers." (Goldman, *Information theory*.)

6/18. Before we go further, the question of "emergent" properties should be clarified.

First let one fact be established. If a number of Black Boxes are given, and each is studied in isolation until its canonical representation is established, and if they are coupled in a known pattern by known linkages, then it follows (S.4/8) that the behaviour of the whole is determinate, and can be predicted. Thus an assembly of Black Boxes, in these conditions, will show no "emergent" properties; i.e. no properties that could not have been predicted from knowledge of the parts and their couplings.

The concept of "emergence" has never been defined with precision, but the following examples will probably suffice as a basis for discussion:

(1) Ammonia is a gas, and so is hydrogen chloride. When the two gases are mixed, the result is a solid—a property not possessed by either reactant.

(2) Carbon, hydrogen and oxygen are all practically tasteless, yet the particular compound "sugar" has a characteristic taste possessed by none of them.

(3) The twenty (or so) amino-acids in a bacterium have none of them the property of being "self-reproducing", yet the whole, with some other substances, has this property.

If these examples are compared in detail with the processes of study and coupling of Black Boxes, it is soon seen that the examples postulate much less knowledge of their parts than is postulated of the Black Boxes. Thus the prediction in regard to ammonia and hydrogen chloride is based on no more knowledge of each substance than that it is a gas. Similarly, of the twenty amino-acids all that is asked is "is it self-reproducing?" Were each amino-acid treated as a Black Box the examination would be far more searching. The input to a molecule is the set of electrical and mechanical forces, in all distributions and combinations, that can affect it; and its output is the set of all states, electrical and mechanical, that it can be in. Were this complete knowledge available, then the method of S.4/8 shows how the behaviour of many coupled amino-acids could be predicted; and among the predicted behaviours would be that of self-reproduction of the whole.

It will be seen that prediction of the whole's behaviour can be based on complete or on incomplete knowledge of the parts. If the knowledge is complete, then the case is that of the Black Box whose canonical representation is known, the inputs or circumstances being all those that may be given by the other Boxes to which it is to be coupled. When the knowledge of the parts is so complete, the prediction can also be complete, and no extra properties can emerge.

Often, however, the knowledge is not, for whatever reason, complete. Then the prediction has to be undertaken on incomplete knowledge, and may prove mistaken. Sometimes all that is known of the parts is that every one has a certain characteristic. There may be no better way of predicting than to use simple extrapolation —to predict that the whole will have it. Sometimes this proves justified; thus, if a whole is of three parts, each of pure copper, then we shall be correct if we predict that the whole is of pure copper. But often the method fails, and a new property can, if we please, be said to "emerge".

It does in fact very commonly happen that when the system becomes large, so that the range of size from part to whole is very large, the properties of the whole are very different from those of the parts. Biological systems are thus particularly likely to show the difference. We must therefore be on guard against expecting the properties of the whole to reproduce the properties of the parts, and vice versa.

The examples of ammonium chloride and sugar mentioned above are simple examples, but more complex cases occur. Consider, for instance, the concept of "localisation" of some function in a system. It may well happen that the view taken when the matter is examined in the small is quite different from that taken in the large. Thus suppose it is asked whether the brewing industry in England is localised. The Exciseman, knowing of every building in his district whether it is or is not part of the brewing trade, will say that brewing is undoubtedly "localised". On the other hand, the map-maker of England, being unable to mark any particular county as being the seat of brewing, will say that it is not localised. Each, of course, is correct. What allows the contradiction is that when the range of size is great, what is true at one end of the scale may be false at the other.

Another example showing how contradictory may be the properties in the small and the large is given by an ordinary piece of elastic. For years physical chemists searched for what made the molecule contractile. They have since discovered that they were making exactly the mistake that this section is attempting to prevent. It is now known that the rubber molecule has no inherent contractility: stretch one out and let it go, and nothing happens! Why then does rubber contract? The point is that "stretching rubber" is not "stretching *one* . . ."; the molecules, when there are more than one, jostle each other and thereby force the majority to take lengths less than their maxima. The result is that a shortening occurs, just as if, on a crowded beach, a rope fifty feet long is drawn out straight: after a few minutes the ends will be less than fifty feet apart!

Further examples are hardly necessary, for the point to be made is the merely negative one that in a large system there is no *a priori* necessity for the properties of the whole to be a simple copy of those of the parts. (S.7/3 adds some further examples.)

6/19. As the system becomes larger, so does the fundamental method of study (S.6/3) become more laborious in application. Eventually the amount of labour necessary becomes prohibitive. What then is the observer to do? The question is of great importance in the biological sciences, whether zoological or sociological, for the size and complexity of the systems is great indeed.

The same difficulty has occurred in other sciences. Thus although the Newtonian theory has, in principle, solved all gravitational problems, yet its application to three bodies is most complex, and its application to half a dozen is prohibitively laborious. Yet astrophysicists want to ask questions about the behaviour of star clusters with 20,000 members! What is to be done?

Experience has shown that in such cases the scientist must be very careful about what questions he asks. He must ask for what he *really* wants to know, and not for what he thinks he wants. Thus the beginner will say simply that he wants to know what the cluster will do, i.e. he wants the trajectories of the components. If this knowledge, however, could be given to him, it would take the form of many volumes filled with numerical tables, and he would then realise that he did not really want all that. In fact, it usually happens that the significant question is something simple, such as "will the cluster contract to a ball, or will it spread out into a disc?"

The physicists, led originally by Poincaré, have now a well developed method for dealing with such matters—that of topology. By its means, unambiguous answers can be given to simple questions, so that the intricacies that would overwhelm the observer are never encountered.

A similar method, applied to complicated differential equations, enables the main important features of the solutions to be deduced in cases where the full solutions would be unmanageably complicated. This is the so-called "stability" theory of these equations.

What is important for us here is that these methods exist. They suggest that if a Black Box (such as a brain) has far too many variables for a study in every detail to be practical then it should be possible for the cybernetically-minded psychologist to devise a "topological" approach that shall enable him to get what information he really wants (not what he thinks he wants!) without his being overwhelmed with useless detail. Lewin attempted such a psychology; but in the '30s topology was not yet developed to be a useful tool. In the '50s, however, it is much better developed, especially in the form published under the pseudonym of *Nicholas Bourbaki*, by the French School. At last we have before us the possibility of a psychology that shall be at once rigorous and practical.

THE INCOMPLETELY OBSERVABLE BOX

6/20. So far, in this chapter, we have assumed that the observer of the Black Box has the necessary means for observing all that pertains to the Box's state, so that he is like a Ship's Engineer (S.6/2) who faces a complete set of dials. Often, however, this is not so—some of the dials are hidden, or missing—and an important part of Black Box theory is concerned with making clear what peculiarities appear when the observer can observe only certain components of the whole state.

The theoretical developments are large, and little explored. They will almost certainly be of importance in psychology; for, to the psychologist, the individual subject, whether a neurotic person or a rat in a maze, is largely a system that is not wholly observable; for the events in the subject's brain are not directly observable at the clinical or experimental session.

It should be noticed that as soon as some of a system's variables become unobservable, the "system" represented by the remainder may develop remarkable, even miraculous, properties. A commonplace illustration is given by conjuring, which achieves (apparently) the miraculous, simply because not all the significant variables are observable. It is possible that some of the brain's "miraculous" properties—of showing "foresight", "intelligence", etc.—are miraculous only because we have not so far been able to observe the events in *all* the significant variables.

6/21. As an example of the profound change that may occur in the observer's opinion about a mechanism if part of it becomes inaccessible to direct observation, consider the following example.

The observer is assumed to be studying a Black Box which consists of two interacting parts, *A* and *Z*. Both are affected by the common input I. (Notice that *A*'s inputs are *I* and *Z*.)

Suppose the important question is whether the part *A* does or does not show some characteristic behaviour *B* (i.e. follow trajectory *B*). Suppose this is shown (followed) only on the simultaneous occurrence of

(1) *I* at state α

and (2) *Z* at state *y*.

Suppose that *Z* is at state *y* only *after I* has had the special value μ.

We (author and reader) are omniscient, for we know everything about the system. Let us, using full knowledge, see how two observers (One and Two) could come to different opinions if they had different powers of observation.

Observer One can see, like us, the values of both A and Z. He studies the various combinations that may lead to the appearance of B, and he reports that B appears whenever the whole shows a state with Z at y and the input at α. Thus, given that the input is at α, he relates the occurrence of B to whether Z is at y now.

Observer Two is handicapped—he can see only I and A, not Z. He will find that knowledge of A's state and of I's state is not sufficient to enable him to predict reliably whether B will be shown; (for sometimes Z will be at y and sometimes at some other state). If however Two turns his attention to *earlier* events at I he finds he can predict B's appearance accurately. For if I has in succession the values μ, α then behaviour B will appear, and not otherwise. Thus, given that the input is at α, he relates the occurrence of B to whether I did have the value μ earlier.

Thus Two, being unable to observe Z directly, can none the less make the whole predictable *by taking into account earlier values of what he* can *observe*. The reason is, the existence of the correspondence:

$$I \text{ at } \mu \text{ earlier} \leftrightarrow Z \text{ at } y \text{ now}$$
$$I \text{ not at } \mu \text{ earlier} \leftrightarrow Z \text{ not at } y \text{ now}.$$

As this correspondence is one-one, information about I's state a step earlier and information about Z's state now are *equivalent*, and each can substitute for the other; for to know one is to know the other.

If One and Two are quarrelsome, they can now fall into a dispute. One can maintain that the system shows no "memory", i.e. its behaviour requires no reference to the past, because the appearance of behaviour B can be fully accounted for by the system's *present* state (at I, A and Z). Two can deny this, and can point out that the system of I and A can be shown as determinate only when past values of I are taken into account, i.e. when some form of "memory" is appealed to.

Clearly, we need not take sides. One and Two are talking of different systems (of $I + A + Z$ or of $I + A$), so it is not surprising that they can make differing statements. What we must notice here is that Two is using the appeal to "memory" as a substitute for his inability to observe Z.

Thus we obtain the general rule: *If a determinate system is only partly observable, and thereby becomes (for that observer) not predictable, the observer may be able to restore predictability by taking the system's past history into account, i.e. by assuming the existence within it of some form of "memory".*

The argument is clearly general, and can be applied equally well if the special, earlier, event (μ) occurred not one step earlier, but many. Thus in general, if earlier events $E_1, E_2, \ldots, E_k$ leave traces $T_1, T_2, \ldots, T_k$ respectively, which persist; and if later the remainder of the system produces behaviours $B_1, B_2, \ldots, B_k$ corresponding to the value of T, then the various behaviours may be related to, or explained by, either

(1) the *present* value of T, in which case there is no need for the invocation of any "memory", or

(2) the *past* value of E, in which case the observer is compelled to postulate some form of "memory" in the system.

Thus *the possession of "memory" is not a wholly objective property of a system*—it is a relation between a system and an observer; and the property will alter with variations in the channel of communication between them.

Thus to invoke "memory" in a system as an explanation of its behaviour is equivalent to declaring that one cannot observe the system completely. The properties of "memory" are not those of the simple "thing" but the more subtle "coding".

Ex. 1: Prove the statement (*Design* .. S.19/22) that in an absolute system we can avoid direct reference to some of the variables provided we use derivatives of the remaining variables to replace them.

Ex. 2: Prove the same statement about equations in finite differences.

Ex. 3: Show that if the system has n degrees of freedom we must, in general, always have at least n observations, each of the type "at time t_i variable x had value X_i" if the subsequent behaviour is to be predictable.

6/22. A clear example showing how the presence of "memory" is related to the observability of a part is given by the digital calculator with a magnetic tape. Suppose, for simplicity, that at a certain moment the calculator will produce a 1 or a 2 according to whether the tape, at a certain point, is magnetised $+$ or $-$, respectively; the act of magnetisation occurred, say, ten minutes ago, and whether it was magnetised $+$ or $-$ depended on whether the operator did or did not, respectively, close a switch. There is thus the correspondence:

$$\text{switch closed} \leftrightarrow + \leftrightarrow 1$$
$$\text{switch open} \quad \leftrightarrow - \leftrightarrow 2$$

An observer who can see the magnetic tape now can argue that any reference to the past is unnecessary, for he can account for the machine's behaviour (i.e. whether it will produce a 1 or a 2) by its state *now*, by examining what the tape carries *now*. Thus to know that it carries a + now is sufficient to allow prediction that the machine's next state will be a 1.

On the other hand, an observer who cannot observe the tape can predict its behaviour only by reference to what was done to the switch ten minutes ago. He will insist that the machine has "memory".

The two observers are not really in conflict, as we can see at once when we realise that they are talking of two "machines" that are not identical. To the first observer, "the machine" means "calculator + tape + switch"; to the second it means "calculator + switch". *They are talking about different systems.* (Again it must be emphasised that in complex systems a mere reference to the material object is often not sufficient to define adequately the system under discussion.) (Compare S.6/14, 12/9.)

Essentially the same difference can occur in a more biological system. Thus, suppose I am in a friend's house and, as a car goes past outside, his dog rushes to a corner of the room and cringes. To me the behaviour is causeless and inexplicable. Then my friend says, "He was run over by a car six months ago." The behaviour is now accounted for by reference to an event of six months ago. If we say that the dog shows "memory" we refer to much the same fact—that his behaviour can be explained, not by reference to his state now but to what his state was six months ago. If one is not careful one says that the dog "has" memory, and then thinks of the dog as *having* some*thing*, as he might have a patch of black hair. One may then be tempted to start looking for the thing; and one may discover that this "thing" has some very curious properties.

Clearly, "memory" is not an objective something that a system either does or does not possess; it is a concept that the *observer* invokes to fill in the gap caused when part of the system is unobservable. The fewer the observable variables, the more will the observer be forced to regard events of the past as playing a part in the system's behaviour. Thus "memory" in the brain is only partly objective. No wonder its properties have sometimes been found to be unusual or even paradoxical. Clearly the subject requires thorough re-examination from first principles.

PART TWO

VARIETY

Now the soldier realised what a capital tinder-box this was. If he struck it once, the dog came who sat upon the chest of copper money; if he struck it twice, the dog came who had the silver; and if he struck it three times, then appeared the dog who had the gold.

("The Tinder-Box")

Chapter 7

QUANTITY OF VARIETY

7/1. In Part I we considered the main properties of the machine, usually with the assumption that we had before us the actual thing, about which we would make some definite statement, with reference to what it is doing here and now. To progress in cybernetics, however, we shall have to extend our range of consideration. The fundamental questions in regulation and control can be answered only when we are able to consider the broader set of what it *might* do, when "might" is given some exact specification.

Throughout Part II, therefore, we shall be considering always *a set* of possibilities. The study will lead us into the subjects of information and communication, and how they are coded in their passages through mechanism. This study is essential for the thorough understanding of regulation and control. We shall start from the most elementary or basic considerations possible.

7/2. A second reason for considering *a set* of possibilities is that science is little interested in some fact that is valid only for a single experiment, conducted on a single day; it seeks always for generalisations, statements that shall be true for all of a set of experiments, conducted in a variety of laboratories and on a variety of occasions. Galileo's discovery of the law of the pendulum would have been of little interest had it been valid only for that pendulum on that afternoon. Its great importance is due precisely to the fact that it is true over a great range of space and time and materials. Science looks for the repetitive (S.7/15).

7/3. This fact, that it is the *set* that science refers to, is often obscured by a manner of speech. "The chloride ion . . .", says the lecturer, when clearly he means his statement to apply to all chloride ions. So we get references to the petrol engine, the growing child, the chronic drunkard, and to other objects in the singular, when the reference is in fact to the set of all such objects.

Sometimes it happens that a statement is equally true of the individual and the set: "the elephant eats with its trunk", for instance. But the commonness of such a double application should not make us overlook the fact that some types of statement are applicable only to the set (or only to the individual) and become misleading and a source of confusion if applied to the other. Thus a gramme of hot hydrogen iodide gas, at some particular moment, may well be 37 per cent ionised; yet this statement must not be applied to the individual molecules, which are all either wholly ionised or not at all; what is true of the set is false of the individuals. Again, the Conservative M.P.s have, at the moment, a majority in Parliament; the statement is meaningless if applied to an individual member. Again, a tyre on a motor-car may well be travelling due west at 50 m.p.h. when considered as a whole; yet the portion in contact with the road is motionless, that at the top is travelling due west at 100 m.p.h., and in fact not a single particle in the tyre is behaving as the whole is behaving.

Again, twenty million women may well have thirty million children, but only by a dangerous distortion of language can we say that Mrs. Everyman has one and a half children. The statement can sometimes be made without confusion only because those who have to take action, those who have to provide schools for the children, for instance, know that the half-child is not a freak but a set of ten million children.

Let us then accept it as basic that a statement true about a **set** may be either true or false (or perhaps meaningless) if applied to the **elements** in the set.

Ex.: The following statements apply to "The Cat", either to the species *Felis domestica* or to the cat next door. Consider the applicability of each statement to (i) the species, (ii) the individual:

1. It is a million years old,
2. It is male,
3. Today it is in every continent,
4. It fights its brothers,
5. About a half of it is female,
6. It is closely related to the Ursidae.

7/4. *Probability.* The exercise just given illustrates the confusion and nonsense that can occur when a concept that belongs properly to the set (or individual) is improperly applied to the other. An outstanding example of this occurs when, of the whole set, some *fraction* of the set has a particular property. Thus, of 100 men in a village 82 may be married. The fraction 0·82 is clearly relevant to the set, but has little meaning for any individual, each of whom either is or is not married. Examine each man as closely as you please, you will find nothing of "0·82" about him; and if he moves to another village this figure may change to another without his having changed at all. Evidently, the "0·82" is a property of the village, not of the individual.

Nevertheless, it is sometimes found convenient to pretend that the fraction has a meaning for the individual, and it may be said that any one person has a "probability" 0·82 of being married. This form of words is harmless provided it is borne in mind that the statement, in spite of its apparent reference to the individual, is really a statement about the village. Let this be forgotten and a host of "paradoxes" arise, as meaningless and silly as that of attempting to teach the "half"-child. Later (in Chapter 9) we shall have to use the concept of probability in conjunction with that of machine; the origin and real nature of the concept should be borne in mind perpetually.

7/5. *Communication.* Another subject in which the concept of a *set* plays an essential part is that of "communication", especially in the theory developed by Shannon and Wiener. At first, when one thinks of, say, a telegram arriving, one notices only the singleness of *one* telegram. Nevertheless, the act of "communication" necessarily implies the existence of a *set* of possibilities, i.e. more than one, as the following example will show.

A prisoner is to be visited by his wife, who is not to be allowed to send him any message however simple. It is understood that they may have agreed, before his capture, on some simple code. At her visit, she asks to be allowed to send him a cup of coffee; assuming the beverage is not forbidden, how is the warder to ensure that no coded message is transmitted by it? He knows that she is anxious to let her husband know whether or not a confederate has yet been caught.

The warder will cogitate with reasonings that will go somewhat as follows: "She might have arranged to let him know by whether the coffee goes in sweetened or not—I can stop that simply by adding lots of sugar and then telling him I have done so. She might have arranged to let him know by whether or not she sends a spoon—I can stop that by taking away any spoon and then telling him that Regulations forbid a spoon anyway. She might do it by sending tea rather than coffee—no, that's stopped because, as they know, the canteen will only supply coffee at this time of day." So his cogitations go on; what is noteworthy is that at each possibility he intuitively attempts to stop the communication by enforcing a reduction of the possibilities to one—always sweetened, never a spoon, coffee only, and so on.   As soon as the possibilities shrink to one, so soon is communication blocked, and the beverage robbed of its power of transmitting information.   The transmission (and storage) of information is thus essentially related to the existence of a *set* of possibilities.   The example may make this statement plausible; in fact it is also supported by all the work in the modern theory of communication, which has shown abundantly how essential, and how fruitful, is the concept of the set of possibilities.

Communication thus necessarily demands a set of messages.   Not only is this so, but the information carried by a particular message depends on the set it comes from.   *The information conveyed is not an intrinsic property of the individual message.*   That this is so can be seen by considering the following example.   Two soldiers are taken prisoner by two enemy countries A and B, one by each; and their two wives later each receive the brief message "I am well".   It is known, however, that country A allows the prisoner a choice from

> *I am well,*
> *I am slightly ill,*
> *I am seriously ill,*

while country B allows only the message

> *I am well*

meaning "I am alive".   (Also in the set is the possibility of " no message ".)   The two wives will certainly be aware that though each has received the same phrase, the informations that they have received are by no means identical.

From these considerations it follows that, in this book, we must give up thinking, as we do as individuals, about "this message". We must become scientists, detach ourselves, and think about "people receiving messages".   And this means that we must turn our attention from any individual message to the set of all the possibilities.

VARIETY

7/6.   Throughout this Part we shall be much concerned with the question, given a set, of how many distinguishable elements it contains.   Thus, if the order of occurrence is ignored, the set

$$c, b, c, a, c, c, a, b, c, b, b, a$$

which contains twelve elements, contains only three *distinct* elements —*a*, *b* and *c*. Such a set will be said to have a **variety** of three elements. (A qualification is added in the next section.)

Though this counting may seem simple, care is needed. Thus the two-armed semaphore can place each arm, independently of the other, in any of eight positions; so the two arms provide 64 combinations. At a distance, however, the arms have no individuality—"arm *A* up and arm *B* down" cannot be distinguished from "arm *A* down and arm *B* up"—so to the distant observer only 36 positions can be distinguished, and the variety is 36, not 64. It will be noticed that a set's variety is not an intrinsic property of the set: the observer and his powers of discrimination may have to be specified if the variety is to be well defined.

Ex. 1: With 26 letters to choose from, how many 3-letter combinations are available for motor registration numbers?

Ex. 2: If a farmer can distinguish 8 breeds of chicks, but cannot sex them, while his wife can sex them but knows nothing of breeds, how many distinct classes of chicks can they distinguish when working together?

Ex. 3: A spy in a house with four windows arranged rectangularly is to signal out to sea at night by each window showing, or not showing, a light. How many forms can be shown if, in the darkness, the position of the lights relative to the house cannot be perceived?

Ex. 4: Bacteria of different species differ in their ability to metabolise various substances: thus lactose is destroyed by *E. coli* but not by *E. typhi*. If a bacteriologist has available ten substances, each of which may be destroyed or not by a given species, what is the maximal number of species that he can distinguish?

Ex. 5: If each Personality Test can distinguish five grades of its own characteristic, what is the least number of such tests necessary to distinguish the 2,000,000,000 individuals of the world's population?

Ex. 6: In a well-known card trick, the conjurer identifies a card thus: He shows 21 cards to a by-stander, who selects, mentally, one of them without revealing his choice. The conjurer then deals the 21 cards face upwards into three equal heaps, with the by-stander seeing the faces, and asks him to say which heap contains the selected card. He then takes up the cards, again deals them into three equal heaps, and again asks which heap contains the selected card; and similarly for a third deal. The conjurer then names the selected card. What variety is there in (i) the by-stander's indications, (ii) the conjurer's final selection?

Ex. 7: (Continued.) 21 cards is not, in fact, the maximal number that could be used. What is the maximum, if the other conditions are unaltered?

Ex. 8: (Continued.) How many times would the by-stander have to indicate which of three heaps held the selected card if the conjurer were finally to be able to identify the correct card out of the full pack of 52?

Ex. 9: If a child's blood group is O and its mother's group is O, how much variety is there in the groups of its possible fathers?

7/7. It will have been noticed that many of the exercises involved the finding of products and high powers. Such computations are often made easier by the use of logarithms. It is assumed that the reader is familiar with their basic properties, but one formula will be given for reference. If only logarithms to base a are available and we want to find the logarithm to the base b of some number N, then

$$\log_b N = \frac{\log_a N}{\log_a b}$$

In particular, $\log_2 N = 3\cdot322 \log_{10} N$.

The word **variety**, in relation to a set of distinguishable elements, will be used to mean either (i) the number of distinct elements, or (ii) the logarithm to the base 2 of the number, the context indicating the sense used. When variety is measured in the logarithmic form its unit is the "bit", a contraction of "BInary digiT". Thus the variety of the sexes is 1 bit, and the variety of the 52 playing cards is 5·7 bits, because $\log_2 52 = 3\cdot322 \log_{10} 52 = 3\cdot322 \times 1\cdot7160 = 5\cdot7$. The chief advantage of this way of reckoning is that multiplicative combinations now combine by simple addition. Thus in Ex. 7/6/2 the farmer can distinguish a variety of 3 bits, his wife 1 bit, and the two together $3 + 1$ bits, i.e. 4 bits.

To say that a set has "no" variety, that the elements are all of one type, is, of course, to measure the variety logarithmically; for the logarithm of 1 is 0.

Ex. 1: In Ex. 7/6/4 how much variety, in bits, does each substance distinguish?

Ex. 2: In Ex. 7/6/5: (i) how much variety in bits does each test distinguish? (ii) What is the variety in bits of 2,000,000,000 distinguishable individuals? From these two varieties check your previous answer.

Ex. 3: What is the variety in bits of the 26 letters of the alphabet?

Ex. 4: (Continued.) What is the variety, in bits, of a block of five letters (not restricted to forming a word)? Check the answer by finding the number of such blocks, and then the variety.

Ex. 5: A question can be answered only by Yes or No; (i) what variety is in the answer? (ii) In twenty such answers made independently?

Ex. 6: (Continued.) How many objects can be distinguished by twenty questions, each of which can be answered only by Yes or No?

Ex. 7: A closed and single-valued transformation is to be considered on six states:

$$\downarrow \begin{array}{cccccc} a & b & c & d & e & f \\ ? & ? & ? & ? & ? & ? \end{array}$$

in which each question mark has to be replaced by a letter. If the replacements are otherwise unrestricted, what variety (logarithmic) is there in the set of all possible such transformations?

Ex. 8: (Continued.) If the closed transformation had *n* states what variety is there?

Ex. 9: If the English vocabulary has variety of 10 bits per word, what is the storage capacity of 10 minutes' speech on a gramophone record, assuming the speech is at 120 words per minute?

Ex. 10: (Continued.) How does this compare with the capacity of a printed page of newspaper (approximately)?

Ex. 11: (Continued.) If a pamphlet takes 10 minutes to be read aloud, how does its variety compare with that of the gramophone record?

Ex. 12: What set is the previous Ex. referring to?

Ex. 13: Can a merely negative event—a light not being lit, a neuron not being excited, a telegram not arriving—be used as a contribution to variety?

CONSTRAINT

7/8. A most important concept, with which we shall be much concerned later, is that of **constraint**. It is a *relation* between two sets, and occurs when the variety that exists under one condition is less than the variety that exists under another. Thus, the variety in the human sexes is 1 bit; if a certain school takes only boys, the variety in the sexes within the school is zero; so as 0 is less than 1, constraint exists.

Another well-known example is given by the British traffic lights, which have three lamps and which go through the sequence (where "+" means lit and "0" unlit):

	(1)	(2)	(3)	(4)	(1)	
Red:	+	+	0	0	+	...
Yellow:	0	+	0	+	0	...
Green:	0	0	+	0	0	...

Four combinations are thus used. It will be noticed that Red is, at various times, both lit and unlit; so is Yellow; and so is Green. So if the three lights could vary independently, eight combinations could appear. In fact, only four are used; so as four is less than eight, constraint is present.

7/9. A constraint may be slight or severe. Suppose, for instance, that a squad of soldiers is to be drawn up in a single rank, and that "independence" means that they may stand in any order they please. Various constraints might be placed on the order of standing, and these constraints may differ in their degree of restriction. Thus, if the order were given that no man may stand next a man whose birthday falls on the same day, the constraint would be slight, for of all the possible arrangements few would be excluded. If, however, the order were given that no man was to stand at the left of a man who was taller than himself, the constraint would be severe; for it would, in fact, allow only one order of standing (unless two men were of exactly the same height). The intensity of the constraint is thus shown by the reduction it causes in the number of possible arrangements.

7/10. It seems that constraints cannot be classified in any simple way, for they include all cases in which a set, for any reason, is smaller than it might be. Here I can discuss only certain types of outstanding commonness and importance, leaving the reader to add further types if his special interests should lead him to them.

7/11. *Constraint in vectors.* Sometimes the elements of a set are vectors, and have components. Thus the traffic signal of S.7/8 was a vector of three components, each of which could take two values. In such cases a common and important constraint occurs if the actual number of vectors that occurs under defined conditions is fewer than the total number of vectors possible without conditions (i.e. when each component takes its full range of values independently of the values taken by the other components). Thus, in the case of the traffic lights, when Red and Yellow are both lit, only Green unlit occurs, the vector with Green lit being absent.

It should be noticed that a set of vectors provides several varieties, which must be identified individually if confusion is not to occur. Consider, for instance, the vector of S.3/5:

$$(\text{Age of car, Horse-power, Colour}).$$

The first component will have some definite variety, and so will the second component, and the third. The three varieties need not be equal. And the variety in the set of vectors will be different again.

The variety in the set of vectors has, however, one invariable relation to the varieties of the components—it cannot exceed their sum (if we think in logarithms, as is more convenient here). Thus, if a car may have any one of 10 ages, of 8 horse-powers, and of 12 colours, then the variety in the types of car cannot exceed $3 \cdot 3 + 3 \cdot 0 + 3 \cdot 6$ bits, i.e. $9 \cdot 9$ bits.

7/12. The components are **independent** when the variety in the whole of some given set of vectors equals the sum of the (logarithmic) varieties in the individual components. If it were found, for instance, that all 960 types of car could be observed within some defined set of cars, then the three components would be said to be "independent", or to "vary independently", within this defined set.

It should be noticed that such a statement refers essentially to what is observed to occur within the set; it need contain no reference to any supposed cause for the independence (or for the constraint).

Ex. 1: When Pantagruel and his circle debated whether or not the time had come for Panurge to marry, they took advisers, who were introduced thus: ". . . Rondibilis, is married now, who before was not—Hippothadeus was not before, nor is yet—Bridlegoose was married once, but is not now—and Trouillogan is married now, who wedded was to another wife before." Does this set of vectors show constraint?

Ex. 2: If each component can be Head (H) or Tail (T), does the set of four vectors (H,H,H), (T,T,H), (H,T,T), (T,H,T) show constraint in relation to the set showing independence?

7/13. *Degrees of freedom.* When a set of vectors does not show the full range of possibilities made available by the components (S.7/11), the range that remains can sometimes usefully be measured by saying how many components with independence would give the same variety. This number of components is called the **degrees of freedom** of the set of vectors. Thus the traffic lights (S.7/8) show a variety of four. If the components continued to have two states apiece, *two* components with independence could give the same variety (of four). So the constraint on the lights can be expressed by saying that the three components, not independent, give the same variety as *two* would if independent; i.e. the three lights have two degrees of freedom.

If all combinations are possible, then the number of degrees of freedom is equal to the number of components. If only one combination is possible, the degrees of freedom are zero.

It will be appreciated that this way of measuring what is left free of constraint is applicable only in certain favourable cases. Thus, were the traffic lights to show three, or five combinations, the equivalence would no longer be representable by a simple, whole, number. The concept is of importance chiefly when the components vary continuously, so that each has available an infinite number of values. A reckoning by degrees of freedom may then still be possible, though the states cannot be counted.

Ex. 1: If a dealer in second-hand cars boasts that his stock covers a range of 10 ages, 8 horse powers, and 12 colours, in all combinations, how many degrees of freedom has his stock?

Ex. 2: The angular positions of the two hands on a clock are the two components of a vector. Has the set of vectors (in ordinary working round the 12 hours) a constraint if the angles are measured precisely?

Ex. 3: (Continued.) How many degrees of freedom has the vector? (Hint: Would removal of the minute-hand cause an essential loss?)

Ex. 4: As the two eyes move, pointing the axes in various directions, they define a vector with four components: the upward and lateral deviations of the right and left eyes. Man has binocular vision; the chameleon moves his two eyes independently, each side searching for food on its own side of the body. How many degrees of freedom have the chameleon's eyes? Man's?

Ex. 5: An arrow, of fixed length, lying in a plane, has three degrees of freedom for position (for two co-ordinates will fix the position of its centre, say, and then one angle will determine its direction). How many degrees of freedom has it if we add the restriction that it must always point in the direction of a given point *P*?

Ex. 6: *T* is a given closed and single-valued transformation, and *a* any of its operands. Consider the set of vectors, each of three components,

$$(a, T(a), T^2(a)),$$

with *a* given all its possible values in turn. How many degrees of freedom has the set?

Ex. 7: In what way does the ordinary graph, of *y* on *x*, show constraint?

Ex. 8: How many degrees of freedom has an ordinary body—a chair say—in three dimensional space?

IMPORTANCE OF CONSTRAINT

7/14. Constraints are of high importance in cybernetics, and will be given prominence through the remainder of this book, because *when a constraint exists advantage can usually be taken of it.*

Shannon's work, discussed chiefly in Chapter 9, displays this thesis clearly. Most of it is directed to estimating the variety that would exist if full independence occurred, showing that constraints (there called "redundancy") exist, and showing how their existence makes possible a more efficient use of the channel.

The next few sections will also show something of the wide applicability and great importance of the concept.

7/15. *Laws of Nature.* First we can notice that the existence of any invariant over a set of phenomena implies a constraint, for its existence implies that the full range of variety does not occur. The general theory of invariants is thus a part of the theory of constraints.

Further, as every law of nature implies the existence of an invariant, it follows that *every law of nature is a constraint.* Thus, the Newtonian law says that, of the vectors of planetary positions and velocities which might occur, e.g. written on paper (the larger set), only a smaller set will actually occur in the heavens; and the law specifies what values the elements will have. From our point of view, what is important is that the law *excludes* many positions and velocities, predicting that they will never be found to occur.

Science looks for laws; it is therefore much concerned with looking for constraints. (Here the larger set is composed of what *might* happen if the behaviour were free and chaotic, and the smaller set is composed of what does actually happen.)

This point of view, it will be noticed, conforms to what was said in S.1/5. Cybernetics looks at the totality, in all its possible richness, and then asks why the actualities should be restricted to some portion of the total possibilities.

Ex. 1: How is the chemist's Law of Simple Proportions a constraint?
Ex. 2: How is the Law of Conservation of Energy a constraint?

7/16. *Object as constraint.* Constraints are exceedingly common in the world around us, and many of our basic concepts make use of it in an essential way. Consider as example the basic concept of a "thing" or "object", as something handled in daily life. A chair is a thing because it has coherence, because we can put it on this side of a table or that, because we can carry it around or sit on it. The chair is also a collection of parts.

Now any free object in our three dimensional world has six degrees of freedom for movement. Were the parts of the chair unconnected each would have its own six degrees of freedom; and this is in fact the amount of mobility available to the parts in the workshop before they are assembled. Thus the four legs, when separate, have 24 degrees of freedom. After they are joined, however, they have only the six degrees of freedom of the single object. That there *is* a constraint is obvious when one realises that if the positions of three legs of an assembled chair are known, then that of the fourth follows necessarily—it has no freedom.

Thus the change from four separate and free legs to one chair corresponds precisely to the change from the set's having 24 degrees of freedom to its having only 6. Thus the essence of the chair's being a "thing", a unity, rather than a collection of independent parts corresponds to the presence of the constraint.

7/17. Seen from this point of view, the world around us is extremely rich in constraints. We are so familiar with them that we take most of them for granted, and are often not even aware that they exist. To see what the world would be like without its usual constraints we have to turn to fairy tales or to a "crazy" film, and even these remove only a fraction of all the constraints.

A world without constraints would be totally chaotic. The turbulent river below Niagara might be such a world (though the physicist would still find some constraint here). Our terrestrial world, to which the living organism is adapted, is far from presenting such a chaos. Later (S.13/5) it will be suggested that the organism can adapt just so far as the real world is constrained, and no further.

Ex.: Attempt to count, during the next one minute, all the constraints that are operating in your surroundings.

7/18. *Prediction and constraint.* That something is "predictable" implies that there exists a constraint. If an aircraft, for instance, were able to move, second by second, from any one point in the sky to any other point, then the best anti-aircraft prediction would be helpless and useless. The latter can give useful information only because an aircraft cannot so move, but must move subject to several constraints. There is that due to continuity—an aircraft cannot suddenly jump, either in position or speed or direction. There is the constraint due to the aircraft's individuality of design, which makes this aircraft behave like an A-10 and that one behave like a Z-20. There is the constraint due to the pilot's individuality; and so on. An aircraft's future position is thus always somewhat constrained, and it is to just this extent that a predictor can be useful.

7/19. *Machine as constraint.* It will now be appreciated that the concept of a "machine", as developed from the inspection of a protocol (S.6/5), comes from recognising that *the sequence in the protocol shows a particular form of constraint.* Were the protocol to show no constraint, the observer would say it was chaotic or unpredictable, like a roulette-wheel.

When it shows the characteristic form of constraint, the observer can take advantage of the fact. He does this by re-coding the whole protocol into a more compact form, containing only:

(i) a statement of the transformation
and (ii) a statement of the actual input given.

Subsequently, instead of the discussion being conducted in terms of a lengthy protocol, it is conducted compactly in terms of a succinct transformation; as we did throughout Part I.

Thus, use of the transformation is one example of how one can turn to advantage the characteristic constraint on behaviour imposed by its being "machine-like".

Ex.: If a protocol shows the constraint characteristic of a machine, what does the constraint exclude?

7/20. Within the set of determinate machines further constraints may be applied. Thus the set can be restricted to those that have a certain set of states as operands, or to those that have only one basin, or to those that are not reducible.

A common and very powerful constraint is that of continuity. It is a constraint because whereas the function that changes arbitrarily can undergo *any* change, the continuous function can change, at each step, only to a neighbouring value. Exercise 4 gives but a feeble impression of the severity of this constraint.

Ex. 1: The set of closed single-valued transformations (absolute systems) on three states a, b, c has 27 members (compare Ex. 7/7/7). How many members remain if we add the restriction that the absolute system is to have no state of equilibrium?

Ex. 2: (Continued.) Similarly, but the restriction is that there must be only one basin.

Ex. 3: (Continued.) Similarly, but the restriction is that the transitions $a \rightarrow b$ and $b \rightarrow c$ may not occur.

Ex. 4: A vector has ten components, each of which can take one of the values: 1, 2, 3, 4. How much variety has the set of vectors if (i) the components vary independently (S.7/12); (ii) under the rule that no two adjacent components may differ in value by more than one unit?

7/21. *Learning and constraint.* For the psychologist, an important example of constraint occurs in learning. Pavlov, for instance, in one experiment gave both thermal and tactile stimuli, as well as reinforcement by meat powder, in the following combinations:

	Thermal	Tactile	Reinforcement
1	+	+	+
2	+	−	−
3	−	+	+
4	−	−	−

(The fourth combination occurred, of course, in the intervals.) Now the total combinations possible are eight; Pavlov presented only four. It was an essential part of the experiment that the full set should not be given, for otherwise there would be nothing particular for the animal to learn. Constraint was an essential feature of the experiment.

The same principle can be seen more simply in learning by association. Suppose one wanted the subject, given a letter, to reply with a number according to the rule

A given : reply with 2
B   ,, :   ,,   ,, 5
C   ,, :   ,,   ,, 3

The subject might then be given a sequence such as A2, B5, C3, B5, C3, A2, A2, C3, and so on.

Now this sequence, as a sequence of vectors with two components, shows constraint; and if learning is to occur the constraint is necessary; for without constraint A would be followed equally by 2, 3 or 5; and the subject would be unable to form any specific associations. Thus *learning is possible only to the extent that the sequence shows constraint.*

The same is true of learning a maze. For this to occur the maze must retain the same pattern from day to day during the period of learning. Were the maze to show no constraint, the animal would be unable to develop the particular (and appropriate) way of behaving. Thus, *learning is worth while only when the environment shows constraint.* (The subject is taken up again in S.13/7.)

VARIETY IN MACHINES

7/22. We can now turn to considering how variety is affected by a machine's activities, making our way towards an understanding of what happens to information when it is handled by a machine. First, let us notice a fundamental peculiarity of the single-valued transformation in its relation to variety.

Consider for instance the single-valued transformation

$$Z: \downarrow \begin{matrix} A & B & C \\ B & C & C \end{matrix}$$

and apply it to some set of the operands, e.g.

$$B\ B\ A\ C\ C\ C\ A\ A\ B\ A$$
The result is $C\ C\ B\ C\ C\ C\ B\ B\ C\ B$

What is important is that the variety in the set has fallen from 3 to 2. A further transformation by Z leads to all C's, with a variety of 1.

The reader can easily satisfy himself that such a set, operated on by a single-valued transformation, can never increase in variety, and usually falls. The reason for the fall can readily be identified. In the graph, a confluence of arrows $\rightarrow\!\!\!\!\!\nearrow$ can occur, but a divergence $\nwarrow\!\!\!\!\!\lt$ is impossible. Whenever the transformation makes two states change to one, variety is lost; and there is no contrary process to replace the loss.

It is not necessary that the transformation should be closed. Thus if the same set of ten letters is transformed by Y:

$$Y: \downarrow \begin{array}{ccc} A & B & C \\ p & q & p \end{array}$$

giving $q\,q\,p\,p\,p\,p\,p\,p\,q\,p$, the variety falls. It is easy to see that only when the transformation is one-one (over the letters that actually occur in the set to be transformed) is the set's variety unchanged; and this is a very special type of transformation.

Ex. 1: Write the letters A to Z in a row; under it, letter by letter, write the first 26 letters of some well known phrase. The transition from upper row to lower now defines a single-valued transformation (u). Write your name in full, find the variety among its letters, transform by u (i.e. "code" it) and find the variety in the new set of letters How has the variety changed? Apply u repeatedly; draw a graph of how the variety changes step by step.

Ex. 2: In a certain genus of parasite, each species feeds off only one species of host. If the varieties (in our sense) of parasites' species and hosts' species are unequal, which is the larger?

Ex. 3: "A multiplicity of genotypes may show the same phenotypic feature." If the change from each genotype to its corresponding phenotype is a transformation V, what change in variety does V cause?

Ex. 4: When a tea-taster tastes a cup of tea, he can be regarded as responsible for a transformation Y converting "sample of leaf" as operand to "opinion" as transform. If the taster is perfect, Y will be one-one. How would he be described if Y were many-one?

Ex. 5: When read to the nearest degree on each of seven occasions, the temperatures of the room and of a thermostatically-controlled water-bath were found to be

Room: 65, 62, 68, 63, 62, 59, 61.
Water-bath: 97, 97, 98, 97, 97, 97, 97.

How much variety is shown (i) by the room's temperatures, (ii) by those of the bath? What would have been said had the variety in (i) exceeded that of (ii)?

*Ex. 6: If the transformation has been formed by letting each state go to one state selected at random from all the states (independently and with equal probabilities), show that if the number of states is large, the variety will fall at the first step, in the ratio of 1 to $1 - 1/e$, i.e. to about two-thirds. (Hint: The problem is equivalent (for a single step) to the following: n hunters come suddenly on a herd of n deer. Each fires one shot at a deer chosen at random. Every bullet hits. How many deer will, on the average, be hit? And to what does the average tend as n tends to infinity?)

7/23. *Set and machine.* We must now be clear about how a *set* of states can be associated with a machine, for no real machine can, at one time, be in more than one state. A set of states can be considered for several reasons.

We may, in fact, not really be considering one machine, however much we speak in the singular (S.7/3), but may really be considering a set of replicates, as one might speak of "the Model T Ford", or "the anterior horn cell", or "the white rat". When this is so we can consider all the replicates together, one in one state and one in another; thus we get a *set* of states for one transformation to act on.

A set of states can also arise even if the machine is unique. For we may wish to consider not only what it may do at one time from one state but also what it may do at another time from another state. So its various possible behaviours at a *set* of times are naturally related to a *set* of states as operands.

Finally, a set may be created by the *fiat* of a theoretician who, not knowing which state a particular machine is at, wants to trace out the consequences of *all* the possibilities. The set now is not the set of what *does* exist, but the set of what *may* exist (so far as the theoretician is concerned). This method is typically cybernetic, for it considers the actual in relation to the wider set of the possible or the conceivable (S.1/3).

7/24. *Decay of variety.* Having, for one of these reasons, a set of states and one single-valued transformation, we can now, using the result of S.7/22, predict that *as time progresses the variety in the set cannot increase and will usually diminish.*

This fact may be seen from several points of view.

In the first place it gives precision to the often made remark that any system, left to itself, runs to some equilibrium. Usually the remark is based on a vague appeal to experience, but this is unsatisfactory, for the conditions are not properly defined. Sometimes the second law of thermodynamics is appealed to, but this is often irrelevant to the systems discussed here (S.1/2). The new formulation shows just what is essential.

In the second place it shows that if an observer has an absolute system, whose transformation he knows but whose states cannot, for any reason, be observed, then as time goes on *his uncertainty about its state can only diminish.* For initially it might be at any one of all its states, and as time goes on so does the number of its possible states diminish. Thus, in the extreme case in which it has only one basin and a state of equilibrium, he can, if initially uncertain, ultimately say with certainty, without making any further observation, at which state it is.

The diminution can be seen from yet another point of view. If the variety in the possible states is associated with information, so that the machine's being at some particular state conveys some particular message, then as time goes on the amount of information it stores can only diminish. Thus one of three messages might be carried to a prisoner by a cup of coffee, the message depending on whether it was hot, tepid, or cold. This method would work satisfactorily if the time between despatch and receipt was short, but not if it were long; for whichever of the three states were selected originally, the states after a short time would be either "tepid" or "cold", and after a long time, "cold" only. Thus the longer the time between despatch and receipt, the less is the system's capacity for carrying information, so far as this depends on its being at a particular state.

Ex. 1: If a ball will rest in any one of three differently coloured basins, how much variety can be stored?

Ex. 2: (Continued.) If in addition another ball of another colour can be placed, by how much is the variety increased?

Ex. 3: That a one-one transformation causes no loss of variety is sometimes used as a parlour trick. A member of the audience is asked to think of two digits. He is then asked to multiply one of them by 5, add 7, double the the result, and add the other number. The result is told to the conjurer who then names the original digits. Show that this transformation retains the original amount of variety. (Hint: Subtract 14 from the final quantity.)

Ex. 4: (Continued.) What is the set for the first measure of variety?

Ex. 5: (Another trick.) A member of the audience writes down a two-digit number, whose digits differ by at least 2. He finds the difference between this number and the number formed by the same digits in reverse order. To the difference he adds the number formed by reversing the digits of the difference. How much variety survives this transformation?

Ex. 6: If a circuit of neurons can carry memory by either reverberating or not, how much variety can the circuit carry? What is the *set* having the variety?

Ex. 7: Ten machines, identical in structure, have run past their transients and now have variety constant at zero. Are they necessarily at a state of equilibrium?

7/25. *Law of Experience.* The previous section showed that the variety in a machine (a set being given and understood) can never increase and usually decreases. It was assumed there that the machine was isolated, so that the changes in state were due only to the inner activities of the machine; we will now consider what happens to the variety when the system is a machine with input.

Consider first the simplest case, that of a machine with one parameter P that changes only at long intervals. Suppose, for clarity, that the machine has many replicates, identical in their transformations but differing in which state each is at; and that we are observing the set of states provided at each moment by the set of machines. Let P be kept at the same value for all and held at that value while the machines change step by step. The conditions are now as in the previous section, and if we measure the variety in state over the set of replicates, and observe how the variety changes with time, we shall see it fall to some minimum. When the variety has reached its minimum under this input-value (P_1), let P be changed to some new value (P_2), the change being made uniformly and simultaneously over the whole set of replicates. The change in value will change the machine's graph from one form to another, as for example (if the machine has states $A, B, \ldots, F,$)

$$
\begin{array}{ccc}
A & B & C \\
\downarrow & \swarrow & \downarrow \\
D & E \leftarrow F
\end{array}
\qquad
\begin{array}{ccc}
A \rightarrow B & C \\
\uparrow & \uparrow \\
D \rightarrow E & F
\end{array}
$$

$$from \qquad\qquad\qquad\qquad to$$

$$(P_1) \qquad\qquad\qquad (P_2)$$

Under P_1, all those members that started at A, B or D would go to D, and those that started at C, E, or F would go to E. The variety, after some time at P_1, would fall to 2 states. When P is changed to P_2, all those systems at D would go, in the first step, to E (for the transformation is single-valued), and all those at E would go to B. It is easy to see, therefore, that, provided the same change is made to all, *change of parameter-value to the whole set cannot increase the set's variety*. This is true, of course, whether D and E are states of equilibrium or not. Now let the system continue under P_2. The two groups, once resting apart at D and E, will now both come to B; here all will have the same state, and the variety will fall to zero. Thus, *change of parameter-value makes possible a fall to a new, and lower, minimum.*

The condition that the change $P_1 \rightarrow P_2$ may lead to a further fall in variety is clearly that two or more of P_1's states of equilibrium lie in the same P_2 basin. Since this will often happen we can make the looser, but more vivid, statement that *a uniform change at the inputs of a set of transducers tends to drive the set's variety down.*

As the variety falls, so does the set change so that all its members tend, at each moment, to be at the same state. In other words, changes at the input of a transducer tend to make the system's state (at a given moment) less dependent on the transducer's individual initial state and more dependent on the particular sequence of parameter-values used as input.

The same fact can be looked at from another point of view. In the argument just given, "the set" was taken, for clarity, to be a set of replicates of one transducer, all behaving simultaneously. The theorem is equally applicable to one transducer on a series of occasions, provided the various initial times are brought into proper correspondence. This point of view would be more appropriate if we were studying some very complex transducer, making fresh experiments on it each day. If it contained great numbers of rather inaccessible parts, there might be difficulty in bringing it each morning back to some standardised state ready for the next experiment. The theorem says that if its input is taken, in the early morning, through some *standardised* routine, then the longer the routine, the more certain is it that the machine will be brought, ready for the experimenter, to some standard state. The experimenter may not be able to name the state, but he can be confident that it tends to be reproducible.

It should be noticed that mere equality of the set's parameter at each step of the sequence is not sufficient; if the effect is to be more than merely nominal (i.e. null) the parameters must undergo actual, non-zero, change.

The theorem is in no way dependent for its truth on the size of the system. Very large systems are exactly as subject to it as small, and may often be expected to show the effect more smoothly and regularly (by the statistical effect of largeness). It may therefore be usefully applicable to the brain and to the social and economic system.

Examples that may correspond to this process are very common. Perhaps something of this sort occurs when it is found that a number of boys of marked individuality, having all been through the same school, develop ways that are more characteristic of the school they attended than of their original individualities. The extent to which this tendency to uniformity in behaviour is due to this property of transducers must be left for further research.

Some name is necessary by which this phenomenon can be referred to. I shall call it the **law of Experience.** It can be described more vividly by the statement that information put in by change at a parameter tends to destroy and replace information about the system's initial state.

Chapter 8

TRANSMISSION OF VARIETY

8/1. The previous chapter has introduced the concept of "variety", a concept inseparable from that of "information", and we have seen how important it is, in some problems, to recognise that we are dealing with a *set* of possibilities.

In the present chapter we shall study how such possibilities are transmitted through a machine, in the sense of studying the relation that exists between the set that occurs at the input and the consequent set that occurs, usually in somewhat coded form, at the output. We shall see that the transmission is, if the machine is determinate, perfectly orderly and capable of rigorous treatment. Our aim will be to work towards an understanding good enough to serve as a basis for considering the extremely complex codings used by the brain.

8/2. *Ubiquity of coding.* To get a picture of the amount of coding that goes on during the ordinary interaction between organism and environment, let us consider, in some detail, the comparatively simple sequence of events that occurs when a "Gale warning" is broadcast. It starts as some patterned process in the nerve cells of the meteorologist, and then becomes a pattern of muscle-movements as he writes or types it, thereby making it a pattern of ink marks on paper. From here it becomes a pattern of light and dark on the announcer's retina, then a pattern of retinal excitation, then a pattern of nerve impulses in the optic nerve, and so on through his nervous system. It emerges, while he is reading the warning, as a pattern of lip and tongue movements, and then travels as a pattern of waves in the air. Reaching the microphone it becomes a pattern of variations of electrical potential, and then goes through further changes as it is amplified, modulated, and broadcast. Now it is a pattern of waves in the ether, and next a pattern in the receiving set. Back again to the pattern of waves in the air, it then becomes a pattern of vibrations traversing the listener's ear-drums, ossicles, cochlea, and then becomes a pattern of nerve-impulses moving up the auditory nerve. Here we can leave it, merely noticing that this very brief account mentions no less than sixteen major transformations through all of which something has been preserved, though the superficial appearances have changed almost out of recognition.

8/3. *Complexity of coding.* When considering such repeated codings the observer may easily over-estimate the amount of complexity that has been introduced. It not uncommonly happens that the amount of complexity is nothing like as large as a first impression might suggest.

A simple example, showing how a complex coding may have hidden simplicities, occurs when a simple one-one coding of the alphabet is applied first to the message, then to the first coded form to give a second (doubly-) coded form, then to the second coded form, and so on for many codings. The final form might be thought to be extremely mixed, and to need for its decoding as many operations backwards as were used forwards; in fact, as can easily be verified, it differs from the original message only by as much as is caused by a *single* application of some one-one coding. The final message can thus be turned back to the original by a single operation.

Ex.: Arrange the cards of a pack in order, and place it on the table face downwards. Cut. Cut again. Cut again and again until you are satisfied that the original order is lost totally. Now pick the pack up and examine its order; how much order has been lost?

8/4. *De-coding.* The general study of codings is best introduced by noticing some of the features of military codings.

We must be careful from the beginning not to interpret "code" too narrowly. At first we tend to think only of those methods that turn each letter of the message to some other letter, but this class is too restricted, for there are many other methods. Thus the "Playfair" code operates on the letters in pairs, turning each pair (a vector with two components) to some other pair. Other codes put the letters into some new arrangement, while others are wholly arbitrary, turning, for instance, "two divisions will arrive" to "Arthur". These considerations make it clear that if the coding is a transformation, the operand is the whole message rather than a letter (though the latter possibility is not excluded). The transformation is therefore essentially of the form

$$U: \downarrow \begin{array}{cccc} M_1 & M_2 & M_3 & \cdots \\ C_1 & C_2 & C_3 & \cdots \end{array}$$

where M_1, M_2, ... are the various messages and C_1, C_2, ... are their coded forms. A coding, then, is specified by a transformation.

Often the method uses a "key-word" or some other factor that is capable of changing the code from one form to another. Such a factor corresponds, of course, to a parameter, giving as many particular codings (or transformations) U_1, U_2, ... as there are values to the factor.

"Decoding" means applying such a transformation to the transform C_i as will restore the original message M_i:

$$V: \downarrow \begin{array}{cccc} C_1 & C_2 & C_3 & \dots \\ M_1 & M_2 & M_3 & \dots \end{array}$$

Such a transformation V is said to be the **inverse** of U; it may then be written as U^{-1}. In general, only one-one transformations have single-valued inverses.

If the original message M_i is to be recoverable from the coded form C_i, whatever value i may have, then both U and U^{-1} must be one-one; for if both M_i and M_j were to be transformed to one form C_k, then the receiver of C_k could not tell which of the M's had been sent originally, and C_k cannot be decoded with certainty.

Next suppose that a set of messages, having variety v, is sent coded by a one-one transformation U. The variety in the set of coded forms will also be v. *Variety is not altered after coding by a one-one transformation.*

It follows that if messages of variety v are to pass through several codes in succession, and are to be uniquely restorable to their original forms, then *the process must be one that preserves the variety in the set at every stage.*

Ex. 1: Is the transformation $x' = \log_{10} x$, applied to positive numbers, a one-one coding? What is "decoding" it usually called?

Ex. 2: Is the transformation $x' = \sin x$, applied to the positive numbers, a one-one coding?

Ex. 3: What transformation results from the application of, first, a one-one transformation and then its inverse?

Ex. 4: What transformation is the inverse of $n' = n + 7$?

Ex. 5: What transformation is the inverse of $x' = 2x + y$, $y' = x + y$?

Ex. 6: If the coded form consists of three English letters, e.g. *JNB*, what is the variety of the possible coded forms (measured logarithmically)?

Ex. 7: (Continued.) How many distinct messages can be sent through such a code, used once?

Ex. 8: Eight horses are running in a race, and a telegram will tell Mr. A. which came first and which second. What variety is there in the set of possible messages?

Ex. 9: (Continued.) Could the set be coded into a single letter, printed either as capital or as lower case (small letters)?

Ex. 10: The concentrations "high" or "low" of sex-hormone in the blood of a certain animal determines whether it will, or will not, go through a ritual of courtship. If the sex-hormone is very complicated chemically and the ritual very complicated ethologically, and if the variable "behaviour" is regarded as a coded form of the variable "concentration", how much variety is there in the set of messages?

8/5. *Coding by machine.* Next we can consider what happens when a message becomes coded by being passed through a machine.

That such questions are of importance in the study of the brain needs no elaboration. Among their other applications are those pertaining to "instrumentation"—the science of getting information from some more or less inaccessible variable or place, such as the interior of a furnace or of a working heart, to the observer. The transmission of such information almost always involves some intermediate stage of coding, and this must be selected suitably. Until recently, each such instrument was designed simply on the principles peculiar to the particular branch of science; today, however, it is known, after the pioneer work of Shannon and Wiener, that certain general laws hold over all such instruments. What they are will be described below.

A "machine" was defined in S.3/4 as any set of states whose changes in time corresponded to a closed single-valued transformation. This definition applies to the machine that is totally isolated, i.e. in constant conditions; it is identical with the absolute system defined in *Design*. . . . In S.4/1 the machine with input was defined as a system that has a closed single-valued transformation for each one of the possible states of a set of parameters. This is identical with the "transducer" of Shannon, which is defined as a system whose next state is determined by its present state and the present values of its parameters. (He also assumes that it can have a finite internal memory, but we shall ignore this for the moment, returning to it in S.9/8.)

Assume then that we have before us a transducer M that can be in some one of the states $S_1, S_2, \ldots, S_n$, which will be assumed here to be finite in number. It has one or more parameters that can take, at each moment, some one of a set of values $P_1, P_2, \ldots, P_k$. Each of these values will define a transformation of the S's. We now find that such a system can accept a message, can code it, and can emit the coded form. By "message" I shall mean simply some succession of states that is, by the coupling between two systems, at once the output of one system and the input of the other. Often the state will be a vector. I shall omit consideration of any "meaning" to be attached to the message and shall consider simply what will happen in these determinate systems.

For simplicity in the example, suppose that M can take any one of four states: A, B, C, and D; that the parameters provide three states Q, R, and S. These suppositions can be shown in tabular form, which shows the essentials of the "transducer" (as in S.4/1):

↓	A	B	C	D
Q	C	C	A	B
R	A	C	B	B
S	B	D	C	D

Given its initial state and the sequence of values given to the parameter, its output can be found without difficulty, as in S.4/1. Thus, suppose it starts at B and that the input is at R; it will change to C. If the input goes next to Q, it will go from C to A. The results so far can be shown in tabular form:

Input-state   : R Q
Transducer-state: B C A

It can now easily be verified that if the initial state is B and the input follows the sequence $R \ Q \ R \ S \ S \ Q \ R \ R \ Q \ S \ R$, the output will follow the sequence $B \ C \ A \ A \ B \ D \ B \ C \ B \ C \ C \ B$.

There is thus no difficulty, given the transducer, its initial state, and the input sequence, in deducing its trajectory. Though the example may seem unnatural with its arbitrary jumps, it is in fact quite representative, and requires only more states, and perhaps the passage to the limit of continuity to become a completely natural representation. In the form given, however, various quantitative properties are made obvious and easily calculable, where in the continuous form the difficult technique of measure theory must be used.

Ex. 1: Pass the same message (R Q R S S Q R R Q S R) through the same transducer, this time starting at A.

Ex. 2: Pass the message "R_1, R_2, R_3, R_1, R_2, R_3" through the transducer of S.4/1, starting it at a.

Ex. 3: (Continued.) Encode the same message through the same transducer, starting it at b.

Ex. 4: (Continued.) Does a transducer's output depend, for given input, on its initial state?

Ex. 5: If the transducer is $n' = n - a$, where a is a parameter, what will its trajectory be if it starts at $n = 10$ and receives the input sequence 2, 1, -3, -1, 2, 1?

Ex. 6: Pass the message "314159 . . ." (the digits of π) through the transducer $n' = n + a - 5$, starting the transducer at $n = 10$.

Ex. 7: If a and b are parameters, so that the vector (a,b) defines a parameter-state, and if the transducer has states defined by the vector (x,y) and transformation

$$\begin{cases} x' = ax + by \\ y' = x \ \ + (a - b)y, \end{cases}$$

complete the trajectory in the table:

a	1	−2	0	−1	2	5	−2
b	−1	1	1	0	1	−2	0
x	2	1	2	?	?	?	?
y	1	4	−11	?	?	?	?

*Ex. 8: A transducer, with parameter u, has the transformation $dx/dt = - (u + 4)x$; it is given, from initial state $x = 1$, the input $u = \cos t$; find the values of x as output.

*Ex. 9: If a is input to the transducer

$$dx/dt = y$$
$$dy/dt = -x -2y + a,$$

with diagram of immediate effects

$$a \rightarrow y \rightleftarrows x,$$

what is the output from x if it is started at $(0,0)$ with input $a = \sin t$? (Hint: Use the Laplace transform.)

*Ex. 10: If a is input and the transducer is

$$dx/dt = k(a - x)$$

what characterises x's behaviour as k is made positive and numerically very large?

INVERTING A CODED MESSAGE

8/6. In S.8/4 it was emphasised that, for a code to be useful as a message-carrier, the possibility of its inversion must exist. Let us attempt to apply this test to the transducer of S.8/5, regarding it as a coder.

There are two transformations used, and they must be kept carefully distinct. The first is that which corresponds to U of S.8/4, and whose operands are the individual messages; the second is that of the transducer. Suppose the transducer of S.8/5 is to be given a "message" that consists of two letters, each of which may be one of Q, R, S. Nine messages are possible:

$$QQ, \ \ QR, \ \ QS, \ \ RQ, \ \ RR, \ \ RS, \ \ SQ, \ \ SR, \ \ SS$$

and these correspond to M_1, M_2, . . ., M_9 of U.   Suppose the transducer is always started at A; it is easy to verify that the corresponding nine outputs will be (if we ignore the initial and invariable A):

$$CA, \ CB, \ CC, \ AC, \ AA, \ AB, \ BC, \ BC, \ BB.$$

These are the C_1, C_2 . . ., C_9 of U.   Now the coding performed by the transducer is not one-one, and there has been some loss of variety, for there are now only eight distinguishable elements, BC being duplicated.   This transducer therefore fails to provide the possibility for complete and exact decoding; for if BC arrives, there is no way of telling whether the original message was SQ or SR.

In this connexion it must be appreciated that an inability to decode may be due to one of two very different reasons.   It may be due simply to the fact that the decoder, *which exists*, is not at hand.   This occurs when a military message finds a signaller without the code-book, or when a listener has a gramophone record (as a coded form of the voice) but no gramophone to play it on.   Quite different is the inability when it is due to the fact that two distinct messages may result in the same output, as when the output BC comes from the transducer above.   All that it indicates is that the original message might have been SQ or SR, and the decoder that might distinguish between them *does not exist*.

It is easy to see that if, in each column of the table, every state had been different then every transition would have indicated a unique value of the parameter; so we would thus have been able to decode any sequence of states emitted by the transducer.   The converse is also true; for if we can decode *any* sequence of states, each transition must determine a unique value of the parameter, and thus the states in a column must be all different.   We have thus identified *the characteristic in the transducer that corresponds to its being a perfect coder.*

Ex. 1: In a certain transducer, which has 100 states, the parameters can take 108 combinations of values; can its output always be decoded?   (Hint: Try simple examples in which the number of transformations exceeds that of the states.)

Ex. 2: (To emphasise the distinction between the two transformations.)   If a transducer's input has 5 states, its output 7, and the message consists of some sequence of 12, (i) how many operands has the transducer's transformation, and (ii) how many has the coding transformation U?

Ex. 3: If a machine is continuous, what does "observing a transition" correspond to in terms of actual instrumentation?

Ex. 4: If the transducer has the transformation $dx/dt = ax$, where a is the input, can its output always be decoded?   (Hint: Solve for a.)

146

8/7. *Designing an inverter.* The previous section showed that, provided the transducer did not lose distinctions in transmission from input to output, the coded message given as output could always be decoded. In this section we shall show that the same process can be done automatically, i.e. given a machine that does not lose distinctions, it is always possible to build another machine that, receiving the first's output as input, *will emit the original message as its own output.*

We are now adopting a rather different point of view from that of the previous section. There we were interested in the possibility of a message being decoded and in whether the decoding could be done or not—by whom did not matter. We are now turning to the question of how a mechanism can be built, by us, so that the mechanism shall do the decoding *automatically.* We seek, not a restored message but a machine. How shall it be built? What we require for its specification, of course, is the usual set of transformations (S.4/1).

A possible method, the one to be used here, is simply to convert the process we followed in the preceding section into mechanistic form, using the fact that *each transition gives information about the parameter-value under which it occurred.* We want a machine, therefore, that will accept a transition as input and give the original parameter value as output. Now to know which transition has occurred, i.e. what are the values of i and j in "$X_i \rightarrow X_j$", is clearly equivalent to knowing what is the value of the vector (i,j); for a transition can also be thought of as a vector having two components. We can therefore feed the transitions into an inverter if the inverter has an input of two parameters, one to take the value of the earlier state and the other to take the value of the later.

Only one difficulty remains: the transition involves two states that do not exist at the same moment of time, so one of the inverter's inputs must behave *now* according to what the transducer's output *was.* A simple device, however, will get over this difficulty. Consider the transducer

↓	q	r	s
Q	q	q	q
R	r	r	r
S	s	s	s

Suppose it is started at state r and is given the input $Q\,S\,S\,R\,Q\,S\,R\,R\,Q$; its output will be $r\,q\,s\,s\,r\,q\,s\,r\,r\,q$, i.e. after the first letter it just repeats the input, but one step later. Two such transducers in series will repeat the message two steps later, and so on.   Clearly there is no difficulty in principle in getting delay.

Suppose that the first transducer, the coder, is:

↓	A	B	C	D
Q	D	A	D	B
R	B	B	B	C
S	A	C	A	D

What we require is a machine that, e.g.

given input A,A will emit S
  „   „   A,B „   „ R
  „   „   A,D „   „ Q
  „   „   B,A „   „ Q
                        etc.

(The input A,C will never actually come to it, for the transition cannot be emitted from the coder.)

The three machines are coupled thus:

→ | Coder | → | Delayer |
            ↘   ↓
              | Inverter | →

The delayer has the simple form:

↓	a	b	c	d
A	a	a	a	a
B	b	b	b	b
C	c	c	c	c
D	d	d	d	d

and the inverter the form:

↓	Q	R	S
(a,A)	S	S	S
(a,B)	R	R	R
(a,C)	(will not occur)		
(a,D)	Q	Q	Q
(b,A)	Q	Q	Q
etc.	etc.		

to which the input is the vector
        (state of delayer, state of coder).

148

The inverter will now emit the same sequence as was put into the coder. Thus suppose Q was put in and caused the transition $A \to D$ in the coder. This implies that the inverter will be receiving at this step, D directly from the coder (for the coder *is* at D), and a from the delayer (for the coder *was* at A the step before). With input (a,D), the inverter goes to state Q, which is the state we supposed. And similarly for the other possible states put in.

Thus, given a transducer that does not lose distinctions, *an automatic inverter can always be built.* The importance of the demonstration is that it makes no reference to the transducer's actual material—it does not matter whether it is mechanical, or electronic, or neuronic, or hydraulic—the possibility of inversion exists. What *is* necessary is the determinateness of the coder's actions, and its maintenance of all distinctions.

Ex. 1: Why cannot the Coder of S.8/5 be used as example?
Ex. 2: Complete the specification of the inverter just given.
Ex. 3: Specify a two-step delayer in tabular form.

8/8. (This section may be omitted at first reading.) Now that the construction of the inverter has been identified in the most general form, we can examine its construction when the transducer is less general and more like the machines of every-day life. The next step is to examine the construction of the inverter when the transformations, of transducer and inverter, are given, not in the abstract form of a table but by some mathematical function.

As a preliminary, consider building an inverter for the transducer with input a, variable n, and transformation $n' = n + a$. A suitable device for delay would be the transducer with parameter n, variable p, and transformation $p' = n$. It is now easily verified that, given the input a as shown, n (if started at 3) and p (if started at 1) will change as:

a:	4	−2	−1	0	2	−1	−1	3
n:	3	7	5	4	4	6	5	4
p:	1	3	7	5	4	4	6	5

It is now obvious that if the inverter, with a variable m, is to receive n and p as input, as vector (n,p), and give back a as output, then M, as transformation, must include such transitions as:

$$M: \downarrow \quad \begin{matrix} (7,3) & (5,7) & (4,5) & (4,4) & \dots \\ 4 & -2 & -1 & 0 & \dots \end{matrix}$$

Examination of these in detail, to find how the transform follows from the operand, shows that in all cases

$$m' = n - p$$

It is easily verified that the whole system will now emit the values that the original input had two steps earlier.

(The reader might be tempted to say that as $n' = n + a$, therefore $a = n' - n$, and the code is solved. This statement is true, but it does not meet our purpose, which is to build a machine (see para. 2 of S.8/7). It enables *us* to decode the message but it is not the specification of a machine. The building or specification requires the complications of the previous paragraph, which finishes with $m' = n - p$, a specification for a machine with input.)

The general rule is now clear. We start with the transducer's equation, $n' = n + a$, and solve it for the parameter: $a = n' - n$. The delaying device has the transformation $p' = n$. The transformation for the inverter is formed by the rules, applied to the equation $a = n' - n$:

1: replace a by the new transducer's symbol m';
2: replace n' by a parameter c;
3: replace n by a parameter d.

Then, if this inverter is joined to the original transducer by putting $d = n$, and to the delayer by $c = p$, it will have the required properties.

If the original transducer has more than one variable, the process needs only suitable expansion. An example, without explanation, will be sufficient. Suppose the original transducer has parameters a_1 and a_2, variables x_1 and x_2, and transformation

$$x_1' = 2x_1 + a_1x_2$$
$$x_2' = 2x_2 + a_1a_2$$

Solving for the parameters gives

$$a_1 = (x_1' - 2x_1)/x_2$$
$$a_2 = x_2(x_2' - 2x_2)/(x_1' - 2x_1)$$

A delayer for x_1 is $p_1' = x_1$, and one for x_2 is $p_2' = x_2$. The equations of the inverter are formed from those for a_1 and a_2 by applying the rules:

1: replace each a_i by a new symbol: $a_1 = m_1'$, $a_2 = m_2'$;
2: replace each x_i' by a parameter c_i: $x_1' = c_1$, $x_2' = c_2$;
3: replace each x_i by a parameter d_i: $x_1 = d_1$, $x_2 = d_2$;

There results the transducer

$$m_1' = (c_1 - 2d_1)/d_2$$
$$m_2' = d_2(c_2 - 2d_2)/(c_1 - 2d_1).$$

If now this transducer is joined to the original transducer by $d_1 = x_1$, $d_2 = x_2$, and to the delayers by $c_1 = p_1$, $c_2 = p_2$, then m_1 and m_2 will give, respectively, the values that a_1 and a_2 had two steps earlier.

Ex. 1: Build an inverter for the transducer $n' = an$.

Ex. 2: Similarly for $n' = n - 2a + 4$.

Ex. 3: Similarly for $x' = ax - by$, $y' = ax + by$.

Ex. 4: Try to build an inverter for the transducer $n' = n + a + b$; why can it not be done?

Ex. 5: Build an inverter for the transducer

$$dx_1/dt = a_1x_1x_2 + a_2$$
$$dx_2/dt = (a_1 - 1)x_1 + a_2x_2.$$

Ex. 6: Why, in the section, does M have to transform (7,3) to 4, and not to -2, as the table a few lines higher might suggest?

8/9. *Size of the inverter.* With the facts of the previous sections, it is now possible to make some estimate of how much mechanism is necessary to invert the output of some given transducer. S.8/7 makes clear that if the original transducer is not to lose distinctions it must have at least as many output values as the input has distinct values. Similarly the inverter must have at least as many, but need not necessarily have more. The delayers will require little, for they are simple. It seems, therefore, that if the inverter is made of similar components to the original transducer then, whatever the complexity or size of the original transducer, *the inverter will have a complexity and size of the same order*.

The importance of this observation is that one sometimes feels, when thinking of the complexities in the cerebral cortex or in an ecological system, that any effect transmitted through the system must almost at once become so tangled as to be beyond all possible unravelling. Evidently this is not so; the complications of coding added by one transducer are often or usually within the decoding powers of another transducer of similar size.

TRANSMISSION FROM SYSTEM TO SYSTEM

8/10. *"Transmitting" variety.* It may be as well at this point to clarify a matter on which there has been some confusion. Though it is tempting to think of variety (or information) as passing through a transducer, or variety passing from one transducer to another, yet the phrase is dangerously misleading. Though an envelope can contain a message, the single message, being unique, cannot show variety; so an envelope, though it can contain a message, cannot contain variety: only a *set* of envelopes can do that. Similarly, variety cannot exist in a transducer (at any given moment), for a particular transducer at a particular moment is in one, and only one, state. A transducer therefore cannot "contain" variety. What *can* happen is that a number of transducers (possibly of identical construction), at some given moment, can show variety in the states occupied; and similarly one transducer, on a number of occasions, can show variety in the states it occupied on the various occasions.

(What is said here repeats something of what was said in S.7/5, but the matter can hardly be over-emphasised.)

It must be remembered always that the concepts of "variety", as used in this book, and that of "information", as used in communication theory, imply reference to some *set*, not to an individual. Any attempt to treat variety or information as a thing that can exist in another thing is likely to lead to difficult "problems" that should never have arisen.

8/11. *Transmission at one step.* Having considered how variety changes in a single transducer, we can now consider how it passes from one system to another, from T to U say, where T is an absolute system and U is a transducer.

$$\boxed{T} \to \boxed{U}$$

As has just been said, we assume that many replicates exist, identical in construction (i.e. in transformation) but able to be in various states independently of each other. If, at a given moment, the T's have a certain variety, we want to find how soon that variety spreads to the U's. Suppose that, at the given moment, the T's are occupying n_T distinct states and the U's are occupying n_U. (The following argument will be followed more easily if the reader will compose a simple and manageable example for T and U on which the argument can be traced.)

T is acting as parameter to U, and to each state of T will correspond a graph of U. The set of U's will therefore have as many graphs as the T's have values, i.e. n_T graphs. This means that from each U-state there may occur up to n_T different transitions (provided by the n_T different graphs), i.e. from the U-state a representative point may pass to any one of not more than n_T U-states. A set of U's that has all its representative points at the same state can thus, under the effect of T's variety, change to a set with its points scattered over not more than n_T states. There are n_U such sets of U's, each capable of being scattered over not more than n_T states, so the total scattering cannot, after one step, be greater than over $n_T n_U$ states. If variety is measured logarithmically, then the variety in U after one step cannot exceed the sum of those initially in U and T. In other words, *the U's cannot gain in variety at one step by more than the variety present in the T's.*

This is the fundamental law of the transmission of variety from system to system. It will be used frequently in the rest of the book.

Ex. 1: A system has states (t,u) and transformation $t' = 2t$, $u' = u + t$, so t dominates u. Eight such systems are started at the states $(0,9)$, $(2,5)$, $(0,5)$, $(1,9)$, $(1,5)$, $(2,5)$, $(0,9)$, $(1,9)$ respectively. How much variety is in the t's? How much in the u's?

Ex. 2: (Continued.) Find the states at the next step. How much variety has t now? Predict an upper limit to u's variety. How much has u now?

Ex. 3: In another system, T has two variables, t_1 and t_2, and U has two, u_1 and u_2. The whole has states (t_1, t_2, u_1, u_2), and transformation $t_1' = t_1 t_2$, $t_2' = t_1$, $u_1' = u_1 + t_2 u_2$, $u_2' = t_1 u_2$, so that T dominates U. Three replicas are started from the initial states $(0,0,0,1)$, $(0,0,1,1)$ and $(1,0,0,1)$. What is T's variety? What is U's?

Ex. 4: (Continued.) Find the three states one step later. What is U's variety now?

8/12. *Transmission at second step.* We have just seen that, at the first step, U may gain in variety by an amount up to that in T; what will happen at the second step? T may still have some variety: will this too pass to U, increasing its variety still further?

Take a simple example. Suppose that every member of the whole set of replicates was at one of the six states (T_i, U_k), (T_i, U_l), (T_i, U_m), (T_j, U_k), (T_j, U_l), (T_j, U_m), so that the T's were all at either T_i or T_j and the U's were all at U_k, U_l or U_m. Now the system as a whole is absolute; so all those at, say (T_i, U_k), while they may change from state to state, will all change similarly, visiting the various states together. The same argument holds for those at each of the other five states. It follows that the set's variety in state cannot exceed six, however many replicates there may be in the set, or however many states there may be in T and U, or for however long the changes may continue. From this it follows that the U's can never show more variety than six U-states. Thus, once U has increased in variety by the amount in T, all further increase must cease. If U receives the whole amount in one step (as above) then U receives no further increase at the second step, even though T still has some variety.

It will be noticed how important in the argument are the *pairings* between the states of T and the states of U, i.e. which value of T and which of U occur in the same machine. Evidently merely knowing the quantities of variety in T and in U (over the set of replicates) is not sufficient for the prediction of how they will change.

8/13. *Transmission through a channel.* We can now consider how variety, or information, is transmitted through a small intermediate transducer—a "channel"—where "small" refers to its number of possible states. Suppose that two large transducers Q and S are connected by a small transducer R, so that Q dominates R, and R dominates S.

$$\boxed{Q} \rightarrow \boxed{R} \rightarrow \boxed{S}$$

As usual, let there be a great number of replicates of the whole triple system. Let R's number of possible states be r. Put $\log_2 r$ equal to ρ. Assume that, at the initial state, the Q's have a variety much larger than r states, and that the R's and S's, for simplicity, have none. (Had they some variety, S.8/11 shows that the new variety, gained from Q, would merely add, logarithmically, to what they possess already.)

Application of S. 8/11 to R and S shows that, at the first step, S's variety will not increase at all. So if the three initial varieties, measured logarithmically, were respectively N, 0 and 0, then after the first step they may be as large as N, ρ, and 0, but cannot be larger.

At the next step, R cannot gain further in variety (by S.8/12), but S can gain in variety from R (as is easily verified by considering an actual example such as Ex. 2). So after the second step the varieties may be as large as N, ρ and ρ. Similarly, after the third step they may be as large as N, ρ and 2ρ; and so on. S's variety can thus increase with time as fast as the terms of the series, 0, ρ, 2ρ, 3ρ, . . ., but not faster. The rule is now obvious: *a transducer that cannot take more than r states cannot transmit variety at more than $\log_2 r$ bits per step.* This is what is meant, essentially, by different transducers having different "capacities" for transmission.

Conversely, as S's variety mounts step by step we can see that *the amount of variety that a transducer (such as R) can transmit is proportional to the product of its capacity, in bits, and the number of steps taken.* From this comes the important corollary, which will be used repeatedly later: *given long enough, any transducer can transmit any amount of variety.*

An important aspect of this theorem is its extreme generality. What sort of a machine it is that is acting as intermediate transducer, as channel, is quite irrelevant: it may be a tapping-key that has only the two states "open" and "closed", or an electric potential that can take many values, or a whole neural ganglion, or a newspaper—all are ruled by the theorem. With its aid, quantitative accuracy can be given to the intuitive feeling that some restriction in the rate of communication is implied if the communication has to take place through a small intermediate transducer, such as when the information from retina to visual cortex has to pass through the lateral geniculate body, or when information about the movements of a predator have to be passed to the herd through a solitary scout.

Ex. 1: An absolute system, of three parts, Q, R and S, has states (q,r,s) and transformation

$$\begin{array}{c} q: \\ q': \end{array} \downarrow \begin{array}{ccccccccc} 1 & 2 & 3 & 4 & 5 & 6 & 7 & 8 & 9 \\ 4 & 6 & 6 & 5 & 6 & 5 & 8 & 8 & 8 \end{array}$$

$$r' = \begin{cases} 0, \text{ if } q + r \text{ is even,} \\ 1, \text{,, ,, ,, ,, odd.} \end{cases}$$

$$s' = 2s - r.$$

Q thus dominates R, and R dominates S. What is R's capacity as a channel?

Ex. 2: (Continued.) Nine replicates were started at the initial states $(1,0,0)$, $(2,0,0)$, . . ., $(9,0,0)$, so that only Q had any initial variety. (i) How did the variety of the Q's change over the first five steps? (ii) How did that of the R's? (iii) That of the S's?

Ex. 3: (Continued.) Had the answer to Ex. 2(iii) been given as "S:1,1,4,5,5", why would it have been obviously wrong, without calculation of the actual trajectories?

8/14. The exercise just given will have shown that when Q, R and S form a chain, S can gain in variety step by step from R even though R can gain no more variety after the first step (S.8/12). The reason is that the output of R, taken step by step as a sequence, forms a vector (S.9/9), and the variety in a vector can exceed that in a component. And if the number of components in a vector can be increased without limit then the variety in the vector can also be increased without limit, even though that in each component remains bounded. Thus a *sequence* of ten coin-spins can have variety up to 1024 values, though each component is restricted to two. Similarly R's values, though restricted in the exercises to two, can provide a sequence that has variety of more than two. As the process of transmission goes on, S is affected (and its variety increased) by the whole sequence, *by the whole vector*, and thus a variety of much more than two can pass through R. A shrinkage in the capacity of a channel can thus be compensated for (to keep the total variety transmitted constant) by an increase in the length of the sequence— a fact already noticed in the previous section, and one that will be used frequently later.

Ex. 1: An absolute system T dominates a chain of transducers $A_1, A_2, A_3, A_4, \ldots$:

$$\boxed{T} \rightarrow \boxed{A_1} \rightarrow \boxed{A_2} \rightarrow \boxed{A_3} \rightarrow \boxed{A_4} \rightarrow \ldots$$

A set of replicates commences with variety in T but with none in A_1, nor in A_2, etc. Show that after k steps the varieties in $A_1, A_2, \ldots, A_k$ may be non-zero but that those in $A_{k+1}, A_{k+2}, \ldots$ must still be zero (i.e. that T's variety "cannot have spread farther than A_k".).

Ex. 2: Of 27 coins, identical in appearance, one is known to be counterfeit and to be light in weight. A balance is available and the counterfeit coin is to be identified by a series of balancings, as few as possible. *Without finding the method*—by regarding the balance as a transducer carrying information from the coins to the observer—give a number below which the number of balancings cannot fall. (Hint: What is the variety at a single balancing if the results can be only: equality, left pan heavier, right pan heavier?)

8/15. *Delay.* The arrangement of the system of S.8/13:

$$\boxed{Q} \rightarrow \boxed{R} \rightarrow \boxed{S}$$

can also be viewed as

$$\boxed{T} \rightarrow \boxed{S}$$

in which Q and R have been regarded as forming a single system T which is, of course, absolute. If now an observer studies the transfer of variety from T to S, with exactly the same events as those of S.8/13 actually occurring, he will find that the variety is moving across in small quantities, step by step, unlike the transfer of S.8/11, which was complete in one step.

The reason for the distinction is simply that in S.8/11 the whole of the dominating system (T) had an immediate effect on the dominated (U), while in S.8/13 T contained a part Q which had no immediate effect on the receiver S. Q's effect had to be exerted through R, and was thereby delayed.

This more time-consuming transfer is common in real systems simply because many of them are built of parts not all of which have an immediate effect on the receiving system. Thus if the cerebral cortex, as receiver, is affected by the environment (which has no immediate effect on the cortex) the action has to take place through a chain of systems: the sense organs, the sensory nerves, the sensory nuclei, and so on; and some delay is thereby imposed. Even within one such part some transfer has to take place from point to point, thereby delaying its transfer to the next part.

Conversely, if a system such as T is found on testing to transmit its variety to another system only over a number of steps, then it may be predicted that T, if examined in detail, will be found to consist of sub-systems coupled so that not all of T's variables have an immediate effect on S.

Ex. 1: If T consists of the sub-systems $A, \ldots, F$ joined to each other and to S as shown in the diagram of immediate effects:

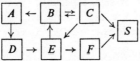

how many steps are necessary for all the variety in T to be transferred to S?

Ex. 2: (Continued.) How long does it take to get a "message", telling of T's state, uniquely from T to S?

Ex. 3: If J, with the variables w, x, y, z, dominates K, with the variable k, by the transformation $w' = w - y$, $x' = w + xz$, $y' = 2wy - z$, $z' = yz^2$, $k' = x - 3k$, how many steps are necessary for all the variety in J to be transferred to K?

Ex. 4: (Continued.) In the same system, how long would it take to get a message from w to z?

8/16. To improve our grasp of these matters, let us next consider the case of two systems joined so that there is feedback:

$$\boxed{T} \rightleftarrows \boxed{U}$$

S.8/11 showed that T will pass variety to U; will U, now having this variety, pass it back to T and thereby increase T's variety still further?

Again the answer is given straightforwardly when we consider a set of replicates. Suppose that initially the variety existed only between the T's, the U's being all at the same state. Divide the whole set into sub-sets, each sub-set consisting of those with T at a particular state, so that set i, say, consists of the systems with T at state T_i. Within such a subset there is now no variety in state, and no variety can develop, for the whole (T,U)-system is absolute. The initial variety of the T's, therefore, will not increase, either at the first step or subsequently. In a determinate system, *feedback does not lead to a regenerative increase in variety.*

What was important in the argument about U's feedback to T is that what U feeds back to T is highly correlated with what is in T, for each U feeds back into the particular T that acted on it a step earlier, and no other. The argument thus demands an accurate treatment of the correspondences between the various T's and U's.

The arguments of the previous few sections have shown that though the matter can be treated in words in the simple cases (those just considered), the attempt to handle complex cases in the verbal form is likely to lead to intolerable complexities. What is wanted is a symbolic machinery, an algebra, which will enable the relations to be handled more or less mechanically, with the rules of the symbolic manipulation looking after the complexities. It seems likely that the theory of sets, especially as developed by Bourbaki and Riguet, will provide the technique. But further research is needed into these questions.

8/17. *Interference.* If acid and alkali are passed along the same pipe they destroy each other; what will happen if two messages are passed along the same channel?—will they interfere with, and destroy, each other?

Simple examples are quite sufficient to establish that the same physical channel may well carry more than one message without interference, each message travelling as if the others did not exist. Suppose, for instance, that a sender wanted to let a recipient know daily, by an advertisement in the personal column of a newspaper, which of 26 different events was being referred to, and suppose he arranged to print a single letter as the coded form. The same channel of "one printed letter" could *simultaneously* be used to carry other messages, of variety two, by letting the letter be printed as lower case or capital. The two messages would then be transmitted with as little interference as if they were on separate pages. Thus, if ten successive messages were sent, N K e S z t y Z w m would transmit both n k e s z t y z w m and 1 1 0 1 0 0 0 1 0 0 completely. It is thus possible for two messages to pass through the same physical thing without mutual destruction.

As an example of rather different type, consider the transformation of Ex. 2/14/11, and regard the position of, say, A''' as a coded form of that of A (with B''' similarly as the coded form of B). Thus treasure might be buried at A and weapons at B, with recording marks left at A''' and B'''. Now a change in the position of B leads to a change of A''', so B's value plays an essential part in the coding of A to A''' (and conversely of A on B'''); so the two messages interact. Nevertheless the interaction is not destructive to the information about where the treasure and the weapons are, for, given the positions of A''' and B''', those of A and B can always be reconstructed, i.e. the messages are still capable of being exactly decoded.

The conditions necessary that two messages should not interfere destructively can be found by considering the basic fact of coding— that a *set* of messages are converted to a set of transforms (S.8/4) —and by using the fact that any two messages of different type can be laid side by side and considered as components of one "vector" message, just as any two variables can always be regarded as components of one vector. Thus if, in the example of the printed letter, x represents the variable "which message of the 26" and y represents the variable "which of the two", then the printed symbol is a coding of the single message (x,y).

Suppose it is given that the two messages x and y do not interfere destructively. This implies that both x's and y's values are reconstructible from the received form. It follows that if two primary messages are distinct, then their coded forms must be distinct (for otherwise unique decoding would not be possible). From this it follows that, if the interaction is to be non-destructive, *the variety in the received forms must be not less than that in the original*. This condition holds in the example of the printed letter, for both the original messages and the printed form have variety of 26 × 2.

The fact that chaos does not necessarily occur when two messages meet in the same channel is of great importance in neuro-physiology, especially in that of the cerebral cortex. Here the richness of connexion is so great that much mixing of messages must inevitably occur, if only from the lack of any method for keeping them apart. Thus a stream of impulses coming from the auditory cortex and carrying information relevant to one reaction may meet a stream of impulses coming from the visual cortex carrying information relevant to some other reaction. It has been an outstanding problem in neurophysiology to know how destructive interaction and chaos is avoided.

The discussion of this section has shown, however, that the problem is badly stated. Chaos does not necessarily occur when two messages meet, even though each affects the same physical set of variables. Through all the changes, provided that no variety is lost and that the mechanism is determinate in its details, the two messages can continue to exist, passing merely from one coding to another. All that is necessary for their recovery is a suitable inverter; and, as S.8/7 showed, its construction is always possible.

Ex. 1: (See Ex. 2/14/11.)   If A''' is at the point (0,0) and B''' at (0,1), reconstruct the position of A.

Ex. 2: A transducer has two parameters: α (which can take the values a or A) and β (which can take the values b or B).   Its states—W,X,Y,Z—are transformed according to:

$\downarrow$	W	X	Y	Z
(a,b)	W	Y	Y	Y
(a,B)	X	X	W	W
(A,b)	Z	W	X	X
(A,B)	Y	Z	Z	Z

Two messages, one a series of α-values and the other a series of β-values, are transmitted simultaneously, commencing together.   If the recipient is interested only in the α-message, can he always re-construct it, regardless of what is sent by β?   (Hint: S.8/6.)

Ex. 3: Join rods by hinge-pins, as shown in Fig. 8/17/1:

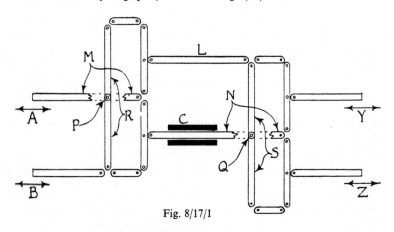

Fig. 8/17/1

(The pinned and hinged joints have been separated to show the construction.) P is a pivot, fixed to a base, on which the rod R can rotate; similarly for Q and S.   The rod M passes over P without connexion; similarly for N and Q.   A tubular constraint C ensures that all movements, for small arcs, shall be to right or left (as represented in the Figure) only.

Movements at A and B will cause movements at L and N and so to Y and Z, and the whole can be regarded as a device for sending the messages "position of A" and "position of B", via L and N, to the outputs Y and Z. It will be found that, with B held fixed, movements at A cause movements of *both* L and N; similarly, with A held fixed, movements at B also affect both L and N.   Simultaneous messages from A and B thus pass through both L and N simultaneously, and evidently meet there.   Do the messages interact destructively?   (Hint: How does Y move if A alone moves?)

Ex. 4: (Continued.)   Find the algebraic relation between the positions at A B, Y and Z.   What does "decoding" mean in this algebraic form?

Chapter   9

INCESSANT TRANSMISSION

9/1. The present chapter will continue the theme of the previous, and will study variety and its transmission, but will be concerned rather with the special case of the transmission that is sustained for an indefinitely long time. This is the case of the sciatic nerve, or the telephone cable, that goes on incessantly carrying messages, unlike the transmissions of the previous chapter, which were studied for only a few steps in time.

Incessant transmission has been specially studied by Shannon, and this chapter will, in fact, be devoted chiefly to introducing his *Mathematical Theory of Communication*, with special emphasis on how it is related to the other topics in this *Introduction*.

What is given in this chapter is, however, a series of notes, intended to supplement Shannon's masterly work, rather than a description that is complete in itself. Shannon's book must be regarded as the primary source, and should be consulted first. I assume that the reader has it available.

9/2. *The non-determinate transformation.* If the transmission is to go on for an indefinitely long time, the variety must be sustained, and therefore not like the case studied in S.8/11, in which *T*'s transmission of variety stopped after the first step. Now any determinate system of finite size cannot have a trajectory that is infinitely long (S.4/5). We must therefore now consider a more comprehensive form of machine and transformation—the non-determinate.

So far all our transformations have been single-valued, and have thus represented the machine that is determinate. An extension was hinted at in S.2/10, and we can now explore the possibility of an operand having more than one transform. Some supplementary restriction, however, is required, so as to keep the possibilities within bounds and subject to some law. It must not become completely chaotic. A case that has been found to have many applications is that in which each operand state, instead of being transformed to a particular new state, may go to some one of the possible states, the selection of the particular state being made by some method or process that gives each state a *constant probability* of being the transform. It is the unchangingness of the probability that provides the law or orderliness on which definite statements can be based.

Such a transformation would be the following: $x' = x + a$, where the value of a is found by spinning a coin and using the rule Head: $a = 1$; Tail: $a = 0$. Thus, if the initial value of x is 4, and the coin gives the sequence $T T H H H T H T T H$, the trajectory will be 4, 4, 4, 5, 6, 7, 7, 8, 8, 8, 9. If the coin gives $H T H H T T T$ $H T T$, the trajectory will be 4, 5, 5, 6, 7, 7, 7, 7, 8, 8, 8. Thus the transformation and the initial state are not sufficient to define a unique trajectory, as was the case in S.2/17; they define only a *set* of trajectories. The definition given here is *supplemented* by instructions from the coin (compare S.4/19), so that a *single* trajectory is arrived at.

The transformation could be represented (uniformly with the previously used representations) as:

$$
\begin{array}{ccccc}
3 & & 4 & & 5 \\
{}^{\frac{1}{2}}\swarrow\ \searrow{}^{\frac{1}{2}} & & {}^{\frac{1}{2}}\swarrow\ \searrow{}^{\frac{1}{2}} & & {}^{\frac{1}{2}}\swarrow\ \searrow{}^{\frac{1}{2}} \quad \text{etc.}\\
3 \quad 4 & & 4 \quad 5 & & 5 \quad 6
\end{array}
$$

where the $\frac{1}{2}$ means that from state 3 the system will change

with probability $\frac{1}{2}$ to state 3,
and   „   „   „ „   „ 4.

Such a transformation, and especially the set of trajectories that it may produce, is called "stochastic", to distinguish it from the single-valued and determinate.

Such a representation soon becomes unmanageable if many transitions are possible from each state. A more convenient, and fundamentally suitable, method is that by matrix, similar to that of S.2/10. A matrix is constructed by writing the possible operands in a row across the top, and the possible transforms in a column down the left side; then, at the intersection of column i with row j, is put the probability that the system, if at state i, will go to state j.

As example, consider the transformation just described. If the system was at state 4, and if the coin has a probability $\frac{1}{2}$ of giving

Head, then the probability of its going to state 5 is $\frac{1}{2}$; and so would be its probability of staying at 4.

↓	...	3	4	5	6	...
...	...	...	...	...	...	...
3	...	$\frac{1}{2}$	0	0	0	...
4	...	$\frac{1}{2}$	$\frac{1}{2}$	0	0	...
5	...	0	$\frac{1}{2}$	$\frac{1}{2}$	0	...
6	...	0	0	$\frac{1}{2}$	$\frac{1}{2}$	...
...	...	...	...	...	...	...

All other transitions have zero probability. So the matrix can be constructed, cell by cell.

This is the **matrix of transition probabilities.** (The reader should be warned that the transposed form, with rows and columns interchanged, is more common in the literature; but the form given has substantial advantages, e.g. Ex. 12/8/4, besides being uniform with the notations used throughout this book.)

We should, at this point, be perfectly clear as to what we mean by "probability". (See also S.7/4.) Not only must we be clear about the meaning, but the meaning must itself be stated in the form of a *practical*, operational test. (Subjective feelings of "degree of confidence" are here unusable.) Thus if two observers differ about whether something has a "constant probability", by what test can they resolve this difference?

Probabilities are frequencies. "A 'probable' event is a frequent event." (Fisher.) Rain is "probable" at Manchester because it is frequent at Manchester, and ten Reds in succession at a roulette wheel is "improbable" because it is infrequent. (The wise reader will hold tight to this definition, refusing to be drawn into such merely speculative questions as to what numerical value shall be given to the "probability" of life on Mars, for which there can be no frequency.) What was said in S.7/4 is relevant here, for the concept of probability is, in its practical aspects, meaningful only over some set in which the various events or possibilities occur with their characteristic frequencies.

The test for a constant probability thus becomes a test for a constant frequency. The tester allows the process to continue for a time until some frequency for the event has declared itself. Thus, if he wished to see whether Manchester had a constant, i.e. unvarying, probability of rain (in suitably defined conditions), he would record the rains until he had formed a first estimate of the frequency. He would then start again, collect new records, and form a second estimate. He might go on to collect third and fourth estimates. If these several estimates proved seriously discrepant he would say that rain at Manchester had no constant probability. If however they agreed, he could, if he pleased, say that the fraction at which they agreed was *the* constant probability. Thus an event, *in a very long sequence*, has a "constant" probability of occurring at each step if every long portion of the sequence shows it occurring with about the same relative frequency.

These words can be stated more accurately in mathematical terms. What is important here is that throughout this book any phrases about "probability" have objective meanings whose validity can be checked by experiment. They do not depend on any subjective estimate.

Ex. 1: Take the five playing cards Ace, 2, 3, 4, 5. Shuffle them, and lay them in a row to replace the asterisks in the transformation *T*:

$$T: \downarrow \quad \begin{matrix} \text{Ace} & 2 & 3 & 4 & 5 \\ * & * & * & * & * \end{matrix}$$

Is the particular transformation so obtained determinate or not? (Hint: Is it single-valued or not?)

Ex. 2: What rule must hold over the numbers that appear in each column of a matrix of transition probabilities?

Ex. 3: Does any rule like that of Ex. 2 hold over the numbers in each row?

Ex. 4: If the transformation defined in this section starts at 4 and goes on for 10 steps, how many trajectories occur in the *set* so defined?

Ex. 5: How does the kinematic graph of the stochastic transformation differ from that of the determinate?

9/3. The stochastic transformation is simply an extension of the determinate (or single valued). Thus, suppose the matrix of transition probabilities of a three-state system were:

↓	A	B	C		↓	A	B	C
first A	0	0·9	0·1	and then A	0	1	0
B	0·9	0	0	B	1	0	0
C	0·1	0·1	0·9	C	0	0	1

The change, from the first matrix to the second, though small (and could be made as small as we please) has taken the system from the obviously stochastic type to that with the single-valued transformation:

$$\downarrow \quad \begin{matrix} A & B & C \\ B & A & C \end{matrix}$$

of the type we have considered throughout the book till now. *The single-valued, determinate, transformation is thus simply a special, extreme, case of the stochastic.* It is the stochastic in which all the probabilities have become 0 or 1. This essential unity should not be obscured by the fact that it is convenient to talk sometimes of the determinate type and sometimes of the types in which the important aspect is the fractionality of the probabilities. Throughout Part III the essential unity of the two types will play an important part in giving unity to the various types of regulation.

The word "stochastic" can be used in two senses. It can be used to mean "all types (with constant matrix of transition probabilities), the determinate included as a special case", or it can mean "all types other than the determinate". Both meanings can be used; but as they are incompatible, care must be taken that the context shows which is implied.

THE MARKOV CHAIN

9/4. After eight chapters, we now know something about how a system changes if its transitions correspond to those of a single-valued transformation. What about the behaviour of a system whose transitions correspond to those of a stochastic transformation? What would such a system look like if we met one actually working?

Suppose an insect lives in and about a shallow pool—sometimes in the water (W), sometimes under pebbles (P), and sometimes on the bank (B). Suppose that, over each unit interval of time, there is a constant probability that, being under a pebble, it will go up on the bank; and similarly for the other possible transitions. (We can assume, if we please, that its actual behaviour at any instant is determined by minor details and events in its environment.) Thus a protocol of its positions might read:

W B W B W P W B W B W B W P W B B W B W P W B W P W
B W B W B B W B W B W B W P P W P W B W B W B B B W

Suppose, for definiteness, that the transition probabilities are

$\downarrow$	B	W	P
B	$\frac{1}{4}$	$\frac{3}{4}$	$\frac{1}{8}$
W	$\frac{3}{4}$	0	$\frac{3}{4}$
P	0	$\frac{1}{4}$	$\frac{1}{8}$

These probabilities would be found (S.9/2) by observing its behaviour over long stretches of time, by finding the frequency of, say, $B \rightarrow W$, and then finding the relative frequencies, which are the probabilities. Such a table would be, in essence, *a summary of actual past behaviour*, extracted from the protocol.

Such a sequence of states, in which, over various long stretches, the probability of each transition is the same, is known as a **Markov chain,** from the name of the mathematician who first made an extensive study of their properties. (Only during the last decade or so has their great importance been recognised. The mathematical books give various types of Markov chain and add various qualifications. The type defined above will give us all we want and will not clash with the other definitions, but an important qualification is mentioned in S.9/7.)

The term "Markov chain" is sometimes applied to a particular trajectory produced by a system (e.g. the trajectory given in Ex. 1) and sometimes to the system (defined by its matrix) which is capable of producing many trajectories. Reference to the context must show which is implied.

Ex. 1: A system of two states gave the protocol (of 50 transitions):

> *A B A B B B A B A B A A B A B A B A B A B B B B B A B A A B A B B A A B*
> *A B B A B A A A B A B B A A B B A B B A.*

Draw up an estimate of its matrix of transition probabilities.

Ex. 2: Use the method of S.9/2 (with the coin) to construct several trajectories, so as to establish that *one* matrix can give rise to *many* different trajectories.

Ex. 3: Use a table of random numbers to generate a Markov chain on two states *A* and *B* by the rule:

Present state	Random number	Then next state
A	0 or 1	*A*
,,	2,3 ... 9	*B*
B	0,1,2,3,4	*A*
,,	5,6,7,8,9	*B*

Ex. 4: (Continued.) What is its matrix of transition probabilities?

9/5. Ex. 9/4/1 shows how the behaviour of a system specifies its matrix. Conversely, the matrix will yield information about the tendencies of the system, though not the particular details. Thus suppose a scientist, not the original observer, saw the insect's matrix of transition probabilities:

$\downarrow$	*B*	*W*	*P*
B	$\frac{1}{4}$	$\frac{3}{4}$	$\frac{1}{8}$
W	$\frac{3}{4}$	0	$\frac{3}{4}$
P	0	$\frac{1}{4}$	$\frac{1}{8}$

He can deduce that if it is in water it will not stay there, for $W \to W$ has probability zero, but will go usually to the bank, for $W \to B$ has the highest probability in the column. From the bank it will probably go to the water, and then back to the bank. If under a pebble it also tends to go to the water. So clearly it spends much of its time oscillating between bank and water. Time spent under the pebbles will be small. The protocol given, which was constructed with a table of random numbers, shows these properties.

Thus the matrix contains information about any particular system's probable behaviour.

Ex. 1: Had the P-column of the matrix a 1 in the lowest cell and zero elsewhere, what could be deduced about the insect's mode of life?

Ex. 2: A fly wanders round a room between positions A, B, C, and D, with transition probabilities:

$\downarrow$	A	B	C	D
A	$\frac{1}{2}$	0	0	$\frac{1}{3}$
B	$\frac{1}{4}$	1	0	$\frac{1}{3}$
C	$\frac{1}{4}$	0	$\frac{1}{2}$	$\frac{1}{3}$
D	0	0	$\frac{1}{2}$	0

One of the positions is an unpleasantly hot stove and another is a fly-paper. Which are they?

Ex. 3: If the protocol and matrix of Ex. 9/4/1 are regarded as codings of each other, which is the direction of coding that loses information?

9/6. *Equilibrium in a Markov chain.*

Suppose now that large numbers of such insects live in the same pond, and that each behaves independently of the others. As we draw back from the pond the individual insects will gradually disappear from view, and all we will see are three grey clouds, three populations, one on the bank, one in the water, and one under the pebbles. These three *populations* now become three quantities that can change with time. If they are d_B, d_W, and d_P respectively at some moment, then their values at one interval later, $d_B{}'$ etc., can be found by considering what their constituent individuals will do. Thus, of the insects in the water, three-quarters will change over to B, and will add their number on to d_B, while a quarter will add their number to d_P. Thus, after the change the new population on the bank, $d_B{}'$, will be $\frac{1}{4}d_B + \frac{3}{4}d_W + \frac{1}{8}d_P$. In general therefore the three *populations* will change in accordance with the transformation (on the vector with three components)

$$
\begin{aligned}
d_B{}' &= \tfrac{1}{4}d_B + \tfrac{3}{4}d_W + \tfrac{1}{8}d_P \\
d_W{}' &= \tfrac{3}{4}d_B + \tfrac{3}{4}d_P \\
d_P{}' &= \tfrac{1}{4}d_W + \tfrac{1}{8}d_P
\end{aligned}
$$

It must be noticed, as fundamentally important, that the system composed of three populations (if large enough to be free from sampling irregularities) is *determinate*, although the individual insects behave only with certain probabilities.

To follow the process in detail let us suppose that we start an experiment by forcing 100 of them under the pebbles and then watching what happens. The initial vector of the three populations (d_B, d_W, d_P) will thus be $(0, 0, 100)$. What the numbers will be at the next step will be subject to the vagaries of random sampling; for it is not *impossible* that each of the hundred might stay under the pebbles. On the average, however (i.e. the average if the whole 100 were tested over and over again) only about 12·5 would remain

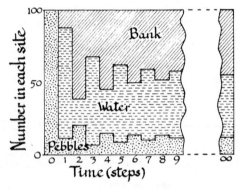

Fig. 9/6/1

there, the remainder going to the bank (12·5 also) and to the water (75). Thus, after the first step the population will have shown the change $(0, 0, 100) \to (12\cdot5, 75, 12\cdot5)$.

In this way the average numbers in the three populations may be found, step by step, using the process of S.3/6. The next state is thus found to be $(60\cdot9, 18\cdot8, 20\cdot3)$, and the trajectory of this system (of three degrees of freedom—not a hundred) is shown in Fig. 9/6/1.

It will be seen that the populations tend, through dying oscillations, to a state of equilibrium, at $(44\cdot9, 42\cdot9, 12\cdot2)$, at which the system will remain indefinitely. Here "the system" means, of course, these three variables.

It is worth noticing that when the system has settled down, and is practically at its terminal populations, there will be a sharp contrast between the populations, which are unchanging, and the insects, which are moving incessantly. The same pond can thus provide two very different meanings to the one word "system". ("Equilibrium" here corresponds to what the physicist calls a "steady state".)

The equilibrial values of a Markov chain are readily computed. At equilibrium the values are unchanging, so d_B', say, is equal to d_B. So the first line of the equation becomes

$$d_B = \tfrac{1}{4}d_B + \tfrac{3}{4}d_W + \tfrac{1}{8}d_P$$

i.e. $$0 = -\tfrac{3}{4}d_B + \tfrac{3}{4}d_W + \tfrac{1}{8}d_P$$

The other lines are treated similarly. The lines are not all independent, however, for the three populations must, in this example, sum to 100; one line (any one) is therefore struck out and replaced by

$$d_B + d_W + d_P = 100.$$

The equations then become, e.g.,

$$-\tfrac{3}{4}d_B + \tfrac{3}{4}d_W + \tfrac{1}{8}d_P = 0$$
$$d_B + d_W + d_P = 100$$
$$\tfrac{1}{4}d_W - \tfrac{7}{8}d_P = 0$$

which can be solved in the usual way. In this example the equilibrial values are $(44 \cdot 9, 42 \cdot 9, 12 \cdot 2)$; as S.9/5 predicted, any individual insect does not spend much time under the pebbles.

Ex. 1: Find the populations that would follow the initial state of putting all the insects on the bank.

Ex. 2: Verify the equilibrial values.

Ex. 3: A six-sided die was heavily biased by a weight hidden in face x. When placed in a box with face f upwards and given a thorough shaking, the probability that it would change to face g was found, over prolonged testing, to be:

	↓	1	2	3	4	5	6
	1	0·1	0·1	0·1	0·1	0·1	0·1
	2	0·1	0·1	0·1	0·1	0·1	0·1
	3	0·5	0·5	0·5	0·5	0·5	0·5
g	4	0·1	0·1	0·1	0·1	0·1	0·1
	5	0·1	0·1	0·1	0·1	0·1	0·1
	6	0·1	0·1	0·1	0·1	0·1	0·1

Which is x? (Hint: Beware!)

Ex. 4: A compound AB is dissolved in water. In each small interval of time each molecule has a 1% chance of dissociating, and each dissociated A has an 0·1% chance of becoming combined again. What is the matrix of transition probabilities of a molecule, the two states being "dissociated" and "not dissociated"? (Hint: Can the number of B's dissociated be ignored?)

Ex. 5: (Continued.) What is the equilibrial value of the percentage dissociated?

Ex. 6: Write out the transformations of (i) the individual insect's transitions, and (ii) the population's transitions. How are they related?

Ex. 7: How many states appear in the insect's transitions? How many in the system of populations?

Ex. 8: If D is the column vector of the populations in the various states, D' the vector one step later, and M the matrix of transition probabilities, show that, in ordinary matrix algebra,

$$D' = MD, \quad D'' = M^2 D, \quad \text{and} \quad D^{(n)} = M^n D.$$

(This simple and natural relation is lost if the matrix is written in transposed form. Compare Ex. 2/16/3 and 12/8/4.)

9/7. *Dependence on earlier values.* The definition of a Markov chain, given in S.9/4, omitted an important qualification: *the probabilities of transition must not depend on states earlier than the operand.* Thus if the insect behaves as a Markov chain it will be found that when on the bank it will go to the water in 75% of the cases, whether before being on the bank it was at bank, water, or pebbles. One would test the fact experimentally by collecting the three corresponding percentages and then seeing if they were all equal at 75%.

Here is a protocol in which the independence does not hold:

$A\,A\,B\,B\,A\,B\,B\,A\,A\,B\,B\,A\,B\,B\,A\,B\,B\,A\,B\,B\,A\,A\,B\,B\,A\,B\,B\,A\,B\,A\,B\,A$

The transitions, on a direct count, are

$\downarrow$	A	B
A	3	10
B	10	8

In particular we notice that B is followed by A and B about equally. If we now re-classify these 18 transitions from B according to what letter preceded the B we get:

$$\ldots AB \text{ was followed by } \begin{cases} A: 2 \text{ times} \\ B: 8 \quad\text{,,} \end{cases}$$

$$\ldots BB \quad\text{,,}\quad\quad\text{,,}\quad\quad\text{,,}\quad \begin{cases} A: 8 \quad\text{,,} \\ B: 0 \quad\text{,,} \end{cases}$$

So what state follows B depends markedly on what state came before the B. Thus this sequence is not a Markov chain. Sometimes the fact can be described in metaphor by saying that the system's "memory" extends back for more than one state (compare S.6/21).

This dependence of the probability on what came earlier is a marked characteristic of the sequences of letters given by a language such as English. Thus: what is the probability that an s will be followed by a t? It depends much on what preceded the s; thus *es* followed by t is common, but *ds* followed by t is rare. Were the letters a Markov chain, then s would be followed by t with the same frequency in the two cases.

These dependencies are characteristic in language, which contains many of them. They range from the simple linkages of the type just mentioned to the long range linkages that make the ending "... of Kantian transcendentalism" more probable in a book that starts "The university of the eighteenth century ..." than in one that starts "The modern racehorse ...".

Ex.: How are the four transitions $C \to C$, $C \to D$, $D \to C$, and $D \to D$, affected in frequency of occurrence by the state that immediately preceded each operand, in the protocol:

D D C C D C C D D C C D C C D D C C D C C D D C C D D D D C C
D D D D C C D D D C C D C C D C?

(Hint: Classify the observed transitions.)

9/8. *Re-coding to Markov form.* When a system is found to produce trajectories in which the transition probabilities depend in a *constant* way on what states preceded each operand, the system, though not Markovian, can be made so by a method that is more important than may at first seem—one re-defines the system.

Thus suppose that the system is like that of Ex. 9/7/1 (the preceding), and suppose that the transitions are such that after the two-state sequence ... *CC* it always goes to *D*, regardless of what occurred earlier, that after ... *DC* it always goes to *C*, that after ... *CD* it goes equally frequently in the long run to *C* and *D*, and similarly after ... *DD*. We now simply define new states that are vectors, having two components—the earlier state as first component and the later one as second. Thus if the original system has just produced a trajectory ending ... *DC*, we say that the new system is *at* the state (D,C). If the original then moves on to state *C*, so that its trajectory is now ... *DCC*, we say that the new system has gone on to the state (C,C). So the new system has undergone the transition $(D,C) \to (C,C)$. These new states *do* form a Markov chain, for their probabilities (as assumed here) do not depend on earlier states; and in fact the matrix is

$\downarrow$	(C,C)	(C,D)	(D,C)	(D,D)
(C,C)	0	0	1	0
(C,D)	1	0	0	0
(D,C)	0	$\frac{1}{2}$	0	$\frac{1}{2}$
(D,D)	0	$\frac{1}{2}$	0	$\frac{1}{2}$

(Notice that the transition $(C,D) \to (C,D)$ is impossible; for any state that ends $(-,D)$ can only go to one that starts $(D,-)$. Some other transitions are similarly impossible in the new system.)

If, in another system, the transition probabilities depend on values occurring n steps back, then the new states must be defined as vectors over n consecutive states.

The method of re-defining may seem artificial and pointless. Actually it is of fundamental importance, for it moves our attention from a system that is not state-determined to one that is. The new system is better predictable, for its "state" takes account of the original system's past history. Thus, with the original form, to know that the system was at state C did not allow one to say more than that it might go to either C or D. With the second form, to know that it was at the state (D,C) enabled one to predict its behaviour with certainty, just as with the original form one could predict with certainty when one knew what had happened earlier. What is important is that the method shows that the two methods of "knowing" a system—by its present state or by its past history—have an exact relation. The theory of the system that is not completely observable (S.6/21) made use of this fact in essentially the same way. We are thus led again to the conclusion that the existence of "memory" in a real system is not an intrinsic property of the system—we hypothesise its existence when our powers of observation are limited. Thus, to say "that system seems to me to have memory" is equivalent to saying "my powers of observation do not permit me to make a valid prediction on the basis of one observation, but I can make a valid prediction after a sequence of observations".

9/9. *Sequence as vector.* In the earlier chapters we have often used vectors, and so far they have always had a finite and definite number of components. It is possible, however, for a vector to have an infinite, or indefinitely large number of components. Provided one is cautious, the complication need cause little danger.

Thus a sequence can be regarded as a vector whose first component is the first value in the sequence, and so on to the n-th component, which is the n-th value. Thus if I spin a coin five times, the result, taken as a whole, might be the vector with five components (H, T, T, H, T). Such vectors are common in the theory of probability, where they may be generated by repeated sampling.

If such a vector is formed by sampling with replacement, it has only the slight peculiarity that each value comes from the same component set, whereas a more general type, that of S.3/5 for instance, can have a different set for each component.

9/10. *Constraint in a set of sequences.* A set of such sequences can show constraint, just as a set of vectors can (S.7/11), by not having the full range that the range of components, if they **were**

independent, would make possible. If the sequence is of finite length, e.g. five spins of a coin, as in the previous paragraph, the constraint can be identified and treated exactly as in S.7/11. When, however, it is indefinitely long, as is often the case with sequences (whose termination is often arbitrary and irrelevant) we must use some other method, without, however, changing what is essential.

What the method is can be found by considering how an infinitely long vector can be specified. Clearly such a vector cannot be wholly arbitrary, in components and values, as was the vector in S.3/5, for an infinity of time and paper would be necessary for its writing down. Usually such indefinitely long vectors are specified by some process. First the value of the initial component is given, and then a specified process (a transformation) is applied to generate the further components in succession (like the "integration" of S.3/9).

We can now deduce what is necessary if a set of such vectors is to show no constraint. Suppose we build up the set of "no constraint", and proceed component by component. By S.7/12, the first component must take its full range of values; then *each* of these values must be combined with each of the second component's possible values; and each of these pairs must be combined with each of the third component's possible values; and so on. The rule is that as each new component is added, *all* its possible values must occur.

It will now be seen that *the set of vectors with no constraint corresponds to the Markov chain that, at each transition, has all the transitions equally probable.* (When the probability becomes an actual frequency, lots of chains will occur, thus providing the *set* of sequences.) Thus, if there are three states possible to each component, the sequences of no constraint will be the set generated by the matrix

$\downarrow$	A	B	C
A	$\frac{1}{3}$	$\frac{1}{3}$	$\frac{1}{3}$
B	$\frac{1}{3}$	$\frac{1}{3}$	$\frac{1}{3}$
C	$\frac{1}{3}$	$\frac{1}{3}$	$\frac{1}{3}$

Ex. 1: The exponential series defines an infinitely long vector with components:

$$(1, \ x, \ \frac{x^2}{2}, \ \frac{x^3}{2.3}, \ \frac{x^4}{2.3.4}, \cdots)$$

What transformation generates the series by obtaining each component from that on its left? (Hint: Call the components $t_1, t_2, \ldots$, etc.; t_i' is the same as t_{i+1}.)

Ex. 2: Does the series produced by a true die show constraint?

Ex. 3: (Continued.) Does the series of Ex. 9/4/3?

ENTROPY

9/11. We have seen throughout S.7/5 and Chapter 8 how information cannot be transmitted in larger quantity than the quantity of variety allows. We have seen how constraint can lessen some potential quantity of variety. And we have just seen, in the previous section, how a source of variety such as a Markov chain has zero constraint when all its transitions are equally probable. It follows that this condition (of zero constraint) is the one that enables the information source, if it behaves as a Markov chain, to transmit the maximal quantity of information (in given time).

Shannon has devised a measure for the quantity of variety shown by a Markov chain at each step—the entropy—that has proved of fundamental importance in many questions relating to incessant transmission. This measure is developed in the following way.

If a set has variety, and we take a sample of one item from the set, by some defined sampling process, then the various possible results of the drawing will be associated with various, corresponding probabilities. Thus if the traffic lights have variety four, showing the combinations

1 Red
2 Red and Yellow
3 Green
4 Yellow,

and if they are on for durations of 25, 5, 25 and 5 seconds respectively, then if a motorist turns up suddenly at irregular times he would find the lights in the various states with frequencies of about 42, 8, 42 and 8% respectively. As probabilities these become 0·42, 0·08, 0·42 and 0·08. Thus the state "Green" has (if this particular method of sampling be used) a probability of 0·42; and similarly for the others.

Conversely, any set of probabilities—any set of positive fractions that adds up to 1—can be regarded as corresponding to some set whose members show variety. Shannon's calculation proceeds from the probabilities by the calculation, if the probabilities are $p_1, p_2, \ldots, p_n$, of

$$-p_1 \log p_1 - p_2 \log p_2 - \ldots - p_n \log p_n,$$

a quantity which he calls the **entropy** of the set of probabilities and which he denotes by H. Thus if we take logs to the base 10, the entropy of the set associated with the traffic lights is

$$-0·42 \log_{10} 0·42 - 0·08 \log_{10} 0·08 - 0·42 \log_{10} 0·42 - 0·08 \log_{10} 0·08$$

which equals 0·492. (Notice that $\log_{10} 0·42 = \bar{1}·6232 = -1·0000$

$+ 0{\cdot}6232 = -0{\cdot}3768$; so the first term is $(-0{\cdot}42)(-0{\cdot}3768)$, which is $+ 0{\cdot}158$; and similarly for the other terms.) Had the logs been taken to the base 2 (S.7/7) the result would have been $1{\cdot}63$ bits.

The word "entropy" will be used in this book solely as it is used by Shannon, any broader concept being referred to as "variety" or in some other way.

Ex. 1: On 80 occasions when I arrived at a certain level-crossing it was closed on 14. What is the entropy of the set of probabilities?

Ex. 2: From a shuffled pack of cards one is drawn. Three events are distinguished:

E_1: the drawing of the King of Clubs,
E_2: the drawing of any Spade,
E_3: the drawing of any other card.

What is the entropy of the variety of the distinguishable events?

Ex. 3: What is the entropy of the variety in one throw of an unbiased die?

Ex. 4: What is the entropy in the variety of the set of possibilities of the outcomes (with their order preserved) of two successive throws of an unbiased die?

Ex. 5: (Continued.) What is the entropy of n successive throws?

*Ex. 6: What is the limit of $-p \log p$ as p tends to zero?

9/12. The entropy so calculated has several important properties. First, it is maximal, for a given number (n) of probabilities, when the probabilities are all equal. H is then equal to $\log n$, precisely the measure of variety defined in S.7/7. (Equality of the probabilities, in each column, was noticed in S.9/10 to be necessary for the constraint to be minimal, i.e. for the variety to be maximal.) Secondly, different H's derived from different sets can, with suitable qualifications, be combined to yield an average entropy.

Such a combination is used to find the entropy appropriate to a Markov chain. Each column (or row if written in the transposed form) has a set of probabilities that sum to 1. Each can therefore provide an entropy. Shannon defines the entropy (of one step of the chain) as the average of these entropies, each being weighted by the proportion in which that state, corresponding to the column, occurs *when the sequence has settled to its equilibrium* (S.9/6). Thus the transition probabilities of that section, with corresponding entropies and equilibrial proportions shown below, are

$\downarrow$	B	W	P
B	$\frac{1}{4}$	$\frac{3}{4}$	$\frac{1}{8}$
W	$\frac{3}{4}$	0	$\frac{3}{4}$
P	0	$\frac{1}{4}$	$\frac{1}{8}$
Entropy:	$0{\cdot}811$	$0{\cdot}811$	$1{\cdot}061$
Equilibrial proportion:	$0{\cdot}449$	$0{\cdot}429$	$0{\cdot}122$

Then the average entropy (per step in the sequence) is

$$0 \cdot 449 \times 0 \cdot 811 + 0 \cdot 429 \times 0 \cdot 811 + 0 \cdot 122 \times 1 \cdot 061 = 0 \cdot 842 \text{ bits.}$$

A coin spun repeatedly produces a series with entropy, at each spin, of 1 bit. So the series of locations taken by one of the insects as time goes on is not quite so variable as the series produced by a spun coin, for $0 \cdot 842$ is less than $1 \cdot 00$. In this way Shannon's measure enables different degrees of variety to be compared.

The reason for taking a weighted average is that we start by finding three entropies: $0 \cdot 811$, $0 \cdot 811$, and $1 \cdot 061$; and from them we want one. Were they all the same we would obviously just use that value, but they are not. We can, however, argue thus: When the system has reached equilibrium, 45% of the insects will be at state B, 43% at W, and 12% at P. This is equivalent, as the insects circulate between all the states, to saying that each insect spends 45% of its time at B, 43% at W, and 12% at P. In other words, 45% of its transitions will be from B, 43% from W, and 12% from P. Thus 45% of its transitions will be with entropy, or variety, of $0 \cdot 811$, 43% also with $0 \cdot 811$, and 12% with $1 \cdot 061$. Thus, transitions with an entropy of $0 \cdot 811$ will be frequent (and the value "$0 \cdot 811$" should count heavily) and those with an entropy of $1 \cdot 061$ will be rather rare (and the value "$1 \cdot 061$" should count little). So the average is weighted: 88% in favour of $0 \cdot 811$ and 12% in favour of $1 \cdot 061$, i.e.

$$\text{weighted average} = \frac{45 \times 0 \cdot 811 + 43 \times 0 \cdot 811 + 12 \times 1 \cdot 061}{45 + 43 + 12}$$

which is, effectively, what was used above.

Ex. 1: Show that the series of H's and T's produced by a spun coin has an average entropy of 1 bit per spin. (Hint: Construct the matrix of transition probabilities.)

Ex. 2: (Continued.)   What happens to the entropy if the coin is biased? (Hint: Try the effect of changing the probabilities.)

9/13.   Before developing the subject further, it is as well to notice that Shannon's measure, and the various important theorems that use it, make certain assumptions. These are commonly fulfilled in telephone engineering but are by no means so commonly fulfilled in biological work, and in the topics discussed in this book. His measure and theorems must therefore be applied cautiously. His main assumptions are as follows.

(1) If applied to a set of probabilities, the various fractions *must add up to* 1; the entropy cannot be calculated over an incomplete set of possibilities.

(2) If applied to an information source, with several sets of probabilities, the matrix of transition probabilities *must be Markovian*; that is to say, the probability of each transition must depend only on the state the system is *at* (the operand) and not on the states it was at earlier (S.9/7). If necessary, the states of the source should first be re-defined, as in S.9/8, so that it becomes Markovian.

(3) The several entropies of the several columns are averaged (S.9/12) using the proportions of the *terminal equilibrium* (S.9/6). It follows that the theorems assume that the system, however it was started, has been allowed to go on for a long time so that the states have reached their equilibrial densities.

Shannon's results must therefore be applied to biological material only after a detailed check on their applicability has been made.

A similar warning may be given before any attempt is made to play loosely, and on a merely verbal level, with the two entropies of Shannon and of statistical mechanics. Arguments in these subjects need great care, for a very slight change in the conditions or assumptions may make a statement change from rigorously true to ridiculously false. Moving in these regions is like moving in a jungle full of pitfalls. Those who know most about the subject are usually the most cautious in speaking about it.

Ex. 1: Work out mentally the entropy of the matrix with transition probabilities

↓	A	B	C
A	0·2	0	0·3
B	0·7	1·0	0·3
C	0·1	0	0·4

(Hint: This is not a feat of calculation but of finding a peculiar simplicity. What does that 1 in the main diagonal mean (Ex. 9/5/1)? So what is the final equilibrium of the system? Do the entropies of columns *A* and *C* matter? And what is the entropy of *B*'s column (Ex. 9/11/6)?)

Ex. 2: (Continued.) Explain the paradox: "When the system is at *A* there *is* variety or uncertainty in the next state, so the entropy cannot be zero."

9/14. A little confusion has sometimes arisen because Shannon's measure of "entropy", given over a set of probabilities $p_1, p_2, \ldots$, is the sum of $p_i \log p_i$ multiplied by -1 whereas the definition given by Wiener in his *Cybernetics* for "amount of information" is the same sum of $p_i \log p_i$ unchanged (i.e. multiplied by $+1$). (The reader should notice that $p \log p$ is necessarily negative, so the multiplier "-1" makes it a positive number.)

There need however be no confusion, for the basic ideas are identical. Both regard information as "that which removes uncertainty", and both measure it by the amount of uncertainty it removes. Both further are concerned basically with the *gain* or increase in information that occurs when a message arrives—the absolute quantities present before or after being of minor interest.

Now it is clear that when the probabilities are well spread, as in *A* of Fig. 9/14/1, the uncertainty is greater than when they are compact, as in *B*.

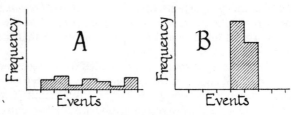

Fig. 9/14/1

So the receipt of a message that makes the recipient revise his estimate, of what will happen, from distribution *A* to distribution *B*, contains a *positive* amount of information. Now $\Sigma p \log p$ (where Σ means "the sum of"), if applied to *A*, will give a more negative number than if applied to *B*; both will be negative but *A*'s will be the larger in absolute value. Thus *A* might give -20 for the sum and *B* might give -3. If we use $\Sigma p \log p$ multiplied by *plus* 1 as amount of information to be associated with each distribution, i.e. with each set of probabilities, then as, in general,

Gain (of anything) = **Final quantity** minus **initial quantity**

so the gain of information will be

$$(-3) - (-20)$$

which is $+ 17$, a positive quantity, which is what we want. Thus, looked at from this point of view, which is Wiener's, $\Sigma p \log p$ should be multiplied by plus 1, i.e. left unchanged; then we calculate the *gain*.

Shannon, however, is concerned throughout his book with the special case in which the received message is known with certainty. So the probabilities are all zero except for a single 1. Over such a set $\Sigma p \log p$ is just zero; so the final quantity is zero, and the *gain* of information is

$$0 - (\text{initial quantity}).$$

In other words, the information in the message, which equals the gain in information, is $\Sigma p \log p$ calculated over the initial distribution, multiplied by *minus* 1, which gives Shannon's measure.

178

Thus the two measures are no more discrepant than are the two ways of measuring "how far is point Q to the right of point P" shown in Fig. 9/14/2.

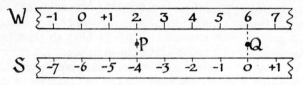

Fig. 9/14/2

Here P and Q can be thought of as corresponding to two degrees of uncertainty, with *more* certainty to the *right*, and with a message shifting the recipient from P to Q.

The distance from P to Q can be measured in two ways, which are clearly equivalent. Wiener's way is to lay the rule against P and Q (as W in the Fig.); then the distance that Q lies to the *right* of P is given by

$$(Q\text{'s reading}) \text{ minus } (P\text{'s reading}).$$

Shannon's way (S in the Fig.) is to lay the zero opposite Q, and then the distance that Q is to the *right* of P is given by

$$\text{minus } (P\text{'s reading}).$$

There is obviously no real discrepancy between the two methods.

9/15. *Channel capacity.* It is necessary to distinguish two ways of reckoning "entropy" in relation to a Markov chain, even after the unit (logarithmic base) has been decided. The figure calculated in S.9/12, from the transition probabilities, gives the entropy, or variety to be expected, at the next, single, step of the chain. Thus if an unbiased coin has already given T T H H T H H H H, the uncertainty of what will come next amounts to 1 bit. The symbol that next follows has also an uncertainty of 1 bit; and so on. So the chain as a whole has an uncertainty, or entropy, of 1 bit *per step*.

Two steps should then have an uncertainty, or variety, of 2 bits, and this is so; for the next two steps can be any one of HH, HT, TH or TT, with probabilities $\frac{1}{4}, \frac{1}{4}, \frac{1}{4}$ and $\frac{1}{4}$, which gives H = 2 bits. Briefly it can be said that *the entropy of a length of Markov chain is proportional to its length* (provided always that it has settled down to equilibrium).

Quite another way of making the measurement on the chain is

introduced when one considers how fast *in time* the chain is being produced by some real physical process. So far this aspect has been ignored, the sole graduation being in terms of the chain's own steps. The new scale requires only a simple rule of proportion for its introduction. Thus if (as in S.9/12) the insects' "unit time" for one step is twenty seconds, then as each 20 seconds produces 0·84 bits, 60 seconds will produce (60/20)0·84 bits; so each insect is producing variety of location at the rate of 2·53 bits *per minute*.

Such a rate is the most natural way of measuring the capacity of a channel, which is simply anything that can be driven by its input to take, at each moment, one of a variety of states, and which can transmit that state to some receiver. The rate at which it can transmit depends both on how fast the steps can succeed one another and on the variety available at each step.

It should be noticed that a "channel" is defined in cybernetics purely in terms of certain *behavioural* relations between two points; if two points are so related then a "channel" exists between them, quite independently of whether any material connexion can be seen between them. (Consider, for instance, Exs. 4/15/2, 6/7/1.) Because of this fact the channels that the cyberneticist sees may be very different from those seen by one trained in another science. In elementary cases this is obvious enough. No one denies the reality of some functional connexion from magnet to magnet, though no experiment has yet demonstrated any intermediate structure.

Sometimes the channel may follow an unusual path. Thus the brain requires information about what happens after it has emitted "commands" to an organ, and usually there is a sensory nerve from organ to brain that carries the "monitoring" information. Monitoring the vocal cords, therefore, may be done by a sensory nerve from cords to brain. An effective monitoring, however, can also be achieved without any nerve in the neck by use of the sound waves, which travel through the air, linking vocal cords and brain, via the ear. To the anatomist this is not a channel, to the communication engineer it is. Here we need simply appreciate that each is right within his own branch of science.

More complex applications of this principle exist. Suppose we ask someone whether 287 times 419 is 118213; he is likely to reply "I can't do it in my head—give me pencil and paper". Holding the numbers 287 and 419, together with the operation "multiply", as parameters he will then generate a process (a transient in the terminology of S.4/5) which will set up a series of impulses passing down the nerves of his arm, generating a series of pencil marks on the paper, then the marks will affect his retina and so on to his brain where an interaction will occur with the trace (whatever that may be) of "118213"; he will then give a final answer. What we must notice here is that this process, from brain, through motor cortex, arm, pencil, marks, light rays, retina, and visual cortex back to brain, is, to the communication engineer, a typical "channel", linking "transmitter" to "receiver". To the cyberneticist, therefore, the white matter, and similar fibres, are not the only channels of communication available to the brain: *some of the communication between part and part may take place through the environment.*

9/16. *Redundancy.* In S.7/14 it was stated that when a constraint exists, advantage can usually be taken of it. An illustration of this thesis occurs when the transmission is incessant.

For simplicity, reconsider the traffic lights—Red, Yellow, and Green—that show only the combinations

(1) Red
(2) Red and Yellow
(3) Green
(4) Yellow.

Each component (each lamp or colour) can be either lit or unlit, so the total variety possible, if the components were independent, would be 8 states. In fact, only 4 combinations are used, so the set shows constraint.

Now reconsider these facts after recognising that a variety of four signals is necessary:

(i) Stop
(ii) Prepare to go
(iii) Go
(iv) Prepare to stop.

If we have components that can each take two values, $+$ or $-$, we can ask *how many* components will be necessary to give this variety. The answer is obviously two; and by a suitable re-coding, such as

$+ +$ = Stop
$+ -$ = Prepare to go
$- -$ = Go
$- +$ = Prepare to stop

the same variety can be achieved with a vector of only two components. The fact that the number of components can be reduced (from three to two) without loss of variety can be expressed by saying that the first set of vectors shows **redundancy,** here of one lamp.

The constraint could clearly be taken advantage of. Thus, if electric lights were very expensive, the cost of the signals, when re-coded to the new form, would be reduced to two-thirds.

Exactly the same lights may also show quite a different redundancy if regarded as the generators of a different set of vectors. Suppose that the lights are clock-operated, rather than traffic-operated, so that they go through the regular cycle of states (as numbered above)

$$\ldots 3, 4, 1, 2, 3, 4, 1, 2, 3, \ldots$$

The sequence that it will produce (regarded as a vector, S.9/9) can only be one of the four vectors:

(i) $(1, 2, 3, 4, 1, 2, \ldots)$
(ii) $(2, 3, 4, 1, 2, 3, \ldots)$
(iii) $(3, 4, 1, 2, 3, 4, \ldots)$
(iv) $(4, 1, 2, 3, 4, 1, \ldots)$

Were there independence at each step, as one might get from a four-sided die, and n components, the variety would be 4^n; in fact it is only 4. To make the matter quite clear, notice that the same variety could be obtained by vectors with only one component:

(i) (1)
(ii) (2)
(iii) (3)
(iv) (4)

all the components after the first being omitted; so all the later components are redundant.

Thus a sequence can show redundancy if at each step the next value has not complete independence of the earlier steps. (Compare S.9/10.) If the sequence is a Markov chain, redundancy will be shown by its entropy having a value less than the maximum.

The fact that the one set of traffic lights provides two grossly different sets of vectors illustrates yet again that great care is necessary when applying these concepts to some *object*, for the object often provides a great richness of sets for discussion. Thus the question "Do traffic lights show redundancy?" is not admissible; for it fails to indicate which of the sets of vectors is being considered; and the answer may vary grossly from set to set.

This injunction is particularly necessary in a book addressed to workers in biological subjects, for here the sets of vectors are often definable only with some difficulty, helped out perhaps with some arbitrariness. (Compare S.6/14.) There is therefore every temptation to let one's grasp of the set under discussion be intuitive and vague rather than explicit and exact. The reader may often find that some intractable contradiction between two arguments will be resolved if a more accurate definition of the set under discussion is achieved; for often the contradiction is due to the fact that the two arguments are really referring to two distinct sets, both closely associated with the same object or organism.

Ex. 1: In a Table for the identification of bacteria by their power to ferment sugars, 62 species are noted as producing "acid", "acid and gas", or "nothing" from each of 14 sugars. Each species thus corresponds to a vector of 14 components, each of which can take one of three values. Is the set redundant? To how many components might the vector be reduced?

Ex. 2: If a Markov chain has no redundancy, how may its matrix be recognised at a glance?

9/17. It is now possible to state what is perhaps the most fundamental of the theorems introduced by Shannon. Let us suppose that we want to transmit a message with H bits per step, as we might want to report on the movements of a single insect in the pool. H is here 0·84 bits per step (S.9/12), or, as the telegraphist would say, per symbol, thinking of such a series as ... P W B W B B B W P P P W B W P W .... Suppose, for definiteness, that 20 seconds elapse between step and step. Since the time-rate of these events is now given, H can also be stated as 2·53 bits per minute. Shannon's theorem then says that any channel with this capacity can carry the report, and that it cannot be carried by any channel with less than this capacity. It also says that a coding always exists by which the channel can be so used.

It was, perhaps, obvious enough that high-speed channels could report more than slow; what is important about this theorem is, first, its great generality (for it makes no reference to any specific machinery, and therefore applies to telegraphs, nerve-fibres, conversation, equally) and secondly its quantitative rigour. Thus, if the pond were far in the hills, the question might occur whether smoke signals could carry the report. Suppose a distinct puff could be either sent or not sent in each quarter-minute, but not faster. The entropy per symbol is here 1 bit, and the channel's capacity is therefore 4 bits per minute. Since 4 is greater than 2·53, the channel *can* do the reporting, and a code can be found, turning positions to puffs, that will carry the information.

Shannon has himself constructed an example which shows exquisitely the exactness of this quantitative law. Suppose a source is producing letters A, B, C, D with frequencies in the ratio of 4, 2, 1, 1 respectively, the successive symbols being independent. A typical portion of the sequence would be ... B A A B D A A A A B C A B A A D A .... At equilibrium the relative frequencies of A, B, C, D would be $\frac{1}{2}, \frac{1}{4}, \frac{1}{8}, \frac{1}{8}$ respectively, and the entropy is $1\frac{3}{4}$ bits per step (i.e. per letter).

Now a channel that could produce, at each step, any one of four states without constraint would have a capacity of 2 bits per step. Shannon's theorem says that there must exist a coding that will enable the latter channel (of capacity 2 bits per step) to transmit such a sequence (with entropy $1\frac{3}{4}$ bits per step) so that any long message requires fewer steps in the ratio of 2 to $1\frac{3}{4}$, i.e. of 8 to 7. The coding, devised by Shannon, that achieves this is as follows. First code the message by

$$\downarrow \quad \begin{array}{cccc} A & B & C & D \\ 0 & 10 & 110 & 111 \end{array}$$

e.g. the message above,

$$\downarrow \begin{array}{c} B . A A B . D . . A A A A B . C . . A B . A A D . . A \\ 1\ 0\ 0\ 0\ 1\ 0\ 1\ 1\ 1\ 0\ 0\ 0\ 0\ 1\ 0\ 1\ 1\ 0\ 0\ 1\ 0\ 0\ 0\ 1\ 1\ 1\ 0 \end{array}$$

Now divide the lower line into pairs and re-code into a new set of letters by

$$\downarrow \quad \begin{array}{cccc} 00 & 01 & 10 & 11 \\ E & F & G & H \end{array}$$

These codes convert any message in "A to D" into the letters "E to H", and conversely, without ambiguity. What is remarkable is that if we take a typical set of eight of the original letters (each represented with its typical frequency) we find that they can be transmitted as seven of the new:

$$\downarrow \begin{array}{cccccccccccccc} A & A & A & A & B & . & B & . & C & . & . & D & . & . \\ 0 & 0 & 0 & 0 & 1 & 0 & 1 & 0 & 1 & 1 & 0 & 1 & 1 & 1 \\ . & E & . & E & . & G & . & G & . & H & . & F & . & H \end{array}$$

thus demonstrating the possibility of the compression, a compression that was predicted quantitatively by the entropy of the original message!

Ex. 1: Show that the coding gives a one-one correspondence between message sent and message received (except for a possible ambiguity in the first letter).

Ex. 2: Printed English has an entropy of about 10 bits per word. We can read about 200 words per minute. Give a lower bound to the channel capacity of the optic nerve.

Ex. 3: If a pianist can put each of ten fingers on any one of three notes, and can do this 300 times a minute, find a lower bound to the channel capacity of the nerves to the upper limbs.

Ex. 4: A bank's records, consisting of an endless sequence of apparently random digits, 0 to 9, are to be encoded into Braille for storage. If 10,000 digits are to be stored per hour, how fast must the Braille be printed if optimal coding is used? (Hint: There are 64 symbols in the Braille "alphabet".)

9/18. One more example will be given, to show the astonishing power that Shannon's method has of grasping the essentials in communication. Consider the system, of states *a*, *b*, *c*, *d*, with transition probabilities

$\downarrow$	a	b	c	d
a	0	0	0·3	0·3
b	0·6	0·6	0	0
c	0·4	0·4	0	0
d	0	0	0·7	0·7

A typical sequence would be

. b b b c a b c a b b c d d a c d a b c a c d d d d d a b b ...

The equilibrial probabilities are 6/35, 9/35, 6/35, 14/35 respectively. The entropy is soon found to be 0·92 bits per letter. Now suppose that the distinction between *a* and *d* is lost, i.e. code by

$$\downarrow \quad \begin{matrix} a & b & c & d \\ X & b & c & X \end{matrix}$$

Surely some information must be lost? Let us see. There are now only three states *X*, *b*, *c*, where *X* means "either *a* or *d*". Thus the previous message would now start ... b b b c X b c X b b c X X X c .... The transition probabilities are found to be

$\downarrow$	X	b	c
X	0·70	0	1
b	0·18	0·6	0
c	0·12	0·4	0

(Thus *c* → *X* must be 1 because *c* always went to either *a* or *d*; the transitions from *a* and from *d* need weighting by the (equilibrial) probabilities of being at *a* or *d*.) The new states have equilibrial probabilities of X, 20/35; b, 9/35; c, 6/35 and entropies of H_X, 1·173; H_b, 0·971; H_c, 0. So the entropy of the new series is 0·92 bits per letter—exactly the same as before!

This fact says uncompromisingly that no information was lost when the d's and a's were merged to X's. It says, therefore, that *there must be some way of restoring the original four-letter message from the three*, of telling which of the X's were a's and which were d's. Closer examination shows that this can be done, strikingly verifying the rather surprising prediction.

Ex.: How is

b b b c X b c X b b c X X X c X X b c X c X X X X X X X b b

to be de-coded to its original form?

NOISE

9/19. It may happen that the whole input to a transducer can be divided into two or more components, and we wish to consider the components individually. This happened in Ex. 8/17/3, where the two messages were sent simultaneously through the same transducer and recovered separately at the output. Sometimes, however, the two inputs are not both completely deducible from the output. If we are interested solely in one of the input components, as a source of variety, regarding the other as merely an unavoidable nuisance, then the situation is commonly described as that of a "message corrupted by noise".

It must be noticed that *noise is in no intrinsic way distinguishable from any other form of variety*. Only when some recipient is given, who will state which of the two is important to him, is a distinction between message and noise possible. Thus suppose that over a wire is coming both some conversation and some effects from a cathode that is emitting irregularly. To someone who wants to hear the conversation, the variations at the cathode are "noise"; but to the engineer who is trying to make accurate measurements of what is going on at the cathode, the conversation is "noise". "Noise" is thus purely relative to some given recipient, who must say which information he wants to ignore.

The point is worth emphasis because, as one of the commonest sources of uninteresting variety in electronic systems is the thermal dance (Brownian movement) of the molecules and electrons, electronic engineers tend to use the word "noise" without qualification to mean this particular source. Within their speciality they will probably continue to use the word in this sense, but workers in other sciences need not follow suit. In biology especially "noise" will seldom refer to this particular source; more commonly, the "noise" in one system will be due to some other macroscopic system from which the system under study cannot be completely isolated.

Should the two (or more) messages be completely and simultaneously recoverable, by de-coding of the output, the concept of noise is of little use. Chiefly it is wanted when the two messages (one wanted, one unwanted) interact with some mutual destruction, making the coding not fully reversible. To see this occur let us go back to the fundamental processes. The irreversibility must mean that the variety is not sustained (S.8/6), and that distinct elements at the inputs are represented at the output by one element. Consider the case in which the input is a vector with two components,

the first having possible values of A, B or C
„ second „ „ „ „ E, F or G.

Suppose the output is a variable that can take values 1, 2, ..., 9, and that the coding was

	AE	AF	AG	BE	BF	BG	CE	CF	CG
$\downarrow$	6	4	2	2	9	1	3	7	5

If now the input message were the sequence $B\,A\,C\,B\,A\,C\,A\,A\,B\,B$, while the "noise" gave simultaneously the sequence $G\,F\,F\,E\,E\,E\,G\,F\,G\,E$, then the output would be

$$1, 4, 7, 2, 6, 3, 2, 4, 1, 2$$

and the de-coding could give, for the first component, only the approximation

$$B, A, C, \overline{A \text{ or } B}, A, C, \overline{A \text{ or } B}, A, B, \overline{A \text{ or } B}.$$

Thus the original message to this input has been "corrupted" by "noise" at the other input.

In this example the channel is quite capable of carrying the message without ambiguity if the noise is suppressed by the second input being held constant, at E say. For then the coding is one-one:

	A	B	C
$\downarrow$	6	2	3

and reversible.

It will be noticed that the interaction occurred because only eight of the nine possible output states were used. By this permanent restriction, the capacity of the channel was reduced.

Ex. 1: What is the coding, of first input to output, if the second output is kept constant (i) at F; (ii) at G?

Ex. 2: A system of three states—P, Q, R—is to transmit changes at two inputs, α and β, each of which can take two states. The states of the inputs and of the system change in step. Is noise-free transmission possible?

9/20. *Distortion.* It should be noticed that falsification of a message is *not* necessarily identical with the effect of noise. "If a particular transmitted signal always produces the same received signal, i.e. the received signal is a definite function of the transmitted signal, then the effect may be called distortion. If this function has an inverse—no two transmitted signals producing the same received signal—distortion may be corrected, at least in principle, by merely performing the inverse functional operation on the received signal." (Shannon.)

Ex. 1: Is the change by which the erect object falls on to the retina inverted a distortion or a corruption?

Ex. 2: A tension applied to a muscle evokes a steady stream of impulses whose frequency is not proportional to the tension. Is the deviation from proportionality a distortion or a corruption?

Ex. 3: (Continued.) If the nerve carrying the impulses is subjected to alcohol vapour of sufficient strength it will cease to conduct for all tensions. Is this a distortion or a corruption?

9/21. *Equivocation.* A suitable measure for the *degree* of corruption has not, so far as I am aware, been developed for use in the basic cases. In the case of the channel that transmits incessantly, however, Shannon has developed the appropriate measure.

It is assumed first that both the original signals and the received signals form Markov chains of the type defined in S.9/4. The data of the messages can then be presented in a form which shows the frequencies (or probabilities) with which all the possible combinations of the vector (symbol sent, symbol received) occur. Thus, to use an example of Shannon's suppose 0's and 1's are being sent, and that the probabilities (here relative frequencies) of the symbols being received are:

Symbol sent	0	0	1	1
Symbol received	0	1	0	1
Probability	0·495	0·005	0·005	0·495

Of every thousand symbols sent, ten arrive in the wrong form, an error of one per cent.

At first sight this "one per cent wrong" might seem the natural measure for the amount of information lost, but this interpretation leads to nonsense. Thus if, in the same transmission, the line were actually cut and the recipient simply tossed a coin to get a "message" he would get about a half of the symbols right, yet no information whatever would have been transmitted. Shannon has shown conclusively that the natural measure is the **equivocation,** which is calculated as follows.

First find the entropy over all possible classes:

$$-0.495 \log 0.495 -0.005 \log 0.005$$
$$-0.005 \log 0.005 -0.495 \log 0.495$$

Call this H_1; it is 1.081 bits per symbol. Next collect together the received signals, and their probabilities; this gives the table

Symbol received	0	1
Probability	0.5	0.5

Find its entropy:

$$-0.5 \log 0.5 -0.5 \log 0.5$$

Call this H_2. It is 1.000 bits per symbol. Then the equivocation is $H_1 - H_2$: 0.081 bits per symbol.

The actual rate at which information is being transmitted, allowance being made for the effect of noise, is the entropy of the source, less the equivocation. The source here has entropy 1.000 bits per symbol, as follows from:

Symbol sent	0	1
Probability	0.5	0.5

So the original amount supplied is 1.000 bits per symbol. Of this 0.919 gets through and 0.081 is destroyed by noise.

Ex. 1: What is the equivocation of the transmission of S.9/19, if all nine combinations of letters occur, in the long run, with equal frequency?

Ex. 2: (Continued.) What happens to the equivocation if the first input uses only the symbols B and C, so that the combinations BE, BF, BG, CE, CF, CG occur with equal frequencies? Is the answer reasonable?

*Ex. 3: Prove the following rules, which are useful when we want to find the value of the expression $-p \log_a p$, and p is either very small or very near to 1:

(i) If $p = xy$, $- p \log_a p = - xy(\log_a x + \log_a y)$;

(ii) If $p = 10^{-z}$, $- p \log_a p = \dfrac{z \times 10^{-z}}{\log_{10} a}$;

(iii) If p is very close to 1, put $1 - p = q$, and $- p \log_a p = \dfrac{1}{\log_e a} (q - \dfrac{q^2}{2}...)$.

Ex. 4: Find $-p \log_2 p$ when p is 0·00025. (Hint: Write p as $2·5 \times 10^{-4}$ and use (i)).

Ex. 5: During a blood count, lymphocytes and monocytes are being examined under the microscope and discriminated by the haematologist. If he mistakes one in every hundred lymphocytes for a monocyte, and one in every two hundred monocytes for a lymphocyte, and if these cells occur in the blood in the ratio of 19 lymphocytes to 1 monocyte, what is his equivocation? (Hint: Use the results of the previous two exercises.)

9/22. *Error-free transmission.* We now come to Shannon's fundamental theorem on the transmission of information in the presence of noise (i.e. when other, irrelevant, inputs are active). It might be thought that when messages are sent through a channel that subjects each message to a definite chance of being altered at random, then the possibility of receiving a message that is correct with certainty would be impossible. Shannon however has shown conclusively that this view, however plausible, is mistaken. Reliable messages can be transmitted over an unreliable channel. The reader who finds this incredible must go to Shannon's book for the proof; here I state only the result.

Let the information to be transmitted be of quantity H, and suppose the equivocation to be E, so that information of amount $H - E$ is received. (It is assumed, as in all Shannon's book, that the transmission is incessant.) What the theorem says is that if the channel capacity be increased by an amount not less than E—by the provision perhaps of another channel in parallel—then it is possible so to encode the messages that the fraction of errors still persisting may be brought *as near zero as one pleases*. (The price of a very small fraction of errors is delay in the transmission; for enough message-symbols must accumulate to make the average of the accumulated material approach the value of the average over all time.)

Conversely, with less delay, one can still make the errors as few as one pleases by increasing the channel capacity beyond the minimal quantity E.

The importance of this theorem can hardly be overestimated in its contribution to our understanding of how an intricately connected system such as the cerebral cortex can conduct messages without each message gradually becoming so corrupted by error and interference as to be useless. What the theorem says is that if plenty of channel capacity is available then the errors may be kept down to any level desired. Now in the brain, and especially in the cortex, there is little restriction in channel capacity, for more can usually be obtained simply by the taking of more fibres, whether by growth in embryogeny or by some functional taking-over in learning.

The full impact of this theorem on neuropsychology has yet to be felt. Its power lies not so much in its ability to solve the problem "How does the brain overcome the ever-increasing corruption of its internal messages?" as in its showing that the problem hardly arises, or that it is a minor, rather than a major, one.

The theorem illustrates another way in which cybernetics can be useful in biology. Cybernetic methods may be decisive in the treatment of certain difficult problems not by a direct winning of the solution but by a demonstration that the problem is wrongly conceived, or based on an erroneous assumption.

Some of today's outstanding problems about the brain and behaviour come to us from mediaeval and earlier times, when the basic assumptions were very different and often, by today's standards, ludicrously false. Some of these problems are probably wrongly put, and are on a par with the problem, classic in mediaeval medicine: what are the relations between the four elements and the four humours? This problem, be it noticed, was never *solved*—what happened was that when chemists and pathologists got to know more about the body they realised that they must ignore it.

Some of our classic problems in the brain—perhaps some of those relating to localisation, causation, and learning—may well be found to be of this type. It seems likely that the new insight given by cybernetics may enable us to advance to a better discrimination; if this happens, it will dispose of some questions by a clear demonstration that they should not be asked.

PART THREE

REGULATION AND CONTROL

The foundation of all physiology must be the physiology of permanence.

(Darlington)

Chapter   10

REGULATION IN BIOLOGICAL
SYSTEMS

10/1. The two previous Parts have treated of Mechanism (and the processes within the system) and Variety (and the processes of communication between system and system). These two subjects had to be studied first, as they are fundamental. Now we shall use them, and in Part III we shall study what is the central theme of cybernetics —regulation and control.

This first chapter reviews the place of regulation in biology, and shows briefly why it is of fundamental importance. It shows how regulation is essentially related to the flow of variety. The next chapter (11) studies this relation in more detail, and displays a quantitative law—that the quantity of regulation that can be achieved is bounded by the quantity of information that can be transmitted in a certain channel. The next chapter (12) takes up the question of how the abstract principles of chapter 11 are to be embodied—what sort of machinery can perform what is wanted. This chapter introduces a new sort of machine, the Markovian, which extends the possibilities considered in Part I. The remaining chapters consider the achievement of regulation and control as the difficulties increase, particularly those that arise when the system becomes very large.

At first, in Part III, we will assume that the regulator is already provided, either by being inborn, by being specially made by a manufacturer, or by some other means. The question of what made the regulator, of how the regulator, which does such useful things, came itself to be made will be taken up at S.13/10.

10/2. The present chapter aims primarily at supplying motive to the reader, by showing that the subjects discussed in the later chapters (11 onwards) are of fundamental importance in biology. The subject of regulation in biology is so vast that no single chapter can do it justice. Cannon's *Wisdom of the Body* treated it adequately so far as internal, vegetative activities are concerned, but there has

195

yet to be written the book, much larger in size, that shall show how all the organism's exteriorly-directed activities—its "higher" activities—are all similarly regulatory, i.e. homeostatic. In this chapter I have had to leave much of this to the reader's imagination, trusting that, as a biologist, he will probably already be sufficiently familiar with the thesis. The thesis in any case has been discussed to some extent in *Design for a Brain*.

The chief purpose of this chapter is to tie together the concepts of regulation, information, and survival, to show how intimately they are related, and to show how all three can be treated by a method that is entirely uniform with what has gone before in the book, and that can be made as rigorous, objective, and unambiguous as one pleases.

10/3. The foundation. Let us start at the beginning. The most basic facts in biology are that this earth is now two thousand million years old, and that the biologist studies mostly that which exists today. From these two facts follow a well-known deduction, which I would like to restate in our terms.

We saw in S.4/23 that if a dynamic system is large and composed of parts with much repetition, and if it contains any property that is autocatalytic, i.e. whose occurrence at one point increases the probability that it will occur again at another point, then such a system is, so far as that property is concerned, essentially unstable in its absence. This earth contained carbon and other necessary elements, and it is a fact that many combinations of carbon, nitrogen, and a few others are self-reproducing. It follows that though the state of "being lifeless" is almost a state of equilibrium, yet this equilibrium is unstable (S.5/6), a single deviation from it being sufficient to start a trajectory that deviates more and more from the "lifeless" state. What we see today in the biological world are these "autocatalytic" processes showing all the peculiarities that have been imposed on them by two thousand million years of elimination of those forms that cannot survive.

The organisms we see today are deeply marked by the selective action of two thousand million years' attrition. Any form in any way defective in its power of survival has been eliminated; and today the features of almost every form bear the marks of being adapted to ensure *survival* rather than any other possible outcome. Eyes, roots, cilia, shells and claws are so fashioned as to maximise the chance of survival. And when we study the brain we are again studying a means to survival.

SURVIVAL

10/4. What has just been said is well enough known. It enables us, however, to join these facts on to the ideas developed in this book and to show the connexion exactly.

For consider what is meant, in general, by "survival". Suppose a mouse is trying to escape from a cat, so that the survival of the mouse is in question. As a dynamic system, the mouse can be in a variety of states; thus it can be in various postures, its head can be turned this way or that, its temperature can have various values, it may have two ears or one. These different states may occur during its attempt to escape and it may still be said to have survived. On the other hand if the mouse changes to the state in which it is in four separated pieces, or has lost its head, or has become a solution of amino-acids circulating in the cat's blood then we do not consider its arrival at one of these states as corresponding to "survival".

The concept of "survival" can thus be translated into perfectly rigorous terms, similar to those used throughout the book. The various states (M for Mouse) that the mouse may be in initially and that it may pass into after the affair with the cat is a set $M_1, M_2, \ldots,$ $M_k, \ldots, M_n$. We decide that, for various reasons of what is practical and convenient, we shall restrict the words "*living* mouse" to mean the mouse in one of the states in some subset of these possibilities, in M_1 to M_k say. If now some operation C (for cat) acts on the mouse in state M_i, and $C(M_i)$ gives, say, M_2, then we may say that M has "survived" the operation of C, for M_2 is in the set $M_1, \ldots, M_k$.

If now a particular mouse is very skilled and always survives the operation C, then all the states $C(M_1), C(M_2), \ldots, C(M_k)$, are contained in the set $M_1, \ldots, M_k$. We now see that this representation of survival is *identical* with that of the "stability" of a set (S.5/5). Thus the concepts of "survival" and "stability" can be brought into an exact relationship; and facts and theorems about either can be used with the other, provided the exactness is sustained.

The states M are often defined in terms of variables. The states $M_1, \ldots, M_k$, that correspond to the living organism are then those states in which certain **essential variables** are kept within assigned ("physiological") limits.

Ex. 1: If n is 10 and k is 5, what would the operation $C(M_7) = M_9$ correspond to?

Ex. 2: (Continued.) What would the operation $C(M_8) = M_4$ correspond to?

Ex. 3: What would be an appropriate definition of "lethal", if C's attack were invariably fatal to M?

10/5. What is it survives, over the ages? Not the individual organism, but certain peculiarly well compounded gene-patterns, particularly those that lead to the production of an individual that carries the gene-pattern well protected within itself, and that, within the span of one generation, can look after itself.

What this means is that those gene-patterns are specially likely to survive (and therefore to exist today) that cause to grow, between themselves and the dangerous world, some more or less elaborate mechanism for defence. So the genes in *Testudo* cause the growth of a shell; and the genes in *Homo* cause the growth of a brain. (The genes that did not cause such growths have long since been eliminated.)

Now regard the system as one of parts in communication. In the previous section the diagram of immediate effects (of cat and mouse) was (or could be regarded as)

$$\boxed{C} \rightarrow \boxed{M}$$

We are now considering the case in which the diagram is

$$\boxed{D} \rightarrow \boxed{F} \rightarrow \boxed{E}$$

in which E is the set of essential variables, D is the source of disturbance and dangers (such as C) from the rest of the world, and F is the interpolated part (shell, brain, etc.) formed by the gene-pattern for the protection of E. (F may also include such parts of the environment as may similarly be used for E's protection—burrow for rabbit, shell for hermit-crab, pike for pike-man, and sword (as defence) for swordsman.)

For convenience in reference throughout Part III, let the states of the essential variables E be divided into a set η—those that correspond to "organism living" or "good"—and not-η—those that correspond to "organism not living" or "bad". (Often the classification cannot be as simple as this, but no difficulty will occur in principle; nothing to be said excludes the possibility of a finer classification.)

To make the assumptions clear, here are some simple cases, as illustration. (Inanimate regulatory systems are given first for simplicity.)

(1) *The thermostatically-controlled water-bath.* E is its temperature, and what is desired (η) is the temperature range between, say 36° and 37°C. D is the set of all the disturbances that may drive the temperature outside that range—addition of cold water, cold draughts blowing, immersion of cold objects, etc. F is the whole

regulatory machinery. F, by its action, tends to lessen the effect of D on E.

(2) *The automatic pilot.* E is a vector with three components—yaw, pitch, and roll—and η is the set of positions in which these three are all within certain limits. D is the set of disturbances that may affect these variables, such as gusts of wind, movements of the passengers in the plane, and irregularities in the thrusts of the engines. F is the whole machinery—pilot, ailerons, rudder, etc.—whose action determines how D shall affect E.

(3) *The bicycle rider.* E is chiefly his angle with the vertical. η is the set of small permissible deviations. D is the set of those disturbances that threaten to make the deviation become large. F is the whole machinery—mechanical, anatomical, neuronic—that determines what the effect of D is on E.

Many other examples will occur later. Meanwhile we can summarise by saying that natural selection favours those gene-patterns that get, in whatever way, a regulator F between the disturbances D and the essential variables E. Other things being equal, the better F is as a regulator, the larger the organism's chance of survival.

Ex.: What variables are kept within limits by the following regulatory mechanisms: (i) the air-conditioner; (ii) the climber's oxygen supply; (iii) the windscreen-wiper; (iv) the headlights of a car; (v) the kitchen refrigerator; (vi) the phototaxic plant; (vii) sun-glasses; (viii) the flexion reflex (a quick lifting of the foot evoked by treading on a sharp stone); (ix) blinking when an object approaches the eye quickly; (x) predictor for anti-aircraft gunfire.

10/6. *Regulation blocks the flow of variety.* On what scale can any particular mechanism F be measured for its value or success as a regulator? The perfect thermostat would be one that, in spite of disturbance, kept the temperature constant at the desired level. In general, there are two characteristics required: the maintenance of the temperature within close limits, and the correspondence of this range with the desired one. What we must notice in particular is that the set of permissible values, η, has less variety than the set of all possible values in E; for η is some set selected from the states of E. If F is a regulator, the insertion of F between D and E *lessens* the variety that is transmitted from D to E. Thus an essential function of F as a regulator is that it shall block the transmission of variety from disturbance to essential variable.

Since this characteristic also implies that the regulator's function is to block the flow of information, let us look at the thesis more closely to see whether it is reasonable.

Suppose that two water-baths are offered me, and I want to decide

199

which to buy. I test each for a day against similar disturbances and then look at the records of the temperatures; they are as in Fig. 10/6/1:

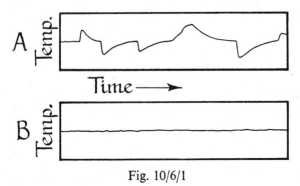

Fig. 10/6/1

There is no doubt that Model *B* is the better; and I decide this precisely because its record gives me no information, as does *A*'s, about what disturbances, of heat or cold, came to it. The thermometer and water in bath *B* have been unable, as it were, to see anything of the disturbances *D*.

The same argument will apply, with obvious modifications, to the automatic pilot. If it is a good regulator the passengers will have a smooth flight whatever the gustiness outside. They will, in short, be *prevented from knowing* whether or not it is gusty outside. Thus a good pilot acts as a barrier against the transmission of that information.

The same argument applies to an air-conditioner. If I live in an air-conditioned room, and can tell, by the hotness of the room, that it is getting hot outside, then that conditioner is failing as a regulator. If it is really good, and the blinds are drawn, I shall be unable to form any idea of what the outside weather is like. The good conditioner blocks the flow inwards of information about the weather.

The same thesis applies to the higher regulations achieved by such activities as hunting for food, and earning one's daily bread. Thus while the unskilled hunter or earner, in difficult times, will starve and will force his liver and tissues (the essential variables) to extreme and perhaps unphysiological states, the skilled hunter or earner will go through the same difficult times with his liver and tissues never taken to extremes. In other words, his skill as a regulator is shown by the fact, among others, that it prevents information

200

about the times reaching the essential variables. In the same way, the skilled provider for a family may go through difficult times without his family realising that anything unusual has happened. The family of an unskilled provider would have discovered it.

In general, then, an essential feature of the good regulator is that *it blocks the flow of variety from disturbances to essential variables.*

10/7. The blocking may take place in a variety of ways, which prove, however, on closer examination to be fundamentally the same. Two extreme forms will illustrate the range.

One way of blocking the flow (from the source of disturbance *D* to the essential variable *E*) is to interpose something that acts as a simple passive block to the disturbances. Such is the tortoise's shell, which reduces a variety of impacts, blows, bites, etc. to a negligible disturbance of the sensitive tissues within. In the same class are the tree's bark, the seal's coat of blubber, and the human skull.

At the other extreme from this static defence is the defence by skilled counter-action—the defence that gets information about the disturbance to come, prepares for its arrival, and then meets the disturbance, which may be complex and mobile, with a defence that is equally complex and mobile. This is the defence of the fencer, in some deadly duel, who wears no armour and who trusts to his skill in parrying. This is the defence used mostly by the higher organisms, who have developed a nervous system precisely for the carrying out of this method.

When considering this second form we should be careful to notice the part played by information and variety in the process. The fencer must watch his opponent closely, and he must gain information in all ways possible if he is to survive. For this purpose he is born with eyes, and for this purpose he learns how to use them. Nevertheless, the end result of this skill, if successful, is shown by his essential variables, such as his blood-volume, remaining within normal limits, much as if the duel had not occurred. Information flows freely to the non-essential variables, but the variety in the distinction "duel or no-duel" has been prevented from reaching the essential variables.

Through the remaining chapters we shall be considering this type of active defence, asking such questions as: what principles must govern it? What mechanisms can achieve it? And, what is to be done when the regulation is very difficult?

Chapter

REQUISITE VARIETY

11/1. In the previous chapter we considered regulation from the biological point of view, taking it as something sufficiently well understood. In this chapter we shall examine the process of regulation itself, with the aim of finding out exactly what is involved and implied. In particular we shall develop ways of *measuring* the amount or degree of regulation achieved, and we shall show that this amount has an upper limit.

11/2. The subject of regulation is very wide in its applications, covering as it does most of the activities in physiology, sociology, ecology, economics, and much of the activities in almost every branch of science and life. Further, the types of regulator that exist are almost bewildering in their variety. One way of treating the subject would be to deal seriatim with the various types; and chapter 12 will, in fact, indicate them. In this chapter, however, we shall be attempting to get at the core of the subject—to find what is common to all.

What is common to all regulators, however, is not, at first sight, much like any particular form. We will therefore start anew in the next section, making no explicit reference to what has gone before. Only after the new subject has been sufficiently developed will we begin to consider any relation it may have to regulation.

11/3. *Play and outcome.* Let us therefore forget all about regulation and simply suppose that we are watching two players, R and D, who are engaged in a game. We shall follow the fortunes of R, who is attempting to score an a. The rules are as follows. They have before them Table 11/3/1, which can be seen by both:

Table 11/3/1

		R		
		α	β	γ
	1	b	a	c
D	2	a	c	b
	3	c	b	a

D must play first, by selecting a number, and thus a particular row. *R*, knowing this number, then selects a Greek letter, and thus a particular column. The italic letter specified by the intersection of the row and column is the **outcome**. If it is an *a*, *R* wins; if not, *R* loses.

Examination of the table soon shows that with this particular table *R* can win always. Whatever value *D* selects first, *R* can always select a Greek letter that will give the desired outcome. Thus if *D* selects 1, *R* selects β; if *D* selects 2, *R* selects α; and so on. In fact, if *R* acts according to the transformation

$$\downarrow \begin{array}{ccc} 1 & 2 & 3 \\ \beta & \alpha & \gamma \end{array}$$

then he can always force the outcome to be *a*.

R's position, with this particular table, is peculiarly favourable, for not only can *R* always force *a* as the outcome, but he can as readily force, if desired, *b* or *c* as the outcome. *R* has, in fact, complete control of the outcome.

Ex. 1: What transformation should *R* use to force *c* as outcome?

Ex. 2: If both *R*'s and *D*'s values are integers, and the outcome *E* is also an integer, given by

$$E = R - 2D,$$

find an expression to give *R* in terms of *D* when the desired outcome is 37.

Ex. 3: A car's back wheels are skidding. *D* is the variable "Side to which the tail is moving", with two values, Right and Left. *R* is the driver's action "Direction in which he turns the steering wheel", with two values, Right and Left. Form the 2 × 2 table and fill in the outcomes.

Ex. 4: If *R*'s play is determined by *D*'s in accordance with the transformation

$$\downarrow \begin{array}{ccc} 1 & 2 & 3 \\ \gamma & \beta & \alpha \end{array}$$

and many games are observed, what will be the variety in the many outcomes?

Ex. 5: Has *R* complete control of the outcome if the table is triunique?

11/4. The Table used above is, of course, peculiarly favourable to *R*. Other Tables are, however, possible. Thus, suppose *D* and *R*, playing on the same rules, are now given Table 11/4/1 in which *D* now has a choice of five, and *R* a choice of four moves.

If *a* is the target, *R* can always win. In fact, if *D* selects 3, *R* has several ways of winning. As every row has at least one *a*, *R* can always force the appearance of *a* as the outcome. On the other hand, if the target is *b* he cannot always win. For if *D* selects 3, there is no move by *R* that will give *b* as the outcome. And if the target is *c*, *R* is quite helpless, for *D* wins always.

203

It will be seen that different arrangements within the table, and different numbers of states available to D and R, can give rise to a variety of situations from the point of view of R.

Table 11/4/1

	R			
	α	β	γ	δ
1	b	d	a	a
2	a	d	a	d
D 3	d	a	a	a
4	d	b	a	b
5	d	a	b	d

Ex. 1: With Table 11/4/1, can R always win if the target is d?

Ex. 2: (Continued.)   What transformation should R use?

Ex. 3: (Continued.)   If a is the target and D, for some reason, never plays 5, how can R simplify his method of play?

Ex. 4: A guest is coming to dinner, but the butler does not know who. He knows only that it may be Mr. A, who drinks only sherry or wine, Mrs. B, who drinks only gin or brandy, or Mr. C, who drinks only red wine, brandy, or sherry.   In the cellar he finds he has only whisky, gin, and sherry.   Can he find something acceptable to the guest, whoever comes?

11/5.   Can any *general* statement be made about R's modes of play and prospects of success?

If full generality is allowed in the Table, the possibilities are so many, arbitrary and complicated that little can be said.   There is one type, however, that allows a precise statement and is at the same time sufficiently general to be of interest.   (It is also fundamental in the theory of regulation.)

From all possible tables let us eliminate those that make R's game too easy to be of interest.   Ex. 11/4/3 showed that if a column contains repetitions, R's play need not be discriminating; that is, R need not change his move with each change of D's move.   Let us consider, then, only those tables in which *no column contains a repeated outcome*.   When this is so R must select his move on *full* knowledge of D's move; i.e. any change of D's move must require a change on R's part.   (Nothing is assumed here about how the outcomes in one column are related to those in another, so these relations are unrestricted.)   Such a Table is 11/5/1.   Now, some target being given, let R specify what his move will be for each move by D.   What is essential is that, win or lose, he must specify

Table 11/5/1

			R	
		α	β	γ
	1	f	f	k
	2	k	e	f
	3	m	k	a
	4	b	b	b
D	5	c	q	c
	6	h	h	m
	7	j	d	d
	8	a	p	j
	9	l	n	h

one and only one move in response to each possible move of D. His specification, or "strategy" as it might be called, might appear:

If D selects 1, I shall select γ
,, ,,   ,,   2, ,, ,,   ,, α
,, ,,   ,,   3, ,, ,,   ,, β
         . . .   . . .
,, ,,   ,,   9, ,, ,,   ,, α

He is, of course, specifying a transformation (which must be single-valued, as R may not make two moves simultaneously):

$$\downarrow \begin{array}{cccccc} 1 & 2 & 3 & \ldots & 9 \\ \gamma & \alpha & \beta & \ldots & \alpha \end{array}$$

This transformation uniquely specifies a set of outcomes—those that will actually occur if D, over a sequence of plays, includes every possible move at least once. For 1 and γ give the outcome k, and so on, leading to the transformation:

$$\downarrow \begin{array}{ccccc} (1,\gamma) & (2,\alpha) & (3,\beta) & \ldots & (9,\alpha) \\ k & k & k & \ldots & l \end{array}$$

It can now be stated that the variety in this set of outcomes cannot be less than

$$\frac{D\text{'s variety}}{R\text{'s variety}}$$

i.e., in this case, 9/3.

It is easily proved. Suppose R marks one element in each row and concentrates simply on keeping the variety of the marked

205

elements as small as possible (ignoring for the moment any idea of a target). He marks an element in the first row. In the second row he must change to a new column if he is not to increase the variety by adding a new, different, element; for in the initially selected column the elements are all different, by hypothesis. To keep the variety down to one element he must change to a new column at each row. (This is the *best* he can do; it may be that change from column to column is not sufficient to keep the variety down to one element, but this is irrelevant, for we are interested only in what is the least possible variety, assuming that everything falls as favourably as possible). So if R has n moves available (three in the example), at the n-th row all the columns are used, so one of the columns must be used again for the next row, and a new outcome *must* be allowed into the set of outcomes. Thus in Table 11/5/1, selection of the k's in the first three rows will enable the variety to be kept to one element, but at the fourth row a second element *must* be allowed into the set of outcomes.

In general: If no two elements in the same column are equal, and if a set of outcomes is selected by R, one from each row, and if the table has r rows and c columns, then *the variety in the selected set of outcomes cannot be fewer than r/c.*

THE LAW OF REQUISITE VARIETY

11/6. We can now look at this game (still with the restriction that no element may be repeated in a column) from a slightly different point of view. If R's move is unvarying, so that he produces the same move, whatever D's move, then *the variety in the outcomes will be as large as the variety in D's moves.* D now is, as it were, exerting full control over the outcomes.

If next R uses, or has available, two moves, then the variety of the outcomes can be reduced to a half (but not lower). If R has three moves, it can be reduced to a third (but not lower); and so on. Thus if the variety in the outcomes is to be reduced to some assigned number, or assigned fraction of D's variety, R's variety *must* be increased to at least the appropriate minimum. *Only variety in R's moves can force down the variety in the outcomes.*

11/7. If the varieties are measured logarithmically (as is almost always convenient), and if the same conditions hold, then the theorem takes a very simple form. Let V_D be the variety of D, V_R that of R, and V_O that of the outcome (all measured logarithmically). Then the previous section has proved that V_O cannot be less, numerically, than the value of $V_D - V_R$. Thus V_O's minimum is $V_D - V_R$.

If V_D is given and fixed, $V_D - V_R$ can be lessened only by a corresponding increase in V_R. Thus *the variety in the outcomes, if minimal, can be decreased further only by a corresponding increase in that of R.* (A more general statement is given in S.11/9.)

This is the law of Requisite Variety. To put it more picturesquely: *only variety in R can force down the variety due to D*; **only variety can destroy variety.**

This thesis is so fundamental in the general theory of regulation that I shall give some further illustrations and proofs before turning to consider its actual application.

11/8. (This section can be omitted at first reading.) The law is of very general applicability, and by no means just a trivial outcome of the tabular form. To show that this is so, what is essentially the same theorem will be proved in the case when the variety is spread out in time and the fluctuation incessant—the case specially considered by Shannon. (The notation and concepts in this section are those of Shannon's book.)

Let D, R, and E be three variables, such that each is an information source, though "source" here is not to imply that they are acting independently. Without any regard for how they are related causally, a variety of entropies can be calculated, or measured empirically. There is $H(D,R,E)$, the entropy of the vector that has the three as components; there is $H_D(E)$, the uncertainty in E when D's state is known; there is $H_{ED}(R)$, the uncertainty in R when both E and D are known; and so on.

The condition introduced in S.11/5 (that no element shall occur twice in a column) here corresponds to the condition that if R is fixed, or given, the entropy of E (corresponding to that of the outcome) is not to be less than that of D, i.e.

$$H_R(E) \geqslant H_R(D).$$

Now whatever the causal or other relations between D, R and E, algebraic necessity requires that their entropies must be related so that

$$H(D) + H_D(R) = H(R) + H_R(D),$$

for each side of the equation equals $H(R,D)$. Substitute $H_R(E)$ for $H_R(D)$, and we get

$$H(D) + H_D(R) \leqslant H(R) + H_R(E)$$
$$\leqslant H(R,E).$$

But always, by algebraic necessity,

$$H(R,E) \leqslant H(R) + H(E)$$

so $\qquad H(D) + H_D(R) \leqslant H(R) + H(E)$

i.e. $\qquad H(E) \geqslant H(D) + H_D(R) - H(R).$

Thus the entropy of the E's has a certain minimum. If this minimum is to be affected by a relation between the D- and R-sources, it can be made least when $H_D(R) = 0$, i.e. *when R is a determinate function of D*. When this is so, then $H(E)$'s minimum is $H(D) - H(R)$, a deduction similar to that of the previous section. It says simply that the minimal value of E's entropy can be forced down below that of D only by an equal *increase* in that of R.

11/9. The theorems just established can easily be modified to give a worth-while extension.

Consider the case when, even when R does nothing (i.e. produces the same move whatever D does) the variety of outcome is *less* than that of D. This is the case in Table 11/4/1. Thus if R gives the reply α to all D's moves, then the outcomes are a, b or d—a variety of three, less than D's variety of five. To get a manageable calculation, suppose that within each column each element is now repeated k times (instead of the "once only" of S.11/5). The same argument as before, modified in that kn rows may provide only one outcome, **leads to** the theorem that

$$V_O \geqslant V_D - \log k - V_R,$$

in which the varieties are measured logarithmically.

An exactly similar modification may be made to the theorem in terms of entropies, by supposing, not as in S.11/8 that

$$H_R(E) \geqslant H_R(D), \text{ but that}$$
$$H_R(E) \geqslant H_R(D) - K.$$

$H(E)$'s minimum then becomes

$$H(D) - K - H(R),$$

with a similar interpretation.

11/10. The law states that certain events are impossible. It is important that we should be clear as to the origin of the impossibility. Thus, what has the statement to fear from experiment?

It has nothing to do with the properties of matter. So if the law is stated in the form "No machine can . . .", it is not to be overthrown by the invention of some new device or some new electronic circuit, or the discovery of some new element. It does not even have anything to do with the properties of the machine in the general sense of Chapter 4; for it comes from the *Table*, such as that of S.11/4; this Table says simply that certain *D-R* combinations lead to certain outcomes, but is quite independent of whatever it is that determines the outcome. Experiments can only *provide* such tables.

The theorem is primarily a statement about possible arrangements in a rectangular table. It says that certain types of arrangement cannot be made. It is thus no more dependent on special properties of machines than is, say, the "theorem" that four objects can be arranged to form a square while three can not. The law therefore owes nothing to experiment.

11/11. *Regulation again.* We can now take up again the subject of regulation, ignored since the beginning of this chapter, for the law of Requisite Variety enables us to apply a *measure* to regulation. Let us go back and reconsider what is meant, essentially, by "regulation".

There is first a set of disturbances *D*, that start in the world outside the organism, often far from it, and that threaten, if the regulator *R* does nothing, to drive the essential variables *E* outside their proper range of values. The values of *E* correspond to the "outcomes" of the previous sections. Of all these *E*-values only a few (η) are compatible with the organism's life, or are unobjectionable, so that the regulator *R*, to be successful, must take its value in a way so related to that of *D* that the outcome is, if possible, always within the acceptable set η, i.e. within physiological limits. Regulation is thus related fundamentally to the game of S.11/4. Let us trace the relation in more detail.

The Table *T* is first assumed to be given. It is the hard external world, or those internal matters that the would-be regulator has to take for granted. Now starts a process. *D* takes an arbitrary value, *R* takes some value determined by *D*'s value, the Table determines an outcome, and this either is or is not in η. Usually the process is repeated, as when a water-bath deals, during the day, with various disturbances. Then another value is taken by *D*, another by *R*, another outcome occurs, and this also may be either in η or not. And so on. If *R* is a well-made regulator—one that works successfully—then *R* is such a transformation of *D* that all the outcomes fall within η. *In this case R and T together are acting as the barrier F* (S.10/5.)

We can now show these relations by the diagram of immediate effects:

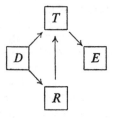

The arrows represent actual channels of communication. For the variety in D determines the variety in R; and that in T is determined by that in both D and R. If R and T are in fact actual machines, then R has an input from D, and T has two inputs.

(When R and T are embodied in actual machines, care must be taken that we are clear about what we are referring to. If some machine is providing the basis for T, it will have (by S.4/1) a set of states that occur step by step. These states, and these steps, are essentially independent of the discrete steps that we have considered to be taken by D, R, and T in this chapter. Thus, T gives the outcome, and any particular outcome may be compared with another, as unit with unit. Each individual outcome may, however, in another context, be analysed more finely. Thus a thirsty organism may follow trajectory 1 and get relief, or trajectory 2 and die of thirst. For some purposes the two outcomes can be treated as units, particularly if they are to be contrasted. If however we want to investigate the behaviour in more detail, we can regard trajectory 1 as composed of a sequence of states, separated by steps in time that are of quite a different order of size from those between successive regulatory acts to successive disturbances.)

We can now interpret the general phenomenon of regulation in terms of communication. If R does nothing, i.e. keeps to one value, then the variety in D threatens to go through T to E, contrary to what is wanted. It may happen that T, without change by R, will block some of the variety (S.11/9), and occasionally this blocking may give sufficient constancy at E for survival. More commonly, a further suppression at E is necessary; it can be achieved, as we saw in S.11/6, only by further variety at R.

We can now select a portion of the diagram, and focus attention on R as a transmitter:

$$\boxed{D} \rightarrow \boxed{R} \rightarrow \boxed{T}$$

The law of Requisite Variety says that *R's capacity as a regulator cannot exceed R's capacity as a channel of communication.*

In the form just given, the law of Requisite Variety can be shown in exact relation to Shannon's Theorem 10, which says that if noise appears in a message, the amount of noise that can be removed by a correction channel is limited to the amount of information that can be carried by that channel.

Thus, his "noise" corresponds to our "disturbance", his "correction channel" to our "regulator *R*", and his "message of entropy *H*" becomes, in our case, a message of entropy zero, for it is *constancy* that is to be "transmitted". Thus the use of a regulator to achieve homeostasis and the use of a correction channel to suppress noise are homologous.

Ex. 1: A certain insect has an optic nerve of a hundred fibres, each of which can carry twenty bits per second; is this sufficient to enable it to defend itself against ten distinct dangers, each of which may, or may not, independently, be present in each second?

Ex. 2: A ship's telegraph from bridge to engine-room can determine one of nine speeds not oftener than one signal in five seconds, and the wheel can determine one of fifty rudder-positions in each second. Since experience has shown that this means of control is normally sufficient for full regulation, estimate a normal upper limit for the disturbances (gusts, traffic, shoals, etc.) that threaten the ship's safety.

Ex. 3: A general is opposed by an army of ten divisions, each of which may manœuvre with a variety of 10^6 bits in each day. His intelligence comes through 10 signallers, each of whom can transmit 60 letters per minute for 8 hours in each day, in a code that transmits 2 bits per letter. Is his intelligence-channel sufficient for him to be able to achieve complete regulation?

Ex. 4: (Continued.) The general can dictate orders at 500 bits/minute for 12 hours/day. If his Intelligence were complete, would this verbal channel be sufficient for complete regulation?

11/12. The diagram of immediate effects given in the previous section is clearly related to the formulation for "directive correlation" given by Sommerhoff, who, in his *Analytical Biology*, uses the diagram

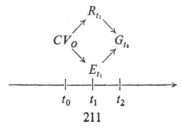

If I am not misinterpreting him, his concepts and those used here are equivalent thus:

Coenetic variable (CV_O) ↔ Disturbance (D)

Response (R_{t_i}) ↔ Response (R)

Environmental circumstances (E_{t_i}) ↔ Table (T)

Subsequent occurrence (G_{t_i}) ↔ Outcome (E)

A reading of his book may thus help to extend much of the theory given in this Part, for he discusses the subject extensively.

11/13. The law now enables us to see the relations existing between the various types of variety and information that affect the living organism.

A species continues to exist (S.10/4) primarily because its members can block the flow of variety (thought of as disturbance) to the gene-pattern (S.10/6), and this blockage is the species' most fundamental need. Natural selection has shown the advantage to be gained by taking a large amount of variety (as information) partly into the system (so that it does not reach the gene-pattern) and then using this information so that the flow via R blocks the flow through the environment T.

This point of view enables us to resolve what might at first seem a paradox—that the higher organisms have sensitive skins, responsive nervous systems, and often an instinct that impels them, in play or curiosity, to bring more variety to the system than is immediately necessary. Would not their chance of survival be improved by an avoidance of this variety?

The discussion in this chapter has shown that variety (whether information or disturbance) comes to the organism in two forms. There is that which threatens the survival of the gene-pattern—the direct transmission by T from D to E. This part must be blocked at all costs. And there is that which, while it may threaten the gene-pattern, can be transformed (or re-coded) through the regulator R and used to block the effect of the remainder (in T). This information is useful, and should (if the regulator can be provided) be made as large as possible; for, by the law of Requisite Variety, the amount of disturbance that reaches the gene-pattern can be diminished only by the amount of information so transmitted. That is the importance of the law in biology.

It is also of importance to *us* as we make our way towards the last chapter. In its elementary forms the law is intuitively obvious and hardly deserving statement. If, for instance, a press photographer would deal with twenty subjects that are (for exposure and distance) distinct, then his camera must obviously be capable of at least twenty distinct settings if all the negatives are to be brought to a uniform density and sharpness. Where the law, in its quantitative form, develops its power is when we come to consider the system in which these matters are not so obvious, and particularly when it is very large. Thus, by how much can a dictator control a country? It is commonly said that Hitler's control over Germany was total. So far as his power of regulation (in the sense of S.10/6) was concerned, the law says that his control amounted to just 1 man-power, and no more. (Whether this statement is true must be tested by the future; its chief virtue now is that it is exact and uncompromising.) Thus the law, though trite in the simple cases, can give real guidance in those cases that are much too complex to be handled by unaided intuition.

CONTROL

11/14. The formulations given in this chapter have already suggested that regulation and control are intimately related. Thus, in S.11/3, Table 11/3/1 enables R not only to achieve a as outcome in spite of all D's variations; but equally to achieve b or c at will.

We can look at the situation in another way. Suppose the decision of what outcome is to be the target is made by some controller, C, whom R must obey. C's decision will affect R's choice of α, β or γ; so the diagram of immediate effects is

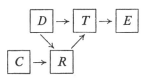

Thus the whole represents a system with two independent inputs, C and D.

Suppose now that R is a perfect regulator. If C sets a as the target, then (through R's agency) E will take the value a, *whatever value D may take.* Similarly, if C sets b as target, b will appear as outcome whatever value D may take. And so on. And if C sets a particular sequence—a, b, a, c, c, a, say—as sequential or compound target, then that sequence will be produced, regardless of D's values during the sequence. (It is assumed for convenience that the components move in step.) Thus the fact that R is a perfect regulator gives *C* complete control over the output, in spite of the entrance of disturbing effects by way of *D*. Thus, *perfect* **regulation** *of the outcome by R makes possible a complete* **control** *over the outcome by C.*

We can see the same facts from yet another point of view. If an attempt at control, by *C* over *E*:

$$C \rightarrow E$$

is disturbed or made noisy by another, independent, input *D*, so that the connexions are

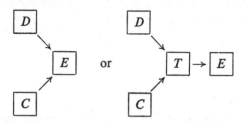

then a suitable regulator *R*, taking information from both *C* and *D*, and interposed between *C* and *T*:

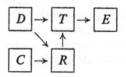

may be able to form, with *T*, a compound channel to *E* that *transmits fully from C while transmitting nothing from D.*

The achievement of control may thus depend necessarily on the achievement of regulation. The two are thus intimately related.

Ex. 1: From Table 11/3/1 form the set of transformations, with *C* as parameter, that must be used by *R* if *C* is to have complete control over the outcome. (Hint: What are the operands?)

Ex. 2: If, in the last diagram of this section, *C* wants to transmit to *E* at 20 bits/second, and a source *D* is providing noise at 5 bits/second, and *T* is such that if *R* is constant, *E* will vary at 2 bits/second, how much capacity must the channel from *D* to *R* have (at least) if *C*'s control over *E* is to be complete?

Ex. 3: (Continued.) How much capacity (at least) is necessary along the channel from *C* to *R*?

Ex. 4: (Continued.) How much along that from *R* to *T*?

11/15. In our treatment of regulation the emphasis has fallen on its property of reducing the variety in the outcome; without regulation the variety is large—with regulation it is small. The limit of this reduction is the regulation that holds the outcome rigorously constant. This point of view is undoubtedly valid, but at first it may seem to contrast sharply with the naive view that living organisms are, in general, anything but immobile. A few words, in addition to what was said in S.11/13, may be useful.

It should be appreciated that the distinction between "constant" and "varying" often depends on the exact definition of what is being referred to. Thus if a searchlight follows an aircraft accurately we may notice either that the searchlight moved through a great range of angles (angles in relation to the earth) or that the angle it made with the aircraft remained constant at zero. Obviously both points of view are valid; there is no real contradiction in this example between "great range" and "constant", for they refer to different variables.

Again, the driver who steers a car accurately from one town to another along a winding lane can be regarded either as one who has caused the steering wheel to show much activity and change or as one who, throughout the trip, has kept the distance between car and verge almost constant.

Many of the activities of living organisms permit this double aspect. On the one hand the observer can notice the great deal of actual movement and change that occurs, and on the other hand he can observe that throughout these activities, so far as they are co-ordinated or homeostatic, there are invariants and constancies that show the degree of regulation that is being achieved.

Many variations are possible on the same theme. Thus if variable x is always doing just the same as variable y, then the quantity $x - y$ is constant at zero. So if y's values are given by some outside factor, any regulator that acts on x so as to keep $x - y$ constant at zero is in fact forcing x to vary, copying y. Similarly, "making x do the opposite to y" corresponds to "keeping $x + y$ at some constant value". And "make the variable w change so that it is always just twice as large as v's (fluctuating) rate of change" corresponds to "keep the quantity $w - 2dv/dt$ constant".

It is a great convenience in exposition and in the processes of general theory to be able to treat all "targets" as if they were of the form "keep the outcome constant at a". The reader must, however, not be misled into thinking that the theory treats only of immobility; he must accustom himself to interchanging the corresponding concepts freely.

SOME VARIATIONS

11/16. In S.11/4 the essential facts implied by regulation were shown as a simple rectangular table, as if it were a game between two players *D* and *R*. The reader may feel that this formulation is much too simple and that there are well known regulations that it is insufficient to represent. The formulation, however, is really much more general than it seems, and in the remaining sections of this chapter we shall examine various complications that prove, on closer examination, to be really included in the basic formulation of S.11/4.

11/17. *Compound disturbance.* The basic formulation of S.11/4 included only one source of disturbance *D*, and thus seems, at first sight, not to include all those cases, innumerable in the biological world, in which the regulation has to be conducted against several disturbances coming simultaneously by several channels. Thus, a cyclist often has to deal both with obstructions due to traffic and with disequilibrations due to gusts.

In fact, however, this case is included; for nothing in this chapter excludes the possibility that *D* may be a vector, with any number of components. A vectorial *D* is thus able to represent all such compound disturbances within the basic formulation.

11/18. *Noise.* A related case occurs when *T* is "noisy"—when *T* has an extra input that is affected by some disturbance that interferes with it. This might be the case if *T* were an electrical machine, somewhat disturbed by variations in the mains' voltage. At first sight this case seems to be not represented in the basic formulation.

It must be appreciated that *D*, *T*, *E*, etc. were defined in S.11/3 in purely *functional* form. Thus "*D*" is "that which disturbs". Given any real system some care may be necessary in deciding what corresponds to *D*, what to *T*, and so on. Further, a boundary drawn provisionally between *D* and *T* (and the other boundaries) may, on second thoughts, require moving. Thus one set of boundaries on the real system may give a system that purports to be of *D*, *T*, etc. yet does not agree with the basic formulation of S.11/4. Then it may be found that a shifting of the boundaries, to give a new *D*, *T*, etc., gives a set that *does* agree with the formulation.

If a preliminary placing of the boundaries shows that this (provisional) *T* is noisy, then the boundaries should be re-drawn so as to get *T*'s input of noise (S.9/19) included *as a component in D*. *D* is now "that which disturbs", and T has no third input; so the formulation agrees with that of S.11/4.

There is, of course, no suggestion here that the noise, as a disturbance, can be allowed for magically by merely thinking differently about it. The suggestion is that if we start again from the beginning, and re-define D and T then some *new* transformation of D may be able to restore regulation. The new transformation will, of course, have to be more complex than the old, for D will have more components.

11/19. *Initial states.* A related case occurs when T is some machine that shows its behaviour by a trajectory, with the outcome E depending on the properties of T's trajectory. The outcomes will then usually be affected by which of T's states is the initial one. How does T's initial state come into the basic formulation of S.11/4?

If the initial state can be controlled, so that the trajectory can be started always from some standardised state, then no difficulty arises. (In this connexion the method of S.7/25 may be useful.) It may however happen, especially if the system is very large, that T's initial state cannot be standardised. Does the basic formulation include this case?

It does; for D, as a vector, can be re-defined to include T's initial state. Then the variety brought to E by the variety in T's initial state is allotted its proper place in the formulation.

11/20. *Compound target.* It may happen that the acceptable states η at E may have more than one condition. Thus of a thermostat it might be demanded that

(i) it shall usually stay between 36° and 37°C;
(ii) if displaced by $\pm 10°$ it shall return to the allowed range within one minute.

This difficulty can be dealt with by the same method as in S.11/17, by recognising that E may be a vector, with more than one component, and that what is acceptable (η) may be given in the form of separate specifications for each component.

Thus, by allowing E to become a vector, the basic formulation of S.11/4 can be made to include all cases in which the target is complex, or conditional, or qualified.

11/21. *Internal complexities.* As a last example, showing how comprehensive the basic formulation really is, consider the case in which the major problem seems to be not so much a regulation as an interaction between several regulations. Thus a signalman may have to handle several trains coming to his section simultaneously. To handle any one by itself would be straightforward, but here the problem is the control of them as a complex whole pattern.

This case is in fact still covered by the basic formulation. For nothing in that formulation prevents the quantities or states or elements in D, R, T, or E from being made of parts, and the parts interrelated. The fact that "D" is a single letter in no way implies that what it represents must be internally simple or unitary.

The signalman's "disturbance" D is the particular set of trains arriving in some particular pattern over space and time. Other arrangements would provide other values for D, which must, of course, be a vector. The outcomes E will be various complex patterns of trains moving in relation to one another and moving away from his section. The acceptable set η will certainly include a component "no collision" and will probably include others as well. His responses R will include a variety of patterns of movements of signals and points. T is what is given—the basic matters of geography, mechanics, signalling techniques, etc., that lead determinately from the situation that has arisen and his reaction pattern to outcome.

It will be seen therefore that the basic formulation is capable, in principle, of including cases of any degree of internal complexity.

Chapter 12

THE ERROR-CONTROLLED REGULATOR

12/1. In the previous chapter we studied the nature of regulation, and showed that certain relations and laws must hold if regulation is to be achieved. There we assumed that regulation was achieved, and then studied what was necessary. This point of view, however, though useful, hardly corresponds with that commonly used in practice. Let us change to a new point of view.

In practice, the question of regulation usually arises in this way: The essential variables E are given, and also given is the set of states η in which they must be maintained if the organism is to survive (or the industrial plant to run satisfactorily). These two must be given before all else. *Before any regulation can be undertaken or even discussed, we must know what is important and what is wanted.* Any particular species has its requirements given—the cat must keep itself dry, the fish must keep itself wet. A servo-mechanism has its aim given by other considerations—one must keep an incubating room hot, another must keep a refrigerating room cold. Throughout this book it is assumed that outside considerations have already determined what is to be the goal, i.e. what are the acceptable states η. Our concern, within the book, is solely with the problem of how to achieve the goal in spite of disturbances and difficulties.

The disturbances D threaten to drive E outside the set η. If D acts through some dynamic system (an environment) T, then the diagram of immediate effects is initially

$$\boxed{D} \to \boxed{T} \to \boxed{E}$$

The organism (or whoever is interested in E), however, has some power of forming another dynamic system R (e.g. a brain or a servo-mechanism) which can be coupled to T and which, if properly made, will form with T a whole, F, so that the diagram of immediate effects becomes

$$\boxed{D} \to \boxed{F} \to \boxed{E}$$

219

and such that F blocks the flow of variety from D to E, so that E stays within η.

T is usually given. It is the environment which the organism is facing together with those parts of the organism that have to be taken as given in the regulation. It cannot just be abolished, but can usually be manipulated. The problem of regulation is then, in general:

Given E, η, T, *and* D, *to form the mechanism* R *so that* R *and* T, *coupled, act to keep* E *within* η.

From now to the end of the book we shall be studying how various types of *data* (E, η, T, and D) can specify the form of machine with input (R) that will give regulation. We want to deduce the form of R.

Were the situation always as simple as it was in Table 11/3/1, the subject would soon be exhausted. As it is, many deviations from that form are possible, so we shall proceed to examine various deviations, as they put various difficulties in the way of the design or specification of the regulator R.

We can now assume, in discussing some particular regulation, that full use has been made of the possibilities of redefining (S.11/16) so that the formulation is either like that of S.11/3, which gave perfect regulation and control, or like those in S.11/4, in which such perfection was impossible. The remainder of the book will be concerned essentially with those cases in which perfect regulation is not possible but in which we wish the regulation to be as good as is possible in the conditions given.

12/2. *Sensory and motor restriction.* A simple introduction to the real difficulties is that given when R's capacity, as a channel for transmitting variety or information from D to T, becomes insufficient, according to the law of Requisite Variety, to reduce the variety in E to that in η. When this happens, the regulation is necessarily imperfect.

Examples of the phenomenon are myriad. First are all the cases of sensory restriction, of deafness, of the driver who cannot see clearly through a rain-obscured windscreen. There are the organisms that cannot see ultra-violet light, and the tabetic who cannot feel where his feet are. These are restrictions in the channel from D to R.

Then there are the restrictions in the channel from R to T, those on the effector side of R. There is the man who has lost an arm, the insect that cannot fly, the salivary gland that cannot secrete, and the rudder that is stuck.

A similar restriction of R's capacity may occur in those cases where R's effect on T is vectorial, i.e. effected through more than one channel or component to T, and some diminution has occurred in the number of T's parameters accessible to R. (Compare S.7/12.) Thus a failure at one of the controls on the dashboard may impair the driver's ability to keep the car running well.

The case when R cannot receive full information about T's initial state (discussed in S.11/19) is really included in the cases mentioned above. Such a difficulty occurs to a railway signalman in a fog. He is well informed that a disturbance "fog" has arrived, but he often has difficulty in ascertaining the present state of the system he is controlling, i.e. the present positions of the trains in his sector. With this restriction in the flow of information from T to R goes the difficulty, or even impossibility, of maintaining full regulation.

12/3.   The basic formulation of S.11/4 assumed that the process of regulation went through its successive stages in the following order:

(1) a particular disturbance threatens at D;
(2) it acts on R, which transforms it to a response;
(3) the two values, of D and R, act on T *simultaneously* to produce T's outcome;
(4) the outcome is a state in E, or affects E.

Thus (3) supposes that if R is an actual material system, it performs all its work before T starts to move. We assumed, in other words, that the regulator R moved at a higher order of speed than T.

This sequence does actually occur in many cases. When the cat approaches, the mouse may react so as to get to its hole before the cat's claws actually strike. We say in general that the organism has reacted to the *threat* (at D) rather than to the *disaster* itself (at E), and has thus forestalled the disaster. The formulation is thus properly representative of many important regulations.

On the other hand, there are many important cases in which this anticipation is not possible—in which R's action cannot be completed before the outcome (at T) starts to be determined. (An example is given in the next section.) In such cases the regulation envisaged in S.11/3 is impossible. What then is to be done?

One method, of course, is to speed up the transmission of information from D to R; and many regulating systems have various devices specially to this end. Primitive nerve fibres develop myelin sheaths, so that the passage to the brain may be faster. Some organisms develop a sense of smell, so that the appropriate response may be prepared in time for the actual bodily encounter. And economic systems send messages by cable rather than by messenger so that the arrival in port of a ship with a perishable cargo can be prepared for.

Sometimes, however, the available resources do not include a speeding-up of the transmission through R; R's reaction cannot be got to T before the outcome commences. In that case, the best that can be done is that the imperfect regulation should at least be as good as it can be made in the circumstances. The succeeding sections will discuss how this can be done.

12/4. *Regulation by error.* A well-known regulator that cannot react directly to the original disturbance D is the thermostat-controlled water-bath, which is unable to say "I see someone coming with a cold flask that is to be immersed in me—I must act now". On the contrary, the regulator gets no information about the disturbance until the temperature of the water (E) actually begins to drop. And the same limitation applies to the other possible disturbances, such as the approach of a patch of sunlight that will warm it, or the leaving open of a door that will bring a draught to cool it.

The same limitation holds over many important regulators. There is, for instance, a mechanism that helps to keep constant the oxygen supply to the tissues: any long-continued lack of oxygen causes eventually an increase in the number of red corpuscles contained in the blood. So people with certain types of heart disease, and those living at high altitudes, where the air is thin, tend to develop such an increase. This regulation draws its information from the harmful effect (the lack of oxygen) itself, not from the cause (D) of the heart disease, or from the decision to live at a higher altitude.

From the point of view of communication, the new phenomena are easily related to those of the old. The difference is simply that now the information from D to R (which must pass if the regulator R is to play any useful part whatever) *comes through T.* Instead of

$$D \rightarrow T \rightarrow E \qquad \text{we have} \qquad D \rightarrow T \rightarrow E$$
$$R \qquad\qquad\qquad\qquad R$$

R is thus getting its information about D by way of T:

$$D \rightarrow T \rightarrow R \rightarrow$$

and the information available for regulatory purposes is whatever survives the coding imposed by its passage through T (S.8/5).

Sometimes the information available to R is forced to take an even longer route, so that R is affected only by the actual effect at E. The diagram of immediate effects is then

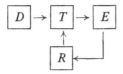

and we have the basic form of the simple "error-controlled servo-mechanism" or "closed loop regulator", with its well-known feedback from E to R. The reader should appreciate that this form differs from that of the basic formulation (S.11/4) only in that the information about D gets to R by the longer route

$$\boxed{D} \rightarrow \boxed{T} \rightarrow \boxed{E} \rightarrow \boxed{R} \rightarrow$$

Again, the information available to R is only such as survives the transmission through T and E.

This form is of the greatest importance and widest applicability. The remainder of the book will be devoted to it. (The other cases are essentially simpler and do not need so much consideration.)

12/5. A fundamental property of the error-controlled regulator is that *it cannot be perfect* in the sense of S.11/3.

Suppose we attempt to formulate the error-controlled system by the method used in S.11/3 and 4. We take a table of double entry, with D and R determining an outcome in E. Each column has a variety equal to that of D. What is new is that the rules must be modified. Whereas previously D made a selection (a particular disturbance), then R, and thus E was determined, the play now is that after D's initial selection, R must take a value that is a determinate function of the outcome E (for R is *error*-controlled). It is easily shown that with these conditions E's *variety will be as large as D's*—i.e. R can achieve no regulation, no matter how R is constructed (i.e. no matter what transformation is used to turn E's value to an R-value).

If the formal proof is not required, a simpler line of reasoning can show why this must be so. As we saw, R gets its information through *T* and *E*. Suppose *R* *is* somehow regulating successfully; then this would imply that the variety at *E* is reduced below that of *D*—perhaps even reduced to zero. This very reduction makes the channel

$$\boxed{D} \rightarrow \boxed{T} \rightarrow \boxed{E} \rightarrow$$

to have a lessened capacity; *if E should be held quite constant then the channel is quite blocked.* So the more successful *R* is in keeping *E* constant, the more does *R* block the channel by which it is receiving its necessary information. Clearly, any success by *R* can at best be partial.

12/6. Fortunately, in many cases complete regulation is not necessary. So far, we have rather assumed that the states of the essential variables *E* were sharply divided into "normal" (*η*) and "lethal", so occurrence of the "undesirable" states was wholly incompatible with regulation. It often happens, however, that the systems show continuity, so that the states of the essential variables lie along a scale of undesirability. Thus a land animal can pass through many degrees of dehydration before dying of thirst; and a suitable reversal from half way along the scale may justly be called "regulatory" if it saves the animal's life, though it may not have saved the animal from discomfort.

Thus the presence of continuity makes possible a regulation that, though not perfect, is of the greatest practical importance. Small errors are allowed to occur; then, by giving their information to *R*, they make possible a regulation against great errors. This is the basic theory, in terms of communication, of the simple feedback regulator.

12/7. The reader may feel that excessive attention has just been given to the error-controlled regulator, in that we have stated with care what is already well known. The accuracy of statement is, however, probably advisable, as we are going now to extend the subject of the error-controlled regulator over a range much wider than usual.

This type of regulator is already well known when embodied in a determinate machine. Then it gives the servo-mechanism, the thermostat, the homeostatic mechanism in physiology, and so on. It can, however, be embodied in a *non*-determinate machine, and it then gives rise to a class of phenomena not yet commonly occurring in industrial machinery but of the commonest occurrence and highest importance in biological systems. The subject is returned to in S.12/11. Meanwhile we must turn aside to see what is involved in this idea of a "non-determinate" machine.

THE MARKOVIAN MACHINE

12/8. We are now going to consider a class of machine more general than that considered in Parts I and II. (Logically, the subject should have been considered earlier, but so much of those Parts was concerned with the determinate machine (i.e. one whose transformations are single-valued) that an account of a more general type might have been confusing.)

A "machine" is essentially a system whose behaviour is sufficiently law-abiding or repetitive for us to be able to make some prediction about what it will do (S.7/19). If a prediction can be made, the prediction may be in one of a variety of forms. Of one machine we may be able to predict its next state—we then say it is "determinate" and is one of the machines treated in Part I. Of another machine we may be unable to predict its next state, but we may be able to predict that, if the conditions are repeated many times, the *frequencies* of the various states will be found to have certain values. This possible constancy in the frequencies has already been noticed in S.9/2. It is the characteristic of the Markov chain.

We can therefore consider a new class of absolute system: it is one whose states change with time not by a single-valued transformation but by a matrix of transition probabilities. For it to remain the *same* absolute system the values of the *probabilities* must be unchanging.

In S.2/10 it was shown that a single-valued transformation could be specified by a matrix of transitions, with 0's or 1's in the cells (there given for simplicity as 0's or +'s). In S.9/4 a Markov chain was specified by a similar matrix containing fractions. Thus a determinate absolute system is a special case of a Markovian machine; it is *the extreme form of a Markovian machine in which all the probabilities have become either 0 or 1.* (Compare S.9/3.)

A "machine with input" was a set of absolute systems, distinguished by a parameter. A **Markovian machine with input** must similarly be a set of Markovian machines, specified by a *set* of matrices, with a parameter and its values to indicate which matrix is to be used at any particular step.

The idea of a Markovian machine is a natural extension of the idea of the ordinary, determinate machine—the type considered throughout Part I. If the probabilities are all 0 or 1 then the two are identical. If the probabilities are all very near to 0 or 1, we get a machine that is almost determinate in its behaviour but that occasionally does the unusual thing. As the probabilities deviate further and further from 0 and 1, so does the behaviour at each step become less and less determinate, and more and more like that of one of the insects considered in S.9/4.

It should be noticed that the definition, while allowing some indeterminacy, is still absolutely strict in certain respects. If the machine, when at state x, goes on 90% of occasions to y and on 10% of occasions to z, then those *percentages* must be constant (in the sense that the relative frequencies must tend to those percentages as the sequence is made longer; and the limits must be unchanging as sequence follows sequence). What this means in practice is that the conditions that determine the percentages must remain constant.

The exercises that follow will enable the reader to gain some familiarity with the idea.

Ex. 1: A metronome-pendulum oscillates steadily between its two extreme states, R and L, but when at the right (R) it has a 1% chance of sticking there at that step. What is its matrix of transition probabilities?

Ex. 2: A determinate machine α has the transformation

$$\downarrow \begin{array}{cccc} A & B & C & D \\ B & D & D & D \end{array}$$

A Markovian machine β has the matrix of transition probabilities

$\downarrow$	A	B	C	D
A	0	0	0	0
B	0·9	0	0	0
C	0	0	0·2	0
D	0·1	1·0	0·8	1·0

How do their behaviours differ? (Hint: Draw α's graph and draw β's graph after letting the probabilities go to 1 or 0.)

Ex. 3: A Markovian machine with input has a parameter that can take three values—p, q, r—and has two states, a and b, with matrices

	(p)			(q)			(r)	
$\downarrow$	a	b	$\downarrow$	a	b	$\downarrow$	a	b
a	$\frac{1}{2}$	1	a	$\frac{1}{4}$	$\frac{3}{4}$	a	$\frac{1}{3}$	$\frac{3}{4}$
b	$\frac{1}{2}$	0	b	$\frac{3}{4}$	$\frac{1}{4}$	b	$\frac{2}{3}$	$\frac{1}{4}$

It is started at state b, and goes one step with the input at q, then one step with it at r, then one step with it at p. What are the probabilities that it will now be at a or b?

Ex. 4: (Continued.) What general rule, using matrix multiplication, allows the answer to be written down algebraically? (Hint: Ex. 9/6/8.)

Ex. 5: Couple the Markovian machine (with states a, b, c and input-states α, β)

$\downarrow$	a	b	c
a	0·2	0·3	0·3
$\alpha: b$	·	0·7	0·2
c	0·8	·	0·5

$\downarrow$	a	b	c
a	0·3	0·9	0·5
$\beta: b$	0·6	0·1	0·5
c	0·1	·	·

to the Markovian machine (with states e, f and input-states δ, ϵ, θ)

$\downarrow$	e	f
$\delta: \begin{matrix} e \\ f \end{matrix}$	$\begin{matrix} 0·7 \\ 0·3 \end{matrix}$	$\begin{matrix} 0·5 \\ 0·5 \end{matrix}$

$\downarrow$	e	f
$\epsilon: \begin{matrix} e \\ f \end{matrix}$	$\begin{matrix} 0·2 \\ 0·8 \end{matrix}$	$\begin{matrix} 0·7 \\ 0·3 \end{matrix}$

$\downarrow$	e	f
$\theta: \begin{matrix} e \\ f \end{matrix}$	$\begin{matrix} 0·5 \\ 0·5 \end{matrix}$	$\begin{matrix} 0·4 \\ 0·6 \end{matrix}$

by the transformations

$$\downarrow \begin{matrix} a & b & c \\ \epsilon & \delta & \theta \end{matrix} \qquad \downarrow \begin{matrix} e & f \\ \beta & \alpha \end{matrix}$$

What is the Markovian machine (without input) that results? (Hint: Try changing the probabilities to 0 and 1, so as to make the systems determinate, and follow S.4/8; then make the probabilities fractional and follow the same basic method.)

Ex. 6: (Continued.) Must the new matrix still be Markovian?

Ex. 7: If M is a Markovian machine which dominates a determinate machine N, show that N's output becomes a Markov chain only after M has arrived at statistical equilibrium (in the sense of S.9/6).

12/9. Whether a given real machine appears Markovian or determinate will sometimes depend on how much of the machine is observable (S.3/11); and sometimes a real machine may be such that an apparently small change of the range of observation may be sufficient to change the appearances from that of one class to the other.

Thus, suppose a digital computing machine has attached to it a long tape carrying random numbers, which are used in some process it is working through. To an observer who cannot inspect the tape, the machine's output is indeterminate, but to an observer who has a copy of the tape it is determinate. Thus the question "Is this machine *really* determinate?" is meaningless and inappropriate unless the observer's range of observation is given exactly. In other words, sometimes the distinction between Markovian and determinate can be made only after the system has been defined accurately. (We thus have yet another example of how inadequate is the defining of "the system" by identifying it with a real object.

227

Real objects may provide a variety of equally plausible "systems", which may differ from one another grossly in those properties we are interested in here; and the answer to a particular question may depend grossly on which system it happens to be applied to.) (Compare S.6/22.)

12/10. The close relation between the Markovian machine and the determinate can also be shown by the existence of mixed forms. Thus, suppose a rat has partly learned the maze, of nine cells, shown in Fig. 12/10/1,

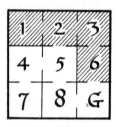

Fig. 12/10/1

in which G is the goal. For reasons that need not be detailed here, the rat can get no sensory clues in cells 1, 2, 3 and 6 (lightly shaded), so when in one of these cells it moves at random to such other cells as the maze permits. Thus, if we put it repeatedly in cell 3 it goes with equal probability to 2 or to 6. (I assume equal probability merely for convenience.) In cells 4, 5, 7, 8 and G, however, clues are available, and it moves directly from cell to cell towards G. Thus, if we put it repeatedly in cell 5 it goes always to 8 and then to G. Such behaviour is not grossly atypical in biological work.

The matrix of its transitions can be found readily enough. Thus, from 1 it can go only to 2 (by the maze's construction). From 2 it goes to 1, 3, or 5 with equal probability. From 4 it goes, say, only to 5. From G, the only transition is to G itself. So the matrix can be built up.

Ex.: Construct a possible matrix of its transition probabilities.

12/11. *Stability.* The Markovian machine will be found on examination to have properties corresponding to those described in Part I, though often modified in an obvious way. Thus, the machine's kinematic graph is constructible; though, as the trans-

228

formation is not single-valued, more than one arrow can go from each state. Thus the Markovian machine

↓	a	b	c
a	0·2	0·3	0·1
b	0·8	0·7	0·5
c	·	·	0·4

has the graph of Fig. 12/11/1, in which each arrow has a fraction indicating the probability that that arrow will be traversed by the representative point.

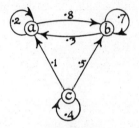

Fig. 12/11/1

In this particular example it can be seen that systems at c will all sooner or later leave it, never to return.

A Markovian machine has various forms of stability, which correspond to those mentioned in Chapter 5. The **stable region** is a set of states such that once the representative point has entered a state in the set it can never leave the set. Thus a and b above form a stable region.

A **state of equilibrium** is simply the region shrunk to a single state. Just as, in the determinate system, all machines started in a basin will come to a state of equilibrium, if one exists, so too do the Markovian; and the state of equilibrium is sometimes called an **absorbing state**. The example of S.9/4 had no state of equilibrium. It would have acquired one had we added the fourth position "on a fly-paper", whence the name.

Around a state of equilibrium, the behaviour of a Markovian machine differs clearly from that of a determinate. If the system has a finite number of states, then if it is on a trajectory leading to a state of equilibrium, any individual *determinate* system must arrive at the state of equilibrium after traversing a particular trajectory and therefore after an exact number of steps. Thus, in the first graph of S.2/17, a system at C will arrive at D in exactly two steps. If the system is Markovian, however, it does not take a unique number of steps; and the duration of the trajectory can be predicted only on the average. Thus suppose the Markovian machine is

$$
\begin{array}{c|cc}
\downarrow & a & b \\
\hline
a & 1 & \frac{1}{2} \\
b & 0 & \frac{1}{2}
\end{array}
$$

with a a state of equilibrium. Start a great number of such systems all at b. After the first step, half of them will have gone to a and half will be still at b. At the second step, a half of those still at b will move over to a and a half (i.e. a quarter óf the whole) will remain at b. By continuing in this way we find that, of those that were started at b,

$$\frac{1}{2} \text{ reach } a \text{ after 1 step}$$
$$\frac{1}{4} \quad ,, \quad ,, \quad ,, \quad 2 \quad ,,$$
$$\frac{1}{8} \quad ,, \quad ,, \quad ,, \quad 3 \quad ,,$$

and so on. The *average* time taken to get from b to a is thus

$$\frac{\frac{1}{2} \times 1 + \frac{1}{4} \times 2 + \frac{1}{8} \times 3 + \ldots}{\frac{1}{2} + \frac{1}{4} + \frac{1}{8} + \ldots} = 2 \text{ steps.}$$

Some of the trajectories will be much longer than 2 steps.

As is now well known, a system around a state of equilibrium behaves as if "goal-seeking", the state being the goal. A corresponding phenomenon appears in the Markovian case. Here, instead of the system going determinately to the goal, it seems to wander, indeterminately, among the states, consistently moving to another when not at the state of equilibrium and equally consistently stopping there when it chances upon that state. The state still appears to have the relation of "goal" to the system, but the system seems to get there by trying a random sequence of states and then moving or sticking according to the state it has arrived at. Thus, *the objective properties of getting success by trial and error are shown when a Markovian machine moves to a state of equilibrium.*

At this point it may be worth saying that the common name of "trial and error" is about as misleading as it can be. "Trial" is in the singular, whereas the essence of the method is that the attempts go on and on. "Error" is also ill-chosen, for the important element is the success at the end. "Hunt and stick" seems to describe the process both more vividly and more accurately. I shall use it in preference to the other.

Movement to a goal by the process of hunt and stick is thus *homologous*, by S.12/8, to movement by a determinate trajectory, for both are the movement of a machine to a state of equilibrium. With caution, we can apply the same set of principles and arguments to both.

Ex. 1: What states of equilibrium has the system of Ex. 12/10/1?

Ex. 2: A Markovian machine has matrix

$\downarrow$	a	b	c	d	e	f
a	$\frac{1}{3}$	$\frac{1}{3}$	.	.	.	.
b	$\frac{1}{3}$	$\frac{1}{3}$	.	.	.	.
c	$\frac{1}{3}$	$\frac{1}{3}$	.	.	.	.
d	.	.	1	.	.	.
e	.	.	.	1	.	.
f	.	.	.	.	1	1

It is started at *a* on many occasions; how would its behaviour be described in the language of rat-maze psychology?

MARKOVIAN REGULATION

12/12. The progression of a single Markovian machine to a state of equilibrium is much less orderly than that of a determinate machine, so the Markovian type is little used in the regulators of industry. In comparison with the smooth and direct regulation of an ordinary servo-mechanism it must seem fumbling indeed. Nevertheless, living organisms use this more general method freely, for a machine that uses it is, on the whole, much more easily constructed and maintained; for the same reason it tends to be less upset by minor injuries. It is in fact often used for many simple regulations where speed and efficiency are not of importance.

A first example occurs when the occupant of a room wishes to regulate the number of flies in the room at, or near, zero. Putting a flypaper at a suitable site causes no *determinate* change in the number of flies. Nevertheless, the only state of equilibrium for each fly is now "on the paper", and the state of equilibrium for "number of flies not on the paper" is zero. The method is primitive but it has the great virtues of demanding little and of working sufficiently well in practice.

A similar method of regulation is that often used by the golfer who is looking for a lost ball in an area known to contain it. The states are his positions in the area, and his rule is, for all the states but one, "go on wandering"; for one however it is "stop the wandering". Though not perhaps ideal, the method is none the less capable of giving a simple regulation.

Another example of regulation, of a low order of efficiency, would be shown by a rat with serious brain damage who cannot remember anything of a maze, but who can recognise food when encountered and who then stops to eat. (Contrast his behaviour with that of a rat who does not stop at the food.) His progression would be largely at random, probably with some errors repeated; nevertheless his behaviour shows a rudimentary form of regulation, for having found the food he will stop to eat it, and will live, while the other rat will keep moving and starve.

Ex. 1: A married couple decide to have children till they have a boy and then to stop. (i) Is the process regulatory? (ii) What is the matrix of transition probabilities?

Ex. 2: Is the game "Heads, I win; Tails, we toss again" regulatory?

12/13. So far we have considered only the way in which a Markovian machine moves to its goal. In principle, its sole difference from a determinate machine is that its trajectory is not unique. Provided we bear this difference in mind, regulation by the Markovian machine can have applied to it all the concepts we have developed in the earlier chapters of this Part.

(The warning given in S.11/11 (para. 5) must be borne in mind. The steps that take a Markovian machine along its trajectory are of a smaller order of magnitude than the steps that separate one act of regulation (one "move" in the sense of S.11/3) from another. The latter steps correspond to change from one trajectory to another —quite different to the change from one point to the next along one trajectory.)

Thus the basic formulation of S.11/4 is compatible with either determinate or Markovian machines in T and R to provide the actual outcome. No difference in principle exists, though if we describe their behaviour in psychological or anthropomorphic terms the descriptions may seem very different. Thus if R is required (for given disturbance) to show its regulatory power by going to some state, then a determinate R will go to it directly, as if it knows what it wants, while a Markovian R will appear to search for it.

The Markovian machine can be used, like the determinate, as a means to control ; for the arguments of S.11/14 apply to both (they were concerned only with which outcomes were obtained, not with *how* they were obtained.) So used, it has the disadvantage of being uncertain in its trajectory, but it has the advantage of being easily designed.

12/14. *Regulation by vetoer.* The basic formulation of S.11/4 is of extremely wide applicability. Perhaps its most important particular case occurs when both T and R are machines (determinate or Markovian) and when the values of E depend on the various states of equilibrium that T may come to, with η as some state (or states) that have some appropriate or desired property. Most physical regulators are of this type. If R and T are Markovian machines, the bringing of T to a desired state of equilibrium η by the action of R can readily be achieved if advantage is taken of the fundamental fact that if two machines (such as T and R are now assumed to be) are coupled, the whole can be at a state of equilibrium only when each part is itself at a state of equilibrium, in the conditions provided by the other. The thesis was stated in S.5/13 for the determinate machine, but it is just as true for the Markovian.

Let the regulator R be built as follows. Let it have an input that can take two values, β and γ. When its input is β (for "bad") let *no* state be one of equilibrium, and when its input is γ (for "good") let them all be equilibrial. Now couple it to T so that all the states in η are transformed, at R's input, to the value γ, and all others to the value β. Let the whole follow some trajectory. The only states of equilibrium the whole can go to are those that have R at a state of equilibrium (by S.5/13); but this implies that R's input must be at γ, and this implies that T's state must be at one of η. Thus the construction of R makes it a vetoer of all states of equilibrium in T save those in η. The whole is thus regulatory; and as T and R are here Markovian, the whole will seem to be hunting for a "desirable" state, and will stick to it when found. R might be regarded as "directing" T's hunting.

(The possibility that T and R may become trapped in a stable region that contains states not in η can be made as small as we please by making R large, i.e. by giving it plenty of states, and by seeing that its β-matrix is richly connected, so that from any state it has some non-zero probability of moving to any other state.)

Ex. 1: What, briefly, must characterise the matrix γ, and what β?
*Ex. 2: Show that the thesis of S.5/13 is equally true for the Markovian machine.

12/15. *The homeostat.* In this form we can get another point of view on the homeostat. In S.5/14 (which the reader should read again) we considered it as a whole which moved to an equilibrium, but there we considered the values on the stepping-switches to be soldered on, given, and known. Thus B's behaviour was determinate. We can, however, re-define the homeostat to include the process by which the values in Fisher and Yates' *Table of Random Numbers* acted as determinants (as they certainly did). If now we ignore (i.e. take for granted) the resistors on the switches, then we can regard part B (of S.5/14) as being composed of a relay and a channel only, to which comes values from the *Table*. We now regard *B* as having two inputs.

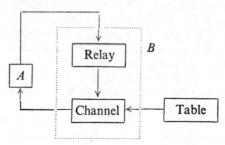

B's state is still a vector of two components—a value provided by the *Table* and the state of the relay (whether energised or not). To an Observer who cannot observe the *Table*, *B* is Markovian (compare S.12/9). Its input from *A* has two states, β and γ; and it has been built so that at β no state is equilibrial, and at γ every state is. Finally it is coupled as in S.5/14.

The whole is now Markovian (so long as the *Table* is not observed). It goes to an equilibrium (as in S.5/14), but will now seem, to this Observer, to proceed to it by the process of hunt and stick, searching apparently at random for what it wants, and retaining it when it gets it.

It is worth noticing that while the relay's input is at β, variety in the *Table* is transmitted to *A*; but when the input comes to γ, the transmission is stopped. The relay thus acts as a "tap" to the flow of variety from the *Table* to *A*. The whole moves to a state of equilibrium, which must be one in which the entry of variety from the *Table* is blocked. It has now gone to a state such that the entry of variety from the *Table* (which would displace it from the state) is prevented. Thus the whole is, as it were, self-locking in this condition. (It thus exemplifies the thesis of S.4/22.)

12/16. The example of the previous section showed regulation occurring in a system that is part determinate (the interactions between the magnets in *A*) and part Markovian (the values taken by the channel in part *B*). The example shows the essential uniformity and generality of the concepts used. Later we shall want to use this generality freely, so that often we shall not need to make the distinction between determinate and Markovian.

Another example of regulation by a Markovian system is worth considering as it is so well known. Children play a game called "Hot or Cold?" One player (call him Tom for T) is blindfolded. The others then place some object in one of a variety of places, and thus initiate the disturbance D. Tom can use his hands to find the object, and tries to find it, but the outcome is apt to be failure. The process is usually made regulatory by the partnership of Rob (for R), who sees where the object is (input from D) and who can give information to Tom. He does this with the convention that the object is emitting heat, and he informs Tom of how this would be felt by Tom: "You're freezing; still freezing; getting a little warmer; no, you're getting cold again; . . .". And the children (if young) are delighted to find that this process is actually regulatory, in that Tom is always brought finally to the goal.

Here, of course, it is Tom who is Markovian, for he wanders, at each next step, somewhat at random. Rob's behaviour is more determinate, for he aims at giving an accurate coding of the relative position.

Regulation that uses Markovian machinery can therefore now be regarded as familiar and ordinary.

DETERMINATE REGULATION

12/17. Having treated the case in which T and R are embodied in machines, and considered that in which the machinery is Markovian, we can now take up again the thread dropped in S.12/7, and can specialise further and consider the case in which the probabilities have all become 0 or 1 (S.12/8), so that the machinery is determinate. We continue with the regulator that is error-controlled. In order, as biologists, to explore thoroughly the more primitive forms of regulation, let us consider the case in which the feedback has a variety of only two states.

An example of such a system occurs in the telephone exchange when a selector starts to hunt for a disengaged line. The selector tries each in turn, in a determinate order, gets from each in turn the information "engaged" or "disengaged", and stops moving (arrives at a state of equilibrium) at the first disengaged line. The set of disturbances here is the set of possible distributions of "engaged" or "disengaged" among the lines. The system is regulatory because, whatever the disturbance, the outcome is always connexion with a disengaged line.

The mechanism is known to be error-controlled, for the information that determines whether it shall move on or stick comes from the line itself.

This case is so simple as to be somewhat degenerate. If we pay no attention to the internal actions between R and T, so that they fuse to form the F of S.10/5, then the case becomes simply that of a determinate system which, when the initial state is given, runs along a determinate trajectory to a state of equilibrium. Thus every basin with a state of equilibrium in η can be said to show a simple form of regulation; for it acts so as to reduce the variety in the initial states (as disturbance D) to the smaller variety in the terminal state.

Much the same can be said of the rat that knows its way about a warehouse; for wherever it gets to it can make its way back to the nest. As much can be said for the computer that is programmed to work by a method of successive approximation; for, at whatever value it is started, the successive values are moved determinately to the goal, which is its only state of equilibrium.

Ex.: A card is to be found in a shuffled pack of 52 by examination of them one by one. How many will have to be examined, on the average, if (i) the cards are examined seriatim, (ii) if one is drawn, examined, returned if not wanted, the pack shuffled, a card drawn, and so on? (Systematic *versus* random searching.)

12/18. When the machinery is all determinate, the problem of S.12/14 may arise—that of getting T to go to some state of equilibrium that has some desired property. When this is so, the solution given there for the Markovian machine is, of course, still valid: one couples on a vetoer.

12/19. *Continuous variation.* After these primitive forms, we arrive at the regulators whose variables can vary continuously. (It must be remembered that the continuous is a special case of the discrete, by S.2/1.) Of the great numbers that exist I can take only one or two for mention, for we are interested here only in their general principles.

Typical is the gas-heated incubator. It contains a capsule which swells as the temperature rises. The mechanism is arranged so that the swelling of the capsule cuts down the size of the gas flame (or of the amount of hot air coming to the incubator); an undue rise of temperature is thus prevented.

The diagram of immediate effects is specially worth noting.   It is

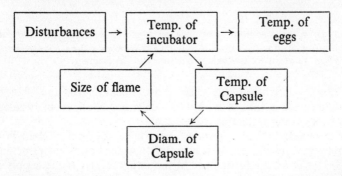

or some equivalent form.   In it, *D*, *T*, *R* and *E* are readily identified (though the distinctions between *T* and *R* and their parts are
somewhat arbitrary).   The whole acts to block the passage of
variety from the Disturbances (whatever they are) to the eggs.   If
the aim of the regulator is re-defined slightly as being to keep
constant the temperature of the incubator, then the regulator is
controlled by the error rather than by the disturbances themselves.

   In this form of regulator, the system must, of course, be stable
for any given disturbance, and the desired temperature must be the
system's state of equilibrium.   The feedback around the circuit
must thus usually be negative.

   Many regulators in the living body are of this simple form, and
Cannon's work has made them well known.   Typical is that which
regulates the *p*H of the blood by the amount of carbon dioxide in it:

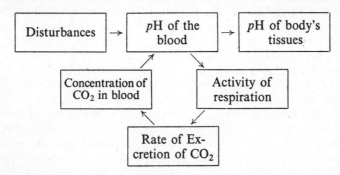

Again the system shows the features just mentioned.

   Among the innumerable examples of such mechanisms should
be included the economic.   Tustin's *Mechanism of Economic*

Systems shows how closely their properties are related to those discussed here.

Ex. 1: Draw the diagram of immediate effects of any regulator known to you.
Ex. 2: (Continued.) Think of some other parameters whose change would affect the regulator's working; add them to the diagram.

12/20. A variant of this class, worth mention for the sake of completeness, is that in which the regulating mechanism becomes active only intermittently.

A reservoir tank, for instance, may have the level of fluid in it kept between two given levels by a siphon which has its inner opening at the lower level and its bend at the upper level. If the supply is usually greater than the demand, the siphon, by coming into action when the fluid reaches the upper level and by stopping its action when it reaches the lower, will keep the level within the desired range.

Many physiological regulators act intermittently. The reaction to cold by shivering is such a case. This particular reaction is of special interest to us (compare S.12/4) in that activity in the regulator can be evoked either by an actual fall in the bodily temperature (error-control, from E) or, before the body has had time to cool, by the sight of things that will bring cold (control from D).

THE POWER AMPLIFIER

12/21. The fact that the discussion in this chapter has usually referred to the output E as being *constant* must not be allowed to obscure the fact that this form can cover a very great number of cases that, at first sight, have no element of constancy in them. The subject was referred to in S.11/15. Here we shall consider an application that is important in many ways already, and that will be needed for reference when we come to Chapter 14. I refer to those regulators and controllers that amplify power.

Power amplifiers exist in many forms. Here I shall describe only one, selecting a form that is simple and clear (Fig. 12/21/1).

Compressed air is supplied freely at A and makes its way past the constriction C before either going into the bellows B or escaping at the valve V. The pressure at A is much higher than the usual working pressure in B, and the aperture at C is small, so air flows past C at a fairly constant rate. It must then either escape at V or accumulate in B, driving up the pressure z. How fast the air escapes at V, where a hole is obstructed to some degree by a cone, depends on the movement up or down (x) of the cone, which is attached

to one end of a light stiff rod *J*, which can turn on a pivot *K*.   Thus
if *K* is unmoving, a movement down at the other end *L* will lift the
cone, will allow air to escape, and will cause a fall of the pressure
z inside *B*; conversely, a movement up at *L* will make *z* rise.

The air pressure in *B* works in opposition to a heavy weight *P*,
which is continued upwards as a pillar, the whole weight being
able to move only up or down.   The pillar carries two pivots, *K* and

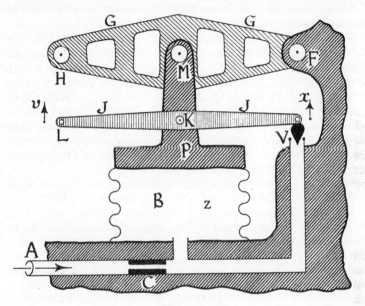

Fig. 12/21/1

M.   *M* is pivot for a strong bar *G*, which is fixed at one end, *F*.
Thus if *P* moves upwards, *M* must move upwards by the same
amount, and *G*'s free end *H* must move upwards by twice the distance.

Now let us see what happens if *L* is moved.   Suppose the operator
lifts *L* by one inch.   The other end (*V*) falls at once by one inch,
the valve is more obstructed, less air escapes, and more accumulates
in *B*, sending up the pressure.   The increased pressure will lift *P*, and
thus *M* and *H*.   Thus *H*'s *movements tend simply to copy L's.*   (We
can notice that the upward movement of *P* (*L* being fixed after its
one inch rise) will make the valve *V* open, so the response of the
whole system to *L*'s movement will be self-limiting, for the feedback
is negative; subject to certain quantitative details, which would

require exact treatment in any particular embodiment, the system is thus stable at a state of equilibrium whose position is determined by L's position.)

The whole can thus also be regarded as a stable system that acts so that, while a movement of, say, one inch at L would tend to cause, at V, a movement of one inch also, the reaction of the system annuls this. So the system can also be regarded as one *that acts so as to keep the position of* V *constant.*

We can now see how it can become a power amplifier, and be used as a crane.

The designer takes care to see that the lever J is light, and that the valve is shaped so that the escaping air, or the pressure z, has little effect on the force required at L. He also takes care that B shall have a large area of action on P, and that the average working pressure z shall be high (with the pressure at A higher still). If he is successful, a small force at L, raising it through one inch, will be sufficient to evoke a large force at H sufficient to raise a heavy mass through the same distance. Thus a force of 1 lb. moving through one inch at L may result in a force of 1000 lbs. moving through one inch at H. It is thus a work- (or power-) amplifier.

So far it has given merely a simple and clear exemplification of the principles of regulation and control described earlier. Later (S.14/1) we shall return to it, for we shall have to be clear about how we can have, simultaneously, a law saying that energy cannot be created, and also a power-*amplifier*.

Ex. 1: How many degrees of freedom for movement have the three bodies P, J, G?

Ex. 2: Modify the arrangement so as to make H move oppositely to L while keeping the equilibrium stable.

Ex. 3: Modify the arrangement so that the equilibrium is unstable.

GAMES AND STRATEGIES

12/22. The subjects of regulation and control are extremely extensive, and what has been said so far only begins to open up the subject. Another large branch of the subject arises when D and R are vectors, and when the compounding that leads eventually to the outcome in T or E is so distributed in time that the components of D and R occur alternately. In this case the whole disturbance presented and the whole response evoked each consists of a sequence of sub-disturbances and sub-responses.

This, for instance, may be the case in wild life when a prey attempts to regulate against an attack by a predator, when the whole struggle progresses through alternating stages of threat and parry. Here the predator's whole attack consists of a sequence of actions $D_1, D_2, D_3 \ldots$, each of which evokes a response, so that the whole response is also a sequence, $R_1, R_2, R_3, \ldots$. The whole struggle thus consists of the double sequence

$$D_1, R_1, D_2, R_2, D_3, R_3, \ldots$$

The outcome will depend on some relation between the predator's whole attack and the prey's whole response.

We are now considering an even more complex interpretation of the basic formulation of S.11/4. It is common enough in the biological world however. In its real form it is the Battle of Life; in its mathematical form it is the Theory of Games and Strategies. Thus in a game of chess the outcome depends on what particular sequence of moves by White and Black

$$W_1, B_1, W_2, B_2, W_3, B_3, \ldots,$$

has been produced. (What was called a "move" in S.11/4 corresponds, of course, to a play here.)

This theory, well founded by von Neumann in the '30s, though not yet fully developed, is already too extensive for more than mention here. We should, however, take care to notice its close and exact relation to the subject in this book. It will undoubtedly be of great scientific importance in biology; for the inborn characteristics of living organisms are simply the strategies that have been found satisfactory over centuries of competition, and built into the young animal so as to be ready for use at the first demand. Just as many players have found "P—Q4" a good way of opening the game of Chess, so have many species found "Grow teeth" to be a good way of opening the Battle of Life.

The relation between the theory of games and the subjects treated in this book can be shown precisely.

The first fact is that the basic formulation of S.11/4—the Table of Outcomes, on which the theory of regulation and control has been based—is *identical* with the "Pay-off matrix" that is fundamental in the theory of games. By using this common concept, the two theories can readily be made to show their exact relation in special cases.

The second fact is that the theory of games, as formulated by von Neumann and Morgenstern, is isomorphic with that of certain machines with input. Let us consider the machine that is equivalent to his generalised game (Fig. 12/22/1). (In the Figure, the letters correspond with those used by von Neumann in his Chapter 2, which should be consulted; his T's do not correspond to the usage in this book.)

There is a machine M with input. Its internal structure (its transformations) is known to the players, T_i. It has three types of input: Γ, V, and T. A parameter Γ, a switch perhaps, determines which structure it shall have, i.e. which game is to be played. Other inputs V_i allow random moves to be made (e.g. effects from a roulette wheel or pack of shuffled cards to be injected; cf. S.12/15). Each player, T_i, is a determinate dynamic system, coupled to M

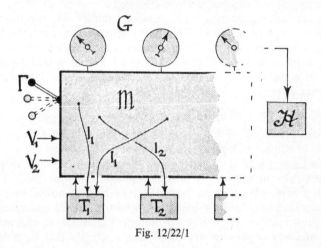

Fig. 12/22/1

both ways. He receives information from M by specified channels I_i and then acts determinately on M. The site of connexion of the I's is defined by Γ. Effects from each T, together with those of the other T's and the V's, exert, through M, complex controls over the dials G. When the play, i.e. trajectory, is completed, the umpire $\mathcal{H}$ reads the G's and then makes corresponding payments to the T's.

What we have here is evidently the case of several regulators, each trying to achieve a goal in G, working simultaneously, and interacting competitively within M. (The possibility of competition between regulators has not been considered explicitly in these chapters till now.)

If the system is ultrastable, each T's behaviour will be determined by parameters, behaving as step-functions. If a particular player is "satisfied" by the payment from $\mathcal{H}$, his parameters will retain their values and his strategy will be unchanged; but if dissatisfied (i.e. if the payment falls below some critical value) the step-functions will change value, and the loser, at the next play, will use a new strategy.

A related subject is the theory of military codings and de-codings. Shannon's *Communication theory of secrecy systems* has shown how intimately related are these various subjects. Almost any advance in our knowledge of one throws light on the others.

More than this cannot be said at present, for the relationships have yet to be explored and developed. It seems to be clear that the theory of regulation (which includes many of the outstanding problems of organisation in brain and society) and the theory of games will have much to learn from each other. If the reader feels that these studies are somewhat abstract and devoid of applications, he should reflect on the fact that the theories of games and cybernetics are simply the foundations of the theory of How to get your Own Way. Few subjects can be richer in applications than that!

12/23. We are now at the end of the chapter, and the biologist may feel somewhat dissatisfied, for this chapter has treated only of systems that were sufficiently small and manageable to be understood. What happens, he may ask, when regulation and control are attempted in systems of biological size and complexity? What happens, for instance, when regulation and control are attempted in the brain or in a human society?

Discussion of this question will occupy the remaining chapters.

Chapter 13

REGULATING THE VERY LARGE SYSTEM

13/1. Regulation and control in the very large system is of peculiar interest to the worker in any of the biological sciences, for most of the systems he deals with are complex and composed of almost uncountably many parts. The ecologist may want to regulate the incidence of an infection in a biological system of great size and complexity, with climate, soil, host's reactions, predators, competitors, and many other factors playing a part. The economist may want to regulate against a tendency to slump in a system in which prices, availability of labour, consumer's demands, costs of raw materials, are only a few of the factors that play some part. The sociologist faces a similar situation. And the psychotherapist attempts to regulate the working of a sick brain that is of the same order of size as his own, and of fearful complexity. These regulations are obviously very different from those considered in the simple mechanisms of the previous chapter. At first sight they look so different that one may well wonder whether what has been said so far is not essentially inapplicable.

13/2. This, however, is not so. To repeat what was said in S.4/18, many of the propositions established earlier are stated in a form that leaves the size of the system irrelevant. (Sometimes the number of states or the number of variables may be involved, but in such a way that the proposition remains true whatever the actual number.)

Regulation in biological systems certainly raises difficult problems —that can be admitted freely. But let us be careful, in admitting this, not to attribute the difficulty to the wrong source. Largeness in itself is not the source; it tends to be so regarded partly because its obviousness makes it catch the eye and partly because variations in size tend to be correlated with variations in the source of the real difficulty. What is usually the main cause of difficulty *is the variety in the disturbances that must be regulated against.*

The size of the dynamic system that embodies T tends to be correlated with the variety in D for several reasons. If T is made of many parts, and there is uncertainty about the initial state of any part, then that variety will be allocated to D (S.11/19); so in general, other things being equal, the greater the number of parts the greater the variety in D. Secondly, if each part is not completely isolated from the world around, each part's input will contribute some variety which will be allocated to D; so in general, the greater the number of parts the greater the number of components in D; and therefore, if the components have some independence, the greater the variety in D. (There may be other reasons as well but these will suffice.)

Thus, when the effects of size are distinguished from those that affect the variety in D, it will usually be found that the former is, in itself, irrelevant, and that what matters is the latter.

It now follows that when the system T is very large and the regulator R very much smaller (a common case in biology), the law of Requisite Variety is likely to play a dominating part. Its importance is that, if R is fixed in its channel capacity, the law places an absolute limit to the amount of regulation (or control) that can be achieved by R, no matter how R is re-arranged internally, or how great the opportunity in T. Thus the ecologist, if his capacity as a channel is unchangeable, may be able at best only to achieve a fraction of what he would like to do. This fraction may be disposed in various ways —he may decide to control outbreaks rather than extensions, or virus infections rather than bacillary—but the *quantity* of control that he can exert is still bounded. So too the economist may have to decide to what aspect he shall devote his powers, and the psychotherapist may have to decide what symptoms shall be neglected and what controlled.

The change in the point of view suggested here is not unlike that introduced into statistics by the work of Sir Ronald Fisher. Before him, it was taken for granted that, however clever the statistician, a cleverer could get more information out of the data. Then he showed that any given extraction of information had a maximum, and that the statistician's duty was simply to get near the maximum— beyond that no man could go. Similarly, before Shannon's work it was thought that any channel, with a little more skill, could be modified to carry a little more information. He showed that the engineer's duty is to get reasonably near the maximum, for beyond it no-one can go. The law of Requisite Variety enforces a similar strategy on the would-be regulator and controller: he should try to get near his maximum—beyond that he cannot go. Let us therefore approach the very large system with no extravagant ideas of what is achievable.

13/3. Before we proceed we should notice that when the system is very large the distinction between D, the source of the disturbances, and T, the system that yields the outcome, may be somewhat vague, in the sense that the boundary can often be drawn in a variety of ways that are equally satisfactory.

This flexibility is particularly well-marked among the systems that occur on this earth (for the terrestrial systems tend markedly to have certain general characteristics). On this earth, the whole dynamic biological and ecological system tends to consist of many sub-systems loosely coupled (S.4/20); and the sub-systems themselves tend to consist of yet smaller systems, again more closely coupled internally yet less closely coupled between one another; and so on. Thus in a herd of cattle, the coupling between members is much looser than the couplings within one member and between its parts (e.g. between its four limbs); and the four limbs are not coupled as closely to one another as are the molecules within one bone. Thus if some portion of the totality is marked out as T, the chief source D of disturbance is often other systems that are loosely coupled to T, and often sufficiently similar to those in T that they might equally reasonably have been included in it. In the discussion that follows, through the rest of the book, this fact must be borne in mind: that sometimes an equally reasonable demarcation of T and D might have drawn the boundary differently, without the final conclusions being affected significantly. Arbitrary or not, however, *some* boundary must always be drawn, at least in practical scientific work, for otherwise no definite statement can be made.

13/4. When the system T is very large—when the organism as regulator faces a very large and complex environment with limited resources—there are various ways that *may* make regulation possible. (If regulation is not possible, the organism perishes—an extremely common outcome that must not be forgotten; but this case needs no detailed consideration.)

Sometimes regulation may be made possible by a re-defining of what is to be regarded as acceptable—by a lowering of standards. This is a somewhat trivial solution, though not to be forgotten as a possibility.

Another possibility is to increase the scope and power of R, until R's capacity is made adequate. This method must obviously never be forgotten; but we shall give it no detailed consideration. Let us consider more fully the interesting case in which the regulation, apparently most difficult or impossible, is actually possible.

13/5. *Constraints.* What this means, by the law of **Requisite** Variety, is that the variety in the disturbances D is not really as large as it seems; in other words, by S.7/8, the disturbances show a constraint.

Thus the case we are led to is the following: D has many components, each of which shows variety. The first estimate of D's variety puts it too high, and we are in danger of deducing (if the regulator's capacity is given) that regulation of E to a certain degree is not possible. Further examination of D may, however, show that the components are not independent, that constraint exists, and that the real variety in D is much lower than the first estimate. It may be found that, with R's capacity given, this smaller variety *can* be regulated against, and full regulation or control achieved at E. Thus the discovery of a constraint may convert "regulation impossible" to "regulation possible". If R's capacity is fixed, it is the *only* way.

We are thus led again to the importance and usefulness of discovering constraints, and to yet another example of the thesis that when a constraint exists it can be turned to use (S.7/14).

Let us then consider the question of what constraints may occur in the disturbances that affect very large systems, and how they may be turned to use. The question is of major practical importance, for if R's capacity is not easily increased and the other methods are not possible, then the law of Requisite Variety says that the discovery of a constraint is the would-be regulator's only hope.

13/6. As was said in S.7/10, constraints do not fall into a few simply-described classes. Having indicated some of the more interesting possibilities in Chapter 7, I can only continue to mention those classes that are of peculiar interest to us now. With this brief reference I shall pass by a vast subject, that comprises a major part of all human activity.

Accordingly we shall study one particular form of constraint. It is of great interest in itself, it will illustrate the thesis of the last chapter, and it is of considerable practical importance in the regulation of the very large system.

REPETITIVE DISTURBANCE

13/7. Though little reference has been made to the fact in the last few chapters, many disturbances (and the corresponding regulatory responses) are repetitive, especially if the system is viewed over a long time. The cough reflex is regulatory and useful not merely because it removes *this* particle of dust but because, in a lifetime, it removes particles again and again—as many times as are necessary. Most of the physiological regulators act again and again, as often as is necessary. And the coastal lifeboat saves lives not once but again and again. If, in the last few chapters, we have spoken of "the regulatory response" in the singular, this is only because the single action is typical of the set, not because the set necessarily has only one element.

So many of the well-known regulations are repetitive that it is difficult to find a regulation that acts once only. A possible example is given by an observatory making plans so as to have everything ready in case a supernova should occur, an event not likely to occur twice in the director's lifetime. Various possibilities would have to be considered—in which part of the sky it might appear, whether during day or night, the spectral and other peculiarities which would determine what particular type of plate and filter should be used in photographing it, and so on. In making his plans, the director would, in fact, draw up a table like that of S.11/4, showing the uncertainties (D) to be feared, the resources (R) available, and the outcomes (E). Inspection of the table, as in Ex. 11/4/4, would then enable him to decide whether, in all cases, he would get what he wanted.

There are, therefore, cases in which the regulation has to be exerted against a non-repetitive disturbance, but they are uncommon.

From here on we shall consider the case in which the disturbance, and the regulatory response, occur more than once; for such cases show constraint, of which advantage can be taken.

13/8. The constraint occurs in the following way.

The basic formulation of the regulatory process referred to a set of disturbances but assumed only that the separate elements in the set were distinct, nothing more. Like any other quantity, a disturbance may be simple or a vector. In the latter case, at least two main types are distinguishable.

The first type was discussed in S.11/17: the several components of the disturbance act simultaneously; as an air-conditioner might, at each moment, regulate both temperature and humidity.

The second type is well shown by the thermostatically-controlled water bath; it can be regarded as a regulator, over either short or long intervals of time. Over the short interval, "the disturbance" means such an event as "the immersion of this flask", and "its response" means "what happens over the next minute". Its behaviour can be judged good or bad according to what happened in that minute. There is also the long interval. After it has worked for a year someone may ask me whether it has proved a good regulator over the year. While deciding the reply, I think of the whole year's disturbance as a sort of Grand Disturbance (made up of many individual disturbances, with a small d), to which it has produced a Grand Response (made up of many individual responses, with a small r). According to some standard of what a bath should do over a year (e.g. never fail badly once, or have an average deviation of less than $\frac{1}{2}°$, etc.) I form an opinion about the Grand Outcome—whether it was Good or Bad—and answer the question accordingly.

It should be noticed that what is "Good" in the Grand Outcome does not follow necessarily from what is "good" (η) in the individual outcomes; it must be defined anew. Thus, if I go in for a lottery and have three tickets, a win on one (and consequent loss on the other two) naturally counts as "Good" in the Grand Outcome; so here 1 good + 2 bad = Good. On the other hand, if I am tried three times for murder and am found not guilty for one, the individual results are still 1 good + 2 bad, but in this case the Grand Outcome must naturally count as Bad. In the case when the individual disturbances each threaten the organism with death, Good in the Grand Outcome must naturally correspond to "good in every one of the individual outcomes".

These Grand Disturbances are vectors whose components are the individual disturbances that came hour by hour. These vectors show a form of constraint. Thus, go back to the very first example of a vector (S.3/5). It was A; contrast it with B:

A		B	
Age of car:	....	Age of Jack's car:	....
Horse power:	....	,, ,, Jill's ,,	....
Colour:	....	,, ,, Tom's ,,	....

Obviously B is restricted in a way that A is not. For the variety in the left-hand words in A's three rows is three; in B's three rows it is one.

Vectors like B are common in the theory of probability, where they occur under the heading "sampling with replacement". Thus, the spin of a coin can give only two results, H or T. A coin spun six times in succession, however, can give results such as (H, H, T, H, T, H), or (T, T, H, H, T, H), and so on for 64 possibilities. (Compare S.9/9.)

What is important here is that, in such a set of vectors (in those whose components all come from the same basic class, as in B),

249

two varieties can be distinguished: there is (i) the variety within the basic class (2 for the coin, the number of distinct possible ages in B), and (ii) the variety built up by using the basic class n times over (if the vector has n components). In the example of the coin, the two varieties are 2 and 64. In general, if the variety within the basic class is k, and the vector has n components, each a member of the class, then the two varieties are, at most, k, and k^n. In particular it should be noticed that if the variety in the basic class has some limit, then a suitably large value of n will enable the second variety to be made larger than the limit.

13/9. These considerations are applicable in many cases of regulation. Suppose, for definiteness, that the water bath may be affected in each minute by one of the three individual disturbances:

(a) a draught of air cooling it,
(b) sunshine warming it,
(c) a cold object being immersed in it.

The variety is three, but this number is hardly representative of the variety that will actually occur over a long time. Over a year, say, the Grand Disturbance is a vector with perhaps some hundreds of components. Thus one Grand Disturbance might be the vector (i.e. the sequence) with 400 components:

$$(a, b, a, b, b, a, c, b, b, c, c, b, b, \ldots c, b, a, b).$$

And if the individually correct responses are, respectively α, β, and γ, then the Grand Response appropriate to this particular Disturbance would be the vector (i.e. sequence)

$$(\alpha, \beta, \alpha, \beta, \beta, \alpha, \gamma, \beta, \beta, \gamma, \gamma, \beta, \beta, \ldots \gamma, \beta, \alpha, \beta).$$

If there is no constraint in the Disturbance from component to component as one goes from left to right, the whole set of possible Disturbances has variety of 3^{400}; and the Grand Response must have at least as much if full regulation is to be obtained.

We now come to the point: the double sequence, as it occurred in time, shows *the characteristic constraint of a machine*, i.e. it defines a machine up to an isomorphism. Thus, in the example just given, the events occurred in the order, from left to right:

$$a \ b \ a \ b \ b \ a \ c \ b \ b \ c \ c \ \ldots, \text{etc.}$$
$$\alpha \ \beta \ \alpha \ \beta \ \beta \ \alpha \ \gamma \ \beta \ \beta \ \gamma \ \gamma \ldots, \text{etc.}$$

(though not necessarily at equal time-intervals). It is now easily verified that this sequence, as a protocol, defines the machine with input:

$$
\begin{array}{c|ccc}
\downarrow & \alpha & \beta & \gamma \\
\hline
a & \alpha & \alpha & \alpha \\
b & \beta & \beta & \beta \\
c & \gamma & \gamma & \gamma
\end{array}
$$

Thus when the Grand Disturbance is a vector whose components are all from a basic set of disturbances, the Grand Response can either be a vector of equal variety or the output of a suitable machine with input.

13/10. Suppose that the regulation discussed throughout Part III is the responsibility of some entity Ω, often the possessor of the essential variables E. Through the previous chapters we have studied how the regulator R must behave. We have now seen that in the case when the disturbances are repetitive, Ω has the option of either *being* the regulator (i.e. acting as R) or of *building a machine* that, once built, will act as R and will carry out a regulation of indefinite length without further action by Ω. We have thus arrived at the question: should Ω achieve the regulation directly, by his own actions, or should he build a machine to undertake the work?

The question would also have arisen for another reason. From the beginning of Part III we took for granted that the regulator existed, and we then asked what properties it must have. Nothing was said about how the regulator came to be made, about the factors that brought it into existence. Thus, having seen in S.10/5 how advantageous it would be if the organism could have a regulator, we showed no means by which the advantage could be gained.

For both these reasons we must now start to consider how a regulatory machine is actually to be designed and made. Here we shall be thinking not so much of the engineer at his bench as of the brain that, if it is to achieve regulation in its learned reactions, must somehow cause the development of regulatory machinery within the nervous material available; or of the sociologist who wants a regulatory organisation to bring harmony into society.

To understand what is involved, we must look more closely at what is implied, in principle, in the "designing" of a regulatory machine.

DESIGNING THE REGULATOR

13/11. *Design as communication.* Let us forget, temporarily, all about "regulation", and turn simply to certain questions related to the design and construction of a machine, any machine.

Our treatment of it, while losing nothing in precision, must be very broad—that is to say, abstract—for, as biologists, we want to consider machines of far wider type than those of steel and brass. Within the formula

Entity Ω designs machine M

we want to include such cases as

(1) The genes determining the formation of the heart.
(2) A mechanic making a bicycle.
(3) One part of the brain determining the internal connexions in a nerve-net.
(4) A works-manager laying out a factory to get production going along certain lines.
(5) A mathematician programming an automatic computer to behave in a certain way.

What we shall be concerned with, if we hold to the cybernetic point of view, is not the more obvious processes of shaping or assembling pieces of matter, but with the less obvious questions of what *determines* the final model, of how it comes to be *selected*. We are interested in tracing long chains of cause and effect, so that we can relate a *set* of possible initial causes to a *set* of final machines issuing as consequence; as a telephone mechanic, with a cable of a hundred wires, relates each one going in at one end to some one coming out at the other. By treating the matter in this way we shall find that certain quantitative relations must hold; on them we can base the ideas of the last chapter. Throughout, we shall be exemplifying the thesis of D. M. MacKay: that quantity of information, as measured here, always corresponds to some quantity, i.e. intensity, of *selection*, either actual or imaginable.

The concepts of selecting, designing, constructing, building (briefly, in any way being responsible for the eventual appearance of) an actual machine share a common property, when one identifies and measures the *varieties* concerned in the process. What might turn up as M has variety—an embryo might produce any one of many forms of muscular blood-pump. In fact, the gene-pattern in *Lumbricus* leads to the production of an earthworm's heart, the gene-pattern in *Rana* leads to the production of a frog's heart, and that in *Homo* to a man's heart. Control, by the gene-pattern over the heart, is clearly involved. So too is regulation, for in whatever state the molecules in *Lumbricus* happen to be initially (there being variety in the possibilities), under the action of the gene-pattern the variety disappears, and a heart of standard worm's form appears.

252

It will be noticed that the concepts of design or construction are essentially applicable to *sets*, in spite of the common linguistic use of the singular. (Compare S.7/3.) Thus "the gene-pattern determines the form of the heart" is a shorthand way of saying that elements in the *set* of gene-patterns among different species can be put into correspondence with those in the *set* of possible hearts in the various species, like the wires at the two ends of a telephone cable. Thus *the act of "designing" or "making" a machine is essentially an act of communication from Maker to Made*, and the principles of communication theory apply to it. In particular the measures that were developed for treating the case in which various possible messages are reduced to *one* message can now be applied to the case when various possible machines are reduced to *one* machine.

A useful conceptual device for forcing this aspect into prominence is to imagine that the act of designing has to take place through the telephone, or by some other specific channel. The quantity of variety can then readily be identified by identification of the actual quantity of variety that will have to be transmitted.

13/12. When a designer selects the final form of the machine, what does "selecting" the machine mean in terms of the general concepts of this book? Consider the following sequence of examples, in which the final machine is a radio receiver.

The first is the case of the buyer who has three machines before him, and he selects one. The second case, equivalent to the first from the abstract point of view, occurs when the designer of a radio set, wavering between three possible circuits, finally selects one. The third case, abstractly equivalent to the previous two, occurs when the owner of a radio set that has three circuits built into it, moves a switch to one of three positions and thereby selects which circuit shall actually be used. Thus, from the abstract point of view, selecting one machine from three is equivalent to selecting one value from three at a parameter. For example, suppose the choice is to be between the three machines α, β, and γ (each on the states a and b);

$$\alpha: \downarrow \begin{matrix} a & b \\ b & a \end{matrix} \qquad \beta: \downarrow \begin{matrix} a & b \\ a & a \end{matrix} \qquad \gamma: \downarrow \begin{matrix} a & b \\ b & b \end{matrix}$$

Suppose β is selected and the selector finishes with the machine

$$\downarrow \begin{matrix} a & b \\ a & a \end{matrix}$$

253

Abstractly this selection is identical with having initially a machine with three-valued input:

↓	a	b
α	b	a
β	a	a
γ	b	b

and then deciding that the input shall be fixed permanently at β. (The processes are identical in the sense that if some observer watches only the results of the processes, he cannot tell which has occurred except by reference to other, unmentioned, criteria.)

In this example, fixing the input at β leaves the resulting machine an absolute system, without input. If the result of the selection is to be a machine with input, then the original machine must start with two or more inputs, so that the fixing of one by the act of design-selection leaves the others free for further variation as ordinary inputs.

The designer's act of selecting one model from many is equivalent to some determining factor fixing an input at a permanent value.

13/13. (This section treats a minor complication.)

In the examples above, the choice has been between machines whose transformations have had the same set of operands, i.e. the same set of states in the machine. What if the choice were to lie between, say,

$$\downarrow \begin{array}{cc} a & b \\ b & a \end{array} \quad \text{and} \quad \downarrow \begin{array}{ccc} p & q & r \\ r & q & r \end{array} \;?$$

Can such a selection be represented by the fixing of an input value? Such a choice might occur in the early stages of design, as when the first decision is made whether the components shall be electronic or hydraulic.

In fact this case is contained in the former, and can be represented in it by a mere change of notation. Thus the choice just mentioned can equally be represented as that between μ and ν in the (reducible) machine, whose states are couples:

↓	(a,p)	(a,q)	(a,r)	(b,p)	(b,q)	(b,r)
μ	(b .)	(b .)	(b .)	(a .)	(a .)	(a .)
ν	(. r)	(. q)	(. r)	(. r)	(. q)	(. r)

(In the transformation, dots represent values that do not matter.) If now μ is chosen, one part gives the machine

$$\downarrow \begin{array}{cc} a & b \\ b & a \end{array}$$

the other components being ignored; while if ν is chosen, the other part gives

$$\downarrow \begin{array}{ccc} p & q & r \\ r & q & r \end{array}$$

Thus the initial formulation is really quite general.

13/14. *Design in a Black Box.* It will be noticed that the operation of "design", as understood here, can be carried out within a Black Box, if it has an input. In fact, the owner of the radio set (S.13/12), if he knows nothing of its contents, but does know how the output is affected by the switch, *does* perform the act of "design in a Black Box" when he sets the switch and gets the desired behaviour.

Other examples extend the range of the same theme. The Black Box, or the radio set, may be dominated by another machine, whose activities and values determine the switch's position. If so, we can say (provided we remember the sense in which we are using the words) that the dominating machine, when it sets the switch at a particular position, "designs" the radio set. What is important is that the dominating machine shows to the radio set those properties that are *objectively* shown by the behaviour of a designer.

The same point of view may be applied to the brain, and we can see how one part of a brain can show towards another part the objective behavioural relationship of designer to machine. We can begin to see how one part—a basal structure perhaps—can act as "designer" towards a part it dominates, towards a neural network, say.

Thus the idea of one machine designing another can be stated in exact and general terms—exact in the sense that experiment can be used to show objectively whether or not this relationship holds.

QUANTITY OF SELECTION

13/15. This aspect of design—of the reduction in numbers that occurs when the many initial possibilities are reduced to the final few or one—can easily be measured. We can use the same scales as are used for measuring variety and information (S.7/7 and 9/11) and they can be measured either directly or logarithmically.

The measure, besides being convenient, has the natural property that it specifies the capacity that the channel *C* must have

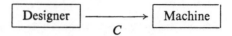

if the transmission of the necessary variety or information from Designer to Machine is to be possible.

It will be noticed that this method does nothing to answer the question "how much design is there *in* this machine (without reference to what it might have been)?" for the measure exists only over the set of possibilities.   It applies, not to the thing that results, but *to the act of communication* (S.13/11).

The exercises will help to give reality to the somewhat abstract arguments, and will show that they agree satisfactorily with what is evident intuitively.

Ex. 1: At one stage in the design of a certain electrical machine, three distinct ohmic resistances must have their values decided on.   Each may have any one of the values 10, 15, 22, 33, 47, 67 or 100 ohms independently.   How much variety must the designer supply (by the law of Requisite Variety) if the possibilities are to be reduced to one?

Ex. 2: (Continued.)   A similar three is to have its resistances selected to the nearest ohm, i.e. from the set 10, 11, 12, ..., 99, 100.   How much variety must the designer now supply?

Ex. 3: Three resistances can each have the value of 10, 20 or 30 ohms.   If they are connected in parallel, how much variety must the designer supply if the possible electrical properties are to be reduced to one?

Ex. 4: How much design is needed if the decision lies between the two machines, both with states *a, b, c, d*:

$$\begin{matrix} & a & b & c & d \\ \downarrow & & & & \\ & b & a & b & c \end{matrix} \quad \text{and} \quad \begin{matrix} & a & b & c & d \\ \downarrow & & & & \\ & c & b & c & a \end{matrix} \quad ?$$

Ex. 5: How much design goes to the production of a penny stamp, (i) as consisting of 15,000 half-tone dots each of which may be at any one of 10 intensities? (ii) as the final form selected by Her Majesty from three submitted forms?   Explain the lack of agreement.

Ex. 6: How much variety must be supplied to reduce to one the possible machines on a given *n* states?   (Hint: Ex. 7/7/8.)

Ex. 7: (Continued.)   Similarly when the machine's states number *n* and the input's states (after design) number *i*.

13/16. Exactly the same measure may be applied to the design of a Markovian machine. Thus the variety between the two Markovian machines

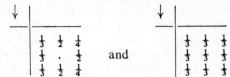

is just 1 bit, for we are choosing *between* two objects, whose inner contents—the various fractions—are here irrelevant. (This quantity of 1 bit is, of course, different from the 1·58 bits that would be associated with the right-hand matrix regarded as an information source that produces 1·58 bits on the average, at each step (S.9/12).)

13/17. *Selection in stages.* The process of selection may be either more or less spread out in time. In particular, it may take place in discrete stages.

The driver about to choose a new car often proceeds in this way. He first says, perhaps, "It must cost less than £1000". This criterion effects some reduction in the number of possibilities. Then perhaps he adds that it must also be able to take five people. So he goes on. Each new criterion makes the surviving possibilities fewer. If he can buy only one car then the criteria must eventually reduce the possibilities to one. Somehow this reduction must be made, even if the spin of a coin has to be used as final selector.

The abstract selection (or design) of a machine can similarly take place in stages. Thus suppose the machine has the four states *a, b, c, d*. The transformation *T*

$$T: \downarrow \begin{matrix} a & b & c & d \\ * & * & * & * \end{matrix}$$

—in which the asterisks are not yet decided on—leaves all possibilities open. The change to transformation *U*

$$U: \downarrow \begin{matrix} a & b & c & d \\ c & * & b & * \end{matrix}$$

represents a partial selection. *U* also represents a *set* of transformations, though a smaller set. So does *V*:

$$V: \downarrow \begin{matrix} \overbrace{a} & b & c & d \\ b \text{ or } c & * & * & * \end{matrix}$$

257

which excludes all single-valued transformations that include the transitions $a \to a$ or $a \to d$. A machine can thus be selected in stages, and the stages may be defined in various ways.

What is fundamental quantitatively is that the overall selection achieved cannot be more than the sum (if measured logarithmically) of the separate selections. (Selection is measured by the fall in variety.) Thus if a pack of cards is taken, and a 2-bit selection is made and then a 3-bit, a unique card cannot be indicated unless a further selection of at least $0 \cdot 7$ bits is made, for $\log_2 52$ is $5 \cdot 7$. The limitation is absolute, and has nothing to do (if a machine is selected) with the type of machine or with the mode of selection used.

Ex. 1: How many possibilities are removed when, to the closed, single-valued transformation on a, b and c with all 27 forms initially possible, the restriction is added "It must have no state of equilibrium"?

Ex. 2: (Continued.) When the restriction is "It must have three states of equilibrium"?

Ex. 3: In logarithmic measure, how much selection was exerted in Ex. 1?

**Ex.* 4: How much selection is exerted on an absolute system of n states, a_1, $a_2, \ldots, a_n$, with all transformations initially possible, if the restriction is added "It must contain no state of equilibrium?" (Hint: To how many states may a_1 now transform, instead of to the n previously?) (Cf. Ex. 1.)

**Ex.* 5: (Continued.) To what does this quantity tend as n tends to infinity? (Hint: Calculate it for $n = 10, 100, 1000$.) (This estimation can be applied to the machine of S.12/15.)

**Ex.* 6: If, as described in this section, the cards of a shuffled pack are searched (without further shuffling) one by one in succession for a particular card, how much information is gained, on the average, as the first, second, third, etc., cards are examined? (Systematic searching.)

**Ex.* 7: (Continued.) How much if, after each failure, the wrong card is replaced and the pack shuffled before the next card is drawn? (Random searching.)

13/18. *Supplementation of selection.* The fact that selection can often be achieved by stages carries with it the implication that the whole selection can often be carried out by more than one selector, so that the action of one selector can be *supplemented* by the action of others.

An example would occur if a husband, selecting a new car from the available models, first decided that it must cost less than £1000, and then allowed his wife to make the remainder of the selection. It would occur again if the wife, having reduced the number to two models, appealed to the spin of a coin to make the final decision.

Examples are ubiquitous. (Those that follow show supplementation by random factors, as we shall be interested in them in the next chapter.) At Bridge, the state of the game at the moment when the first card is led has been selected partly by the bids of the players and partly by chance—by the outcome of the statistically standardised act of shuffling—which has selected the distribution of the cards. (Compare Fig. 12/22/1.) The Rules of Bridge ensure, in fact, that a definite part of the whole determination shall be assigned to chance, i.e. to shuffling carried out in a prescribed way. Such an appeal to chance was frequently used in the past as a method for supplementing selection. The Roman general, for instance, after having made many decisions, would often leave the remainder to be determined by some other factor such as the flight of the next flock of birds, or the configurations shown in the entrails of a freshly-killed sheep. (Supplementation was used earlier in this book in S.4/19 and 12/15.)

In scientific work the first deliberate use of wholly uncorrelated selectors to provide "random" determination to complete the selection imposed by the experimenter, was made apparently by Sir Ronald Fisher; for he first appreciated its fundamental importance and usefulness.

(By saying a factor is **random**, I do not refer to what the factor is in itself, but to the relation it has with the main system. Thus the successive digits of π are as determinate as any numbers can be, yet a block of a thousand of them might serve quite well as random numbers for agricultural experiments, not because they *are* random but because they are probably *uncorrelated* with the peculiarities of a particular set of plots. Supplementation by "chance" thus means (apart from minor, special requirements) supplementation by taking effects (or variety) *from a system whose behaviour is uncorrelated with that of the main system.* An example was given in S.12/15. Thus if a chance variable were required, yesterday's price of a gold-share might be suitable if the main system under study was a rat in a maze, but it would not be suitable if the main system were a portion of the financial-economic system.)

SELECTION AND MACHINERY

13/19. *Selection by machine.* In the preceding sections we have considered the questions of communication involved when a machine is to be selected. Whatever does the selecting is, however, on general cybernetic principles, also to be considered as a mechanism. Thus, having considered the system

$$\boxed{L} \rightarrow \boxed{M}$$

when L acts so as to design or select the machine M, we must now consider L as a machine, in some way acting as designer or selector.

How can a machine select? The answer must, of course, be given in terms compatible with those already used in this Part.

Perhaps the simplest process of selection occurs when a machine goes along a particular trajectory, so that after state i (say) it goes to state j (say) and not to any other of its states. This is the ordinary selection that a machine makes when its "message" (the protocol from it) says that the machine has *this* transformation and no other.

Another process of selection shown by a machine is that noticed in S.7/24: every determinate machine shows selection as it reduces the variety in its possible states from the maximum initially to the number of its basins finally.

Another process of selection was treated in S.5/13, when one part of a whole can select from states of equilibrium in the other part by "vetoing" some of them. This is perhaps the most obvious form of selection, for, as the two are watched, the imaginative observer can almost hear the vetoing part say ". . . no good, still no good, I won't have it, still no good, Hold It!—yes, we'll keep that permanently." If a machine is to be built as a selector (perhaps to carry out the programme hinted at in the final section) it will, so far as I can see, have to be built to act in this way. It is the way of the second-order feedback in Fig. 5/14/1 (supplemented in S.12/15).

There are doubtless other methods, but these will suffice for illustration, and they are sufficient to give definiteness to the idea of a machine "selecting"; (though special consideration is hardly necessary, for in Shannon's theory *every* act of communication is also one of selection—that by which the particular message is caused to appear).

13/20. *Duration of selection.* At this point a word should be said about how long a given act of selection may take, for when actual cases are examined, the time taken may, at first estimate, seem too long for any practical achievement. The question becomes specially important when the regulator is to be developed for regulation of a very large system. Approximate calculation of the amount of selection likely to be necessary may suggest that it will take a time far surpassing the cosmological; and one may jump to the conclusion that the time taken in actually achieving the selection would have to be equally long. This is far from being the case, however.

The basic principles have been made clear by Shannon, especially in his *Communication theory of secrecy systems.* He has shown that if a particular selection is wanted, of 1 from N, and if the selector can indicate (or otherwise act appropriately) only as to whether the required element is or is not in a given set, then the method that achieves the whole selection in the fewest steps is selection by successive dichotomies, so that the early selections are between group and group, not between elements. This method is much faster than the method of examining the N one by one, seriatim. And if N becomes very large, the method of selecting among groups becomes almost incomparably faster. Lack of space prohibits an adequate treatment of this important subject, but it should not be left until I have given an example to show something of how enormously faster the dichotomising method is.

Let us consider a really big selection. Suppose that, somewhere in the universe (as visible to the astronomer) there is a unique atom; the selector wants to find it. The visible universe contains about 100,000000 galaxies, each of which contains about 100000,000000 suns and their systems; each solar system contains about 300000 bodies like the earth, and the earth contains about 1,000000,000000 cubic miles. A cubic mile contains about 1000,000000,000000,000000 dust particles, each of which contains about 10000,000000,000000 atoms. He wants to find a particular one!

Let us take this as a unit of very large-scale selection, and call it 1 *mega-pick*; it is about 1 from 10^{73}. How long will the finding of the particular atom take?

Two methods are worth comparing. By the first, the atoms are examined one at a time, and a high-speed electronic tester is used to examine a million in each second. Simple calculation shows that the number of *centuries* it would take to find the atom would require more than the width of this page to write down. Thus, following this method dooms the selection to failure (for all practical purposes).

In the second method he uses (assuming it possible) the method of dichotomy, asking first: is the atom in this half or that? Then, taking what is indicated, is it in this half or that?. And so on. Suppose this could be done only at one step in each second. How long would this method take? The answer is: just over four minutes! With this method, success has become possible.

This illustration may help to give conviction to the statement that the method of selection by groups is *very much* faster than the method of searching item by item. Further, it is precisely when the time of searching item by item becomes excessively long that the method of searching by groups really shows its power of keeping the time short.

13/21. *Selection and reducibility.* What does this mean when a particular machine is to be selected? Suppose, for definiteness that it has 50 inputs, that each input can take any one of 25 values, and that a particular one of the possible forms is sought.   This selection is just about 1 megapick, and we know that the attempt to select seriatim is hopeless.   Can the selection be made by groups? We can if there can be found some *practical* way of grouping the input-states.

A particular case, of great practical importance, occurs when the whole machine is reducible (S.4/14) and when the inputs go separately to the various sub-systems.   Then the sequence: select the right value for part 1, on part 1's input; select the right value for part 2, on part 2's input; and so on—corresponds to the selection being conducted by groups, by the fast method.   *Thus, if the machine is reducible the fast method of selection can be used.*

In fact, reducibility is extremely common in our terrestrial systems.   It is so common that we usually take it for granted, but he who would learn how to regulate the very large system must become fully aware of it.

To get some idea of how much the world we live in shows reducibility, compare its ordinary behaviour with what would happen if, suddenly, the reducibility were lost, i.e. if every variable had an effect, immediate or delayed, on every other variable.   The turning over of a page of this book, instead of being just that and nothing more, might cause the lights to change, the table to start moving, the clock to change its rate, and so on throughout the room.   Were the world really to be irreducible, regulation would be so difficult as to be impossible, and no organised form of life could persist (S.7/17).

The subject must be left now, but what was said in *Design* . . . on "Iterated systems", and in the chapters that followed, expands the thesis.   Meanwhile we can draw the conclusion that if a responsible entity Ω (S.13/10) is to design (i.e. select) a machine to act as regulator to a very large system, so that the regulator itself is somewhat large, the achieving of the necessary selection within a reasonably short time is likely to depend much on whether the regulator can be made in reducible form.

13/22.   *Whence the Regulator*?   Now at last we can answer the question that has been latent throughout Part III: how is the desired regulator to be brought into being?   The question was raised in S.13/10, but since then we have explored a variety of topics, which had to be discussed before the threads could be pulled together. Let us now survey the position.

The process of arriving eventually at a particular machine with desired properties implies selection, and it also implies that the responsible entity Ω (of S.13/10) has worked successfully to a goal. With whatever variety the components were initially available, and with whatever variety the designs (i.e. input values) might have varied from the final appropriate form, the maker Ω acted in relation to the goal so as to achieve it.   He therefore acted as a regulator.   Thus, *the making of a machine of desired properties* (in the sense of getting it rather than one with undesired properties) *is an act of regulation.*

Suppose now that this machine of desired properties is the regulator discussed throughout Part III—how is it to be made? The answer is inescapable: by another regulator.

Is this a reductio ad absurdum of our whole position?   I think not.   For the obvious question "where does it all start?" is readily answered.   As biologists, our fundamental fact (S.10/3) is that the earth has now existed for a long time, that selection has acted throughout this time, and that selection favours the appearance of regulators (S.10/5).   These facts alone are sufficient to account for the presence on the earth today of many good regulators.   And no further explanation is *necessary* if it should be found that some of these regulators have as goal the bringing of some mechanism to standard form, even if the standard form is that of a regulator (with goal, of course, distinct from that of the first).   The scientist would merely be mildly curious as to why something that could be done directly, in one stage, is actually done indirectly, in two.

We can thus answer this section's question by saying that a regulator can be selected from some general set of mechanisms (many non-regulatory) only by being either the survivor of some process of natural selection or by being made (another process of selection) by another regulator.

13/23. Is not this making of the desired regulator by two stages wasteful?   That it should be arrived at in two stages suggests that the problem of getting a regulator always has to be solved before it can be tackled!

Again, what does this imply when the very large system to be regulated is the social and economic world and the responsible entity Ω is some set, of sociologists perhaps, whose capacity, as a regulator, is limited to that available to the members of the species *Homo*?   Does this imply that no advance in regulation is possible (for the regulator will have to be built by members of the species)?

It does not; for when regulation is achieved in stages—when a regulator R_1 acts so as to bring into existence a regulator R_2—*the capacity of R_2 is not bounded by that of R_1.*   The possibility arises that R_2 may be of capacity greater than R_1, so that an *amplification* occurs. This possibility is studied in the next chapter, where we shall see that, far from being necessarily wasteful, the method of regulation by stages opens up some remarkable possibilities.

Chapter

AMPLIFYING REGULATION

14/1. *What is an amplifier?* An amplifier, in general, is a device that, if given a little of something, will emit a lot of it. A sound-amplifier, if given a little sound (into a microphone) will emit a lot of sound. A power-amplifier, such as the one described in S.12/21, if given a little power (enough to move L) will emit a lot of power (from H). And a money-amplifier would be a device that, if given a little money, would emit a lot.

Such devices work by having available a generous reservoir of what is to be emitted, and then using the input to act as controller to the flow from the reservoir. Rarely an amplifier acts by directly magnifying the input, as does the cine-projectionist's lens; but more commonly it works by supplementation. Thus the power-amplifier has some source that will provide power abundantly (the compressed air at A in Fig. 12/21/1), and it is this source that provides most of the power in the output, the input contributing little or nothing towards the output. Similarly, the work performed by the crane-driver on the control-handle does nothing directly towards lifting the main weight, for the whole of his work is expended in moving electrical or other switch gear.

It will be seen that in the power amplifier (e.g. that of Fig. 12/21/1) the whole process—that of lifting a heavy weight at H, by a force at L—goes in two stages, by two coupled systems. It is this separation into two stages that makes power-amplification possible, for otherwise, i.e. in one stage, the law of conservation of energy would make any simple and direct amplification of power impossible. Stage 1 consists of the movement, by the operator, of the point L against the friction at K and the pressure at V; over this stage energy, or power, is conserved strictly. Stage 2 consists of the movement of compressed air into or out of B and the lifting of P, G and H; over this stage, also, energy is conserved; for the energy used when the weight at H is lifted is derived from the expansion of the compressed air. Thus the whole system can be regarded as composed of two systems, within each of which energy is conserved strictly, and so coupled that forces of 0, 1, 2 . . . dynes at L correspond *respectively* to forces of 0, 1000, 2000, dynes (or some other multiple) at H.

It is the division into two stages that enables a power-amplifier to be built in spite of the law of conservation of energy, the point being that the energy supplied to the input in stage 1 can be supplemented to give the output in stage 2.

Sometimes the proportionality is important, as in the radio amplifier. Then the machine has to be made so that the ratio has the same value all along the scale. In other cases the exact value of the ratio is of little importance, as in the crane, the essential point in it being that the input values shall all be within some given limit (that set by the strength of the crane driver's arm) and that the output shall be supplemented generously, so that it much exceeds the value of the input.

Ex. : Design a " water-amplifier ", i.e. a device that, if water is pumped into the input at *x* ml/sec will emit, from its output, water at 100*x* ml/sec.

14/2. The process of amplification can thus be looked at from two very different points of view, which are apt to lead to two very different opinions about whether amplification does or does not occur.

On the one side stands the theoretician—a designer of cranes, perhaps, who must understand the inner nature of the process if he is to make the crane effective. To him there is no real amplification: the power emitted does not exceed the (total) power supplied. He knows that the operator at the control is successful simply because the operator can, as it were, rob other sources of energy (coal, oil, etc.) to achieve his end. Had Nature not provided the coal as a generous source of supplementation, the operator would not be able to lift the heavy load. The operator gets "amplification" simply by calling in King Coal to help him. So the basic type of amplifier is the boy who can lift big weights—because his father is willing to lift them for him!

All this is true; yet on the other side stands the practical man who wants to *use* the thing, the man who decides what machinery to install at the quay-side, say. If he has access to an abundant source of cheap power, then for him "amplification" becomes very real and practical. It means the difference between the ships being loaded quickly and easily by movements of a control handle, or slowly and laboriously by hand. When the load is larger, a locomotive for instance, the non-availability of a power-amplifier might mean that the job could not be done at all. Thus, to the practical man the possibility of such an apparent amplification is of great importance.

Obviously, both points of view are right. Designers of cranes should be well aware that they are not really amplifiers, but the users of them should think of them as if they were.

14/3. We can now see how we should view the question of amplifying regulation. During the designing (in this chapter) we shall have to be clearly aware that the designer is really achieving only a supplementation, by robbing some easily available and abundant source of it. When he comes to use it, however (a matter for the future), he should forget the fact, and should know only that he is now like a workman equipped with power-operated tools, able to achieve tasks impossible to the unaided workman.

14/4. *Regulation and selection.* In S.13/10 we started to consider what would get the regulator (previously assumed to be given) into actual existence, either as a formula for behaving, contained within the organism (Ω) that wants the regulation, or as a material machine built by the organism to act for him. We saw that the *quantity* of design that goes to it can be measured (by the amount of selection necessary) and we saw (S.13/18) that selection can, in a sense, be amplified. To make the matter clearer, let us consider more directly the relation between regulation and selection, especially so far as the quantities of variety or information are concerned. If the diagram of immediate effects is

$$\boxed{\text{Designer}} \xrightarrow{\quad\quad} \boxed{\text{Regulator}}$$
$$C$$

we want to know how much variety or information the channel C between them will have to carry.

To get a regulator made, selection is essential. Here are three examples:

The first regulator we discussed (S.11/3) led to our identifying it as

$$R: \downarrow \begin{array}{ccc} 1 & 2 & 3 \\ \beta & \alpha & \gamma \end{array}$$

and this particular transformation (the regulatory) had to be selected from the set of all transformations possible, which numbered, in this case, 27 (cf. Ex. 7/7/8). Here the regulator is "made" by being unambiguously specified, i.e. distinguished from the others.

In S.13/12 another method was used, and a machine, which might be a regulator, was "designed" by a particular value being selected from the set of possible input-values.

A third method for getting a regulator made is to assemble it in hardware, as a mechanic makes a water bath. Again selection is necessary: components have to be selected (distinguished) from other possible objects, and the mode of assembling and coupling has to be selected from the other, incorrect, modes. The quantity of selection used can be measured; and any dispute about the measurement can be resolved by the method of S.13/11 (final paragraph).

It follows from S.13/18 that if the final regulator can be arrived at by stages (the whole selection occurring in stages) the possibility exists that *the provision of a small regulator at the first stage may lead to the final establishment of a much bigger regulator* (i.e. one of larger capacity) so that the process shows amplification.

This is the sense in which "amplifying" regulation is to be understood. The law of Requisite Variety, like the law of Conservation of Energy, absolutely prohibits any direct and simple magnification but it does not prohibit supplementation.

14/5. Let us consider some examples which will actually show such amplification of regulation.

Suppose the disturbances are fluctuations in the mains' voltage, which come to an apparatus owned by Ω at the rate of hundreds a second, and threaten to disturb it. Assume that the variety per second provided by these disturbances far exceeds his capacity as a channel, so it is impossible for him to regulate against them by direct personal action. However, he has available a manufacturer's catalogue, which shows three items:

1: Television set,
2: Mains stabiliser,
3: Frequency changer.

Assume that it is within his capacity for him to make a suitable selection of one from three; if now he performs the appropriate selection, the end result will be that the mains' supply to his apparatus will become stabilised. Thus his three possible primary selections can be put into correspondence with three outcomes, one of which is "mains' voltage stabilised".

The latter regulation (over, say, a year) involves far more selection than of one from three; so over the whole transaction an undoubted amplification has occurred.

In this example the supplementation is so obvious, and his dependence on the manufacturer's power as a designer so blatant, that the reader may be tempted to dismiss this "amplification" as not worth serious consideration. (It is not, however, more blatant than the crane-driver's dependence on a suitable power supply.) This case, however, is only somewhat extreme (having been selected to show one end of the scale). Other cases lie further along the scale, and are of more general interest. The principle, however, remains unaltered.

Next consider the case in which Ω wants a water bath to be restored to a certain temperature; restorations will be required 100 times in each day and over a whole year. This means that on 36,500 occasions the temperature must be corrected by a raising or a lowering—a one-bit selection, say. The whole Grand Disturbance (S.13/8) thus has variety of 2^{36500} possibilities. Ω probably *could* transmit this in the year, but finds it inconvenient. If then his resources are such that he can make a thermostat at a cost of, say, 1000 bits, then by using the fact that the Grand Disturbance is repetitive (S.13/9), the act of selecting appropriately from 1000 bits has as consequence the correct selection from 36,500 bits. So an amplification of about $\times 36$ (if measured on the logarithmic scale) has occurred.

This second example is more ordinary than the first. The fact that its method is widely used in practice shows whether or not the practical man thinks it worth while.

There is, of course, not necessarily any amplification; and the practical man, before he builds a machine to do a job, always makes at least an intuitive assessment of the balance:

| **Cost** (in some sense) of making the machine which will do the job. | **Cost** incurred by doing it himself. |

What this chapter deals with are the actual quantities involved, when our interest is centred on the amount of communication and selection that is required.

Finally let us consider an example in which the possibility of amplification is obvious and of practical use. Suppose twenty men are given the task of keeping two thousand rooms constant in temperature and humidity. If some means of control exists in each room, the twenty may yet find the task beyond their capacity if they try to compensate for all the atmospheric variations by manipulation of the controls directly. It may happen, however, that machines are available such that if the men become mechanics and act as regulators to the machines, the machines can be made into air-conditioners and maintained as such. And it may further happen that the amount of regulation that the mechanics can supply to the conditioners is sufficient to keep the conditioners effectively in control of the two thousand rooms.   Thus the regulation that could not be done in one stage may, if the conditions are suitable, be possible in two.

The quantities of communication (the channel capacities) involved in these regulations could be measured to any desired accuracy, and the exact degree of any amplification ascertained.   Thus if amplification had actually occurred, the reality of the fact could be demonstrated beyond dispute.

Whence (in the last example) comes the supplementation?   In general, from whatever supplies the other inputs.   In the example just given, these include the other factors that contributed to the machines' design and manufacture, and also the environment itself, which communicates to the conditioner, and *not to the mechanic*, what is the temperature and humidity at each moment.   As a result, these sources of information play a part in the total regulation, without using the mechanic as a channel.

The example just given shows two levels of regulation, but there is no reason why the number should stop at two.   A doctor who looks after the set of mechanics and keeps them healthy and able to work might claim, so far as the rooms were concerned, to be a regulator at the third level.   The matter need not be pursued further once the principle is clear, especially since many cases will probably not show the various regulators arranged in a simple hierarchy.

14/6. *Amplification in the brain.* We can now understand quantitatively why this indirect method has proved superior—why it is the method used by those organisms that have the most powerful resources for regulation—it allows amplification.

The gene-pattern, as a store or channel for variety, has limited capacity.   Survival goes especially to those species that use the capacity efficiently.   It can be used directly or indirectly.

The direct use occurs when the gene-pattern is used directly to specify the regulator.   The regulator is made (in the embryo) and the organism passes its life responding to each disturbance as the gene-pattern has determined.   Amplification does not occur (from our present point of view, though some advantage is gained (S.13/9) if the disturbances recur frequently in the organism's lifetime).

The indirect use occurs when the gene-pattern builds a regulator (R_1) whose action is to build the main regulator (R_2), especially if this process is raised through several orders or levels.   By achieving the ultimate regulation through stages, the possibility of large-scale supplementation occurs, and thus the possibility of an ultimate regulation far greater than could be achieved by the gene-pattern directly.

A clear example of how one regulator can act so as to cause the development of another occurred in S.12/15. Part *B* of the homeo-stat was built and thus became the primary regulator R_1. Coupled to Part *A*, it acts so as to cause *A* to become stable with its needles at the centre. When this is achieved, *A* acts as a regulator (R_2) towards disturbances coming to it that would make the needles diverge. Though the R_2 of this particular example is extremely simple, nothing in principle separates this case from those in which the regulator R_2 is of any degree of complexity.

The method of achieving regulation in two stages, by which the gene-pattern makes R_1, and R_1 makes R_2, is the method of the mammals, whose gene-pattern is used, in its action on the embryo brain, to determine the development at birth of some fundamental regulators (R_1) whose action is not immediately to the organism's advantage. From birth onwards, however, they act towards the cerebral cortex so as to develop in it a vast regulatory mechanism (R_2) that, by the time adulthood arrives, is a much better regulator (i.e. of larger capacity) than could have been produced by the action of the gene-pattern directly.

Whence comes the supplementation? From random sources as in S.12/15 and from the environment itself! For it is the environment that is forced to provide much of the determination about how the organism shall act. Thus gene-pattern and environment both contribute to the shaping of the fully developed adult, and in this way the quantity of design supplied by the gene-pattern is supplemented by design (as variety and information) coming from the environment. Thus the adult eventually shows more regulatory capacity than could have been determined by the gene-pattern alone. The amplification of regulation is thus no new thing, for the higher animals, those that adapt by learning, discovered the method long ago.

May it not be possible that the amplification can be increased even further? If so, is there not a possibility that we can use our present powers of regulation to form a more highly developed regulator, of much more than human capacity, that can regulate the various ills that occur in society, which, in relation to us, is a very large system?

14/7. *Amplifying intelligence.* This book is intended to be an Introduction, and for twelve chapters it has kept to its purpose. The last two chapters, however, have developed the subject somewhat speculatively, partly to give the reader practice in applying the earlier methods, and partly to show what lies ahead, for the prospects are exciting.

In S.13/18 we saw that selection can be amplified. Now "problem solving" is largely, perhaps entirely, a matter of appropriate selection. Take, for instance, any popular book of problems and puzzles. Almost every one can be reduced to the form: out of a certain set, indicate one element. Thus of all possible numbers of apples that John might have in his sack we are asked to find a certain one; or of all possible pencil lines drawn through a given pattern of dots, a certain one is wanted; or of all possible distributions of letters into a given set of spaces, a certain one is wanted. It is, in fact, difficult to think of a problem, either playful or serious, that does not ultimately require an appropriate selection as necessary and sufficient for its solution.

It is also clear that many of the tests used for measuring "intelligence" are scored essentially according to the candidate's power of appropriate selection. Thus one test shows the child a common object and asks its name: out of all words the child must select the proper one. Another test asks the child how it would find a ball in a field: out of all the possible paths the child must select one of the suitable few. Thus it is not impossible that what is commonly referred to as "intellectual power" may be equivalent to "power of appropriate selection". Indeed, if a talking Black Box were to show high power of appropriate selection in such matters—so that, when given difficult problems it persistently gave correct answers—we could hardly deny that it was showing the *behavioral* equivalent of "high intelligence".

If this is so, and as we know that power of selection can be amplified, it seems to follow that intellectual power, like physical power, can be amplified. Let no one say that it cannot be done, for the gene-patterns do it every time they form a brain that grows up to be something better than the gene-pattern could have specified in detail. What is new is that we can now do it synthetically, consciously, deliberately.

But this book must stop; these are not matters for an Introduction.

REFERENCES

ASHBY, W. ROSS. *Design for a brain*. Chapman & Hall, London; 2nd imp., 1954.
Idem. The applications of cybernetics to psychiatry. *Journal of Mental Science*; **100**, 114-124; 1954.
Idem. The effect of experience on a determinate dynamic system. *Behavioral Science*; **1**, 35–42; 1956.
BELLMAN, R. *Stability theory of differential equations*. McGraw-Hill Book Co., New York, 1953.
BOURBAKI, N. *Théorie des ensembles;* fascicule de resultats. A.S.E.I. No. 1141; Hermann & Cie., Paris: 2nd edition, 1951.
Idem. Algèbre, Chapitre 1, A.S.E.I. No. 1144.
Idem. Topologie générale, Chapitre 1, A.S.E.I. No. 1142.
CANNON, WALTER B. *The wisdom of the body*. London, 1932.
FISHER, SIR R. and YATES, F. *Statistical tables*. Oliver & Boyd, Edinburgh, 1943.
GOLDMAN, S. *Information theory*. Constable & Co., London; 1953.
GRANIT, R., LEKSELL, L., and SKOGLUND, C. R. Fibre interaction in injured or compressed region of nerve. *Brain;* **67**, 125 140; 1944.
LASHLEY, K. S. in *Cerebral mechanisms in behavior*. John Wiley & Sons, New York; 1951.
LEWIN, K. *Principles of topological psychology*. McGraw-Hill Book Co., New York; 1936.
MACKAY, D. M. Quantal aspects of scientific information. *Philosophical Magazine;* **41**, 289–311; 1950.
NEUMANN, J. VON, and MORGENSTERN, O. *Theory of games and economic behavior*. Princeton; 1947.
PAVLOV, I. P. *Conditioned reflexes*. Oxford University Press; 1927.
RIGUET, J. *Fondements de la théorie des relations binaires*. Thèse de Paris; 1951.
Idem. Sur les rapports entre les concepts de machine de multipole et de structure algébrique. *Comptes rendues de l'Académie des Sciences;* **237**, 425–7; 1953.
SHANNON, C. E. Communication theory of secrecy systems. *Bell System technical Journal;* **28**, 656–715; 1949.
Idem. The synthesis of two-terminal switching circuits. *Ibid.;* **28**, 59–98; 1949.
Idem. Computers and automata. *Proceedings of the Institute of Radio Engineers;* **41**, 1235–41; 1953.
Idem and WEAVER, W. *The mathematical theory of communication*. University of Illinois Press, Urbana; 1949.
SOMMERHOFF, G. *Analytical biology*. Oxford University Press, London; 1950.
TINBERGEN, N. *The study of instinct*. Oxford University Press, London; 1951.
TUSTIN, A. *The mechanism of economic systems*. Heinemann, London; 1953.
WIENER, N. *Cybernetics*. John Wiley & Sons, New York; 1948.

ANSWERS TO THE EXERCISES

2/4. **1:** No. **2:** No. **3:** A, yes; B, yes; C, no; D, yes. **4:** It must be of the form $a \to a$. **5:** Yes; a position with a player mated can have no transform, for no further legal move exists; if C's transformation is closed, every position his move creates can be followed by another, so his transformation can contain no mating moves.

2/5. **1:** Yes. **2:** No; some operands, e.g. 40, end in 0 and will transform to 0, which is not in the set of operands.

2/6. **1:** $n' = n + 10$ ($n = 1, 2, 3$). **2:** a, $n' = 7n$ ($n = 1, 2, 3$, understood for all); b, $n' = n^2$; c, $n' = 1/n$; d, $n' = 11 - n$; e, $n' = 1$; f, $n' = n$.
3: $\downarrow \begin{matrix} 5 & 6 & 7 \\ 2 & 3 & 4 \end{matrix}$ No. **4:** (i) $\downarrow \begin{matrix} 5 & 6 & 7 \\ 25 & 30 & 35 \end{matrix}$ (ii) $\downarrow \begin{matrix} -1 & 0 & 1 \\ 2 & 0 & 2 \end{matrix}$
5: Yes. **6:** Yes.

2/8. **1:** Many-one; both 1 and 8 are changed to 9.

2/9. **1:** No Sale. **2:** Maiden over.

2/10. **1:** The main diagonal consists exclusively of 1's, and the rest are all zeros. **2:** a: ii; b: iii; c: i. **3:** a: Yes; b: No. **4:** The distributions are the same, the one being merely a reflection of the other. **6:** 16. **7:** 4.

2/11. **1:** $\downarrow \begin{matrix} a & b & c \\ a & a & c \end{matrix}$ **2:** The same as the transformation. **3:** A. **4:** $n' = n + 2$ ($n = 1, 2, \ldots$). **5:** $n' = 49n$ ($n = 1, 2, \ldots$).
6: $\downarrow \begin{array}{|ccc} + & 0 & 0 \\ 0 & 0 & 0 \\ 0 & + & + \end{array}$

2/14. **1:** $n'' = 9n$. **2:** $a'' = a + 16$. **3:** $a''' = 343a$. **4:** $k'' = 9k - 4$. **5:** $m'' = \log(\log m)$. **6:** $p'' = p^4$. **7:** (i) $n' = 4n + 9$; (ii) $n' = n^4 + 2n^3 + 2n^2 + n$; (iii) $n' = 1 + 2\log(1 + 2\log n)$. **8:** $n' = -27n - 7$. **9:** $n' = \dfrac{1+n}{2+n}, \dfrac{2+n}{3+2n}, \dfrac{3+2n}{5+3n}, \dfrac{5+3n}{8+5n}$, etc. **10:** The identity.
12: The limit is at $(\frac{2}{3}, \frac{1}{3})$.

2/15. **1:** 2, 3, 1. **2:** $g: \downarrow \begin{matrix} 6 & 7 & 8 \\ 8 & 7 & 8 \end{matrix}$ **3:** $h: \downarrow \begin{matrix} \alpha & \beta & \gamma & \delta \\ \gamma & \delta & \beta & \alpha \end{matrix}$ **4:** 17. **5:** 0. **6:** $9n$.
7: t.

2/16. **1:** $U^2T: \downarrow \begin{matrix} a & b & c & d \\ d & c & b & d \end{matrix}$ **2:** $UTU: \downarrow \begin{matrix} a & b & c & d \\ c & d & c & b \end{matrix}$

3: They are identical; this equivalence is the chief justification for writing the transformation downwards rather than from left to right. (Cf. Ex. 9/6/8 and 12/8/4.)

274

2/17. **1**: (i) $\begin{array}{c} c \\ \downarrow \\ b \to a \leftarrow d \end{array}$ (ii) $f \rightleftarrows g \, p \rightleftarrows q$. **2**: It contains no arrows, just isolated points. **3**: Each is composed solely of isolated points and/or simple rings without branches.

4: $\begin{array}{ccc} 9 \to 2 & & 5 \leftarrow 6 \\ \uparrow & & \downarrow \\ 4 \to 0 \to 1 & \leftarrow 7 \leftarrow 8 \end{array}$ if 4-figure logs are used
$$\uparrow$$
$$3$$

5: 7, 1, 2, 2. **6:** No. **7:** Yes. **9:** No.

3/1. **1:** Possible answers are: (a) soft-boiled egg → hard-boiled; (b) log → ash; (c) cylinder full of vapour and air → full of flame; (d) unicellular ovum → two-celled; (e) cumulus cloud → thunder storm; (f) oestrus → pregnancy; (g) low price (with short supply) → high price; (h) **cat** seeing mouse → cat chasing mouse; (i) nebulae close → nebulae dispersed.

3/4. **1:** $n' = 2n$. **2:** 2, 4, 8, 16, 32, 64 × 10³. **3:** Graph (ii): 1000 → 2000 → 4000 → ... **4:** $n' = 0.8n$. **5:** (i) 800, 640, 510, 410, 330 × 10⁶; (ii) Zero. **6:** It would run to state 3 at which it remains; 3 is the only state it can stop at. **7:** It runs to a cycle of states 2 and 8, between which it oscillates incessantly. **8:** Four; two with a state of equilibrium and two with a cycle. **9:** $n' = 0.9n + 1,000,000$. **10:** 20, 19, 18·1, 17·3, × 10⁶. **11:** 10,000,000. **12:** If l is its length, its *change* of length over one interval of time is $l' - l$; so $l' - l = 1.2$, and the transformation is $l' = l + 1.2$. **13:** The *increase* in number (not the next number) is $n' - n$; so $n' - n = 10^{-8}n(10^8 - n)$, and the transformation is $n' = n + 10^{-8}n(10^8 - n)$. **14:** 19, 34, 57, 81, 97 × 10⁶.

1: $\downarrow \begin{array}{ccc} (ABC) & (BCA) & (CAB) \\ (BCA) & (CAB) & (ABC) \end{array}$

2: (ABC)
$$\nearrow \quad \searrow$$
$$(CAB) \leftarrow (BCA)$$

3: (1,−1), (1,1), (−1,1), (−1,−1). **4:** A cycle of four elements. **5:** (2,3,5), (3,5,8), (5,8,13).

3/6. **1:** ($\frac{1}{2}$,2), (2,−$\frac{1}{2}$), (−$\frac{1}{2}$,−2), (−2,$\frac{1}{2}$), ($\frac{1}{2}$,2), etc. **2:** (1,2,0,2,2,). **3:** (2,1,0,2,2,) $\rightleftarrows$ (1,2,0,2,2,). **4:** Further cycles of two elements each, and not connected, would be added. **5:** (8,−3,1). **6:** (8,4) transforms to (6,6), at which the system remains. **7:** If the operand is (a,b), $a' = \frac{1}{2}a + \frac{1}{2}b$, $b' = \frac{1}{2}a + \frac{1}{2}b$. **8:** (30,34) → (28,36) → (24,40) → (16,48) → (0,64) → ? What happens next cannot be decided until the permissibility of borrowing is decided. **9:** $a' = \frac{1}{2}(3a - b)$, $b' = \frac{1}{2}(3b - a)$. **10:** Whoever started with most money. **11:** $m' = m - n$, $n' = 2n$. **12:** The vector (m,n). **13:** (150,10) → (140,20) → ... → (0,160), after which the algebraic events no longer parallel the zoological. **14:** $x = 10$, 0, −5, −5, −2$\frac{1}{2}$, 0, 1$\frac{1}{4}$, 1$\frac{1}{4}$, $\frac{5}{8}$; no. **15:** It is heavily damped. **16:** If wages are represented by x, and the price index by y, then the first statement says that $x' - x = y - 100$, and the second says that $y' = x$; so the transformation is $x' = x + y - 100$, $y' = x$. **17:** (110,110) → (120,110) → (130,120) → ... → (1540,990). **18:** No, the system is caught in a "vicious spiral". **19:** (110,110) → (110,100)

$\rightarrow \ldots \rightarrow (100\frac{5}{16}, 100\frac{5}{16})$. **20:** Each is converging to 100. **21:** One system is stable; the other shows self-aggravating inflation. **22:** $(80,120) \rightarrow (100,80) \rightarrow (90,110) \rightarrow \ldots \rightarrow (99\frac{3}{8}, 100\frac{5}{8})$. **24:** Yes. **25:** 3.

3/7. **1:** $\dfrac{d^3x}{dt^3} - \dfrac{d^2x}{dt^2} - 2x\dfrac{dx}{dt} + x^2 = 0$.

2: $dx/dt = y, \; dy/dt = -ax$.

3: $\dfrac{dx}{dt} = y, \; \dfrac{dy}{dt} = (1 - x^2)\dfrac{y}{x} - \dfrac{2}{x(1 + x^2)}$.

4/1. **1:** Three. **2:** Yes. **3:** Under R_1 it goes $c \rightarrow d \rightarrow b$; then under R_2 it goes $b \rightarrow a \rightarrow b$; so it is at b. **4:** (i) R_1 and then R_2 would do; (ii) R_1, R_3, R_2 would do. **5:** It would become $x' = 4, \; y' = 4 - y$; notice that the equation of the first line, belonging to x, is made actually untrue; the fixing forces the machine to behave differently. **6:** Within each column the states must be the same.

4/2. **1:** (i) $g' = 2g - 2h, \; h' = 2g - 2h$; (ii) $g' = g - h, \; h' = 2g$; (iii) $g' = 0$, $h' = 2g + 2h$. **2:** (i) $h' = j, \; j' = e^{-h}$; (ii) $h' = \log(2 + \sin h)$, $j' = 1 + \sin j$. **3:** (i) 0; (ii) 2; (iii) alternately 1 and 2; (iv) $a = 1$ for 90 steps and then $a = 10$. **5:** $PV = 10$; yes, approximately. **6:** $n' = n + a^2$. **7:** Yes; each jump is $n' - n$, and this measures $3a$.

4/3. **1:**

$ab =$	00	01	10	11	20	21
$s' = s$	s	0	t	$-s$	$-s+2t$
$t' = t$	$2t$	$t-1$	$2t$	$t-2$	$2t$

2: 3. **3:** $a = 9/8, \; b = 1/8$. **4:** $a = 9/10, \; b = -1/10$. **5:** Four ($ab = 0, 1, 2$ or 4).

4/4. **1:** Putting a and b always equal, i.e. making the transducer effectively $p' = a(p + q), q' = a(p + q)$.

4/5. **1:** The graph must consist of a single chain that passes through all states. **2:** The sequence (8,4), (6,6).

4/7. **1 and 2:** (omitting brackets) four basins:

$$ai \rightleftarrows bk \qquad dj \rightarrow bi \rightleftarrows ak \qquad bj \rightarrow ci \rightleftarrows dk$$
$$aj \rightarrow di \rightleftarrows ck$$
$$\uparrow$$
$$cj$$

3: $ai \rightarrow ck \rightarrow di \rightarrow bk \rightarrow ci \rightarrow dk \rightleftarrows bi$. **4:** Yes. **5:** $n_1 n_2$. **6:** n^3 **7:** Each part in succession goes to state 0. **8:** The change $\ldots 0,0,1,2,0,0, \ldots$ occurs in each part in turn, somewhat as an impulse passes along a nerve.

4/8. **1:**

$$ce$$
$$\downarrow$$
$$ae \rightarrow df \rightleftarrows bf$$
$$\uparrow$$
$$af \rightarrow cf \leftarrow be \leftarrow de$$

3: In X put all the values of β the same.

4/9. **1:** $p,q; \; r,s,t,u$. **2:** (1,0,1,0,0).

4/11. **1:** Between six pairs, such as AB, there are 6; around four triples, such as ABC, taken in either direction, there are 8; and around all four ($ABCD$, $ABDC$, $ACBD$, $ACDB$, $ADBC$, $ADCB$), there are 6. **2:** $x' = y + z^2, y' = 2z, z' = x - z$. **3:** Yes; the other transformation is $x' = y + z, y' = 2z, z' = x - 1$. **4:** Yes.

4/12. **1:** (with boxes omitted for simplicity): (i) $y \rightarrow x$; y dominates x;

(ii) y a system with feedback;

$$\swarrow \nwarrow$$
$$x \rightarrow z$$

(iii) $u \rightleftarrows x \quad v \rightleftarrows y$; the "whole" actually consists of two unconnected parts; (iv) $u \rightarrow x \rightarrow y \rightarrow z$; a chain of action;

$$u$$
$$\nearrow$$

(v) $y \rightarrow x$; y dominates all the other three;

$$\searrow$$
$$z$$

$$u$$
$$\searrow$$

(vi) $x \rightarrow z$; z is dominated by the other three. **2:** When y is zero.

$$\nearrow$$
$$y$$

4/13. **1:** z dominates x, y is independent of both.

4/14. **1:** (iii) only.

4/15. **1:** If the variables are S = Singing, L = Laughter, X = Organ-playing, Y = Incense-burning, and each take the values 0 or 1 for inactive or active respectively, then the machine with input is soon found to be

	(S,L)			
↓	00	01	10	11
00	01	01	10	10
(X,Y) 01	00	00	11	11
10	11	01	00	10
11	10	00	01	11

One way to (0,0) is: Stop the incense burning for one minute; next stop the incense and play the organ; finally, start burning the incense again; in future keep it burning and never play the organ. **2:** Yes, for the L's transitions are affected by S's values. **3:** No. **4:** $X \rightarrow S \rightleftarrows L \leftarrow Y$.

4/19. **1:** A possible method is roll a die and let its first number give the transform of S_1, and so on. **2:** A possible method is to number six cards from 1 to 6, shuffle them, deal in a row, and then fill in the states in the same order. **5:** See $S.4/20$.

4/20. **1:** Yes, no, no.

5/3. **2:** No. **3:** The only one is (0,0). **4:** All the points on the y-axis are equilibrial. **5:** $j = 0$, $k = -1$. **6:** Yes. **7:** No. **8:** Every arrow returns to its state of origin, so the representative point is immobile. **9:** Identity. **10:** Yes. **11:** Yes.

5/4. **1:** Such is $\downarrow \begin{smallmatrix} a & b & c & d & e & f & g \\ b & a & d & c & e & f & g \end{smallmatrix}$ **3:** No. **4:** No. **5:** No. **6:** Every trajectory is a cycle. **7:** No.

5/5. **1:** $b + c + g$ only. **2:** Yes. **3:** Yes. **4:** Yes.

5/6. **1:** Yes; the sequence $D(c)$, $TD(c)$, $T^2D(c)$, $T^3D(c)$, ... is d, a, c, c, ... **2:** No; the limit is not e. **3:** The system, though displaced out of the set, always comes back to it.

5/7.   **1:** A possible set of transformations is:

↓	a	b	c	d
T	a	b	a	b
D	c	c	.	.
E	b	d	.	.

5/9.   **1:** $a = (100,100)$; D turns it to $(110,110)$—i.e. $\delta_1 = 10$, $\delta_2 = 10$; T is given; it is not stable.   **2:** a and D are as before, but T is changed, and the system is stable.   **3:** Usually the limit will be some state other than a; it is not stable to such D's.   **4:** Yes; the deviations tend to zero, which is a state of equilibrium.   **5:** No; the deviations increase to a degree limited only by extraneous factors such as the shape of the couplings.   **6:** To make any deviation wane rather than wax.   **7:** It is self-aggravating—a perpetual headache to route managers.   **8:** Any displacement from the state of equilibrium would increase until some other limiting factor came in.   **9:** Yes; for all displacements D; thus if D displaces the state to (δ_1, δ_2), then x's successive values are δ_1, $\frac{1}{2}\delta_2$, $\frac{1}{4}\delta_1$, $\frac{1}{8}\delta_2$, ... which obviously converges to 0; similarly for y.

5/13.   **1:** No; for y would have to be in equilibrium at 0 under some value of β; thus β would have to satisfy $0 = 2\beta0 + 3$, which is impossible.

6/3.   **1:** See $S.6/5$.

6/5.   **1:** $\overset{g\searrow}{\underset{h\nearrow}{}} j \to f$.   **2:** $j \to f \to h$ (the protocol gives no evidence about transitions from g with input at β).   **3:** No, the transition from C is not single-valued.   **4:** Yes, so far as the evidence goes.
5:

(x,y) ↓	00	01	02	10	11	12	20	21	22
(x',y')	01	00	11	11	00	21	11	20	11

6: For each input value, n transitions have to be observed, taking at least n steps; so the whole set of transformations cannot be observed in fewer than mn steps.   **7:** Select any two values for x and α, and find what value of x' ensues. Thus "$\alpha = 1$, $x = 4$, and $x' = 4$" shows the Box to be I. An even simpler test is to set $\alpha = 0$ and see whether x increases or decreases in value.

6/7.   **1:** y dominates x.

6/9.   **1:**

↓	a	b	c	d	e
	t	p	r	q	s

  2: Six.

3: Two variables are necessary, the dial reading (v) and its rate of change ($\dot{v}$); $dv/dt = \dot{v}$, $d\dot{v}/dt = k(u - v) - f\dot{v}$, where k represents the strength of the spring and moment of inertia of the mass, and f is the coefficient of friction; (ii) $dy/dt = \dot{y}$, $d\dot{y}/dt = -R\dot{y}/L - y/CL + x$. To be isomorphic in the strict sense defined above, they must have $f = R/L$ and $k = 1/CL$. If this is so they can be shown isomorphic by the one-one transformation

↓	y	$\dot{y}$	x
	v	$\dot{v}$	ku

4:

↓	u	v	w
	z	x	y

6/10.   **1:** They are identical: $p \rightleftarrows q \to r$.   **2:** ii and iv may be changed; i, iii, and v unchanged.   **3:** All are unchanged.

6/11. **1:** Think of x as the price of butter and y as the price of sugar; their difference now is $x - y$; tomorrow's *difference* is $(x - y)'$; and this is the same as tomorrow's price of butter less tomorrow's price of sugar, $x' - y'$.

6/12. **1:** It is if the one-one transformation is regarded as simply an extreme case of the many-one.

6/13. **1:** Even $+$ Even $=$ Even, $E + O = O$, $O + E = O$, $O + O = E$. **2:** (Let "$x + y$" mean "merge x and y"). The systems are: (i) $a + b$, (ii) $c + d$, (iii) $a + b$ and $c + d$, (iv) $b + c + d$, (v) $a + b + c + d$, and (vi) (*ex officio*) the original system with none merged. **3:** The states (x,y) and $(-x,y)$ can be merged, for the change of x's sign does not alter the next state (x',y'); thus, to be told only that the present state is $(\pm 4, -2)$, without specification of x's sign, is still sufficient to show that the next state must be the single one of $(+2, +14)$.

6/16. **1:** System and model would be indistinguishable. **2:** It persists, so does the brain; they are isomorphic at the lowest level. **3:** (i) $a, b+c+d$ is isomorphic with $p, q+r$; (ii) $a+b+c+d$ is isomorphic with $p + q + r$.

7/6. **1:** $26 \times 26 \times 26$, which is 17,576. **2:** 16. **3:** 11. **4:** $2 \times 2 \times 2 \ldots$ ten times, i.e. 1024. **5:** 5^x must be not less than 2×10^9 so, taking logs to any convenient base (10 will do):

$$x \log 5 \geqslant \log 2 + 9 \log 10$$
$$\therefore \ x \geqslant (\log 2 + 9 \log 10)/\log 5$$
$$\geqslant 13 \cdot 3;$$

so at least 14 such tests would be necessary. **6:** (i) 27, (ii) 21. **7:** 27. **8:** $3^3 = 27$ and $3^4 = 81$; so, to select one from 52, *four* indications would be necessary. **9:** Three; the father's group can be A, B or O.

7/7. **1:** One bit. **2:** (i) $2 \cdot 32$ bits, (ii) $30 \cdot 9$ bits. **3:** $4 \cdot 7$ bits. **4:** $5 \times 4 \cdot 7 = 23 \cdot 5$ bits. **5:** (i) 1 bit, (ii) 20 bits. **6:** 2^{20}, i.e. 1,048576. **7:** The replacement of each question mark has variety of $\log_2 6$ bits, so the whole has variety of $6 \log_2 6$ bits, i.e. $15 \cdot 5$ bits. **8:** $n \log_2 n$ bits. **9:** 12000 bits. **10:** A page of 5000 words would carry about 50,000 bits—more than the record. **11:** Other things being equal the varieties must be equal. **12:** That of "all possible pamphlets that are printed in English and that take ten minutes in the reading". The variety belongs not to the pamphlet but to this set. **13:** Certainly; it has only to be *distinct* from the other possibilities.

7/12. **1:** No, for all combinations of past marital state and present marital state are included. **2:** Yes; four possibilities are missing.

7/13. **1:** Three, so far as the quantities mentioned are concerned. **2:** Yes, if the hands are accurately set; thus the hour-hand being midway between two numbers implies that the minute-hand is at the "half-past". **3:** One; for the information given by the minute hand is implied by that given by the hour-hand. **4:** The chameleon's have four; Man has a little more than two, for his eyes can move with slight independence. **5:** Two. **6:** One, for its variety cannot exceed that of a; it would still be 1 however many components the vector had. **7:** Before the graph is given, y might, for given x, have any value over y's range; but after the graph is drawn y's value, for given x, is limited to some one value. **8:** Six.

7/15. **1:** It says that of all the possible rational numbers (infinite in number), the combining proportions will always be found in a small subset (numbering perhaps a few dozen). **2:** Of all geometrically possible trajectories, and all possible heat changes, etc., it allows only a few.

7/19. **1:** Of the transitions (e.g.) $a \rightarrow a$, $a \rightarrow b$, $a \rightarrow c$, etc. all are excluded but one, for the transition from a must be single-valued; similarly from b, etc.

7/20. **1:** 8. **2:** 17. **3:** 12. **4:** (i) 1,048,576; (ii) 21,892.

7/22. **2:** The parasites'; evidently some hosts are food to more than one species of parasite. **3:** V is many-one, and causes a fall. **4:** As lacking in discrimination. **5:** (i) 6 states, (ii) 2 states. "The bath is out of order". **6:** The chance that a particular state S_i will be the transform of a particular state S_j is $1/n$. The chance that S_i will not be the transform of S_j is $1 - 1/n$. The chance that S_i will not be the transform of S_k will also be $1 - 1/n$. So the chance that S_i will not be the transform of any state is $(1 - 1/n)^n$. This gives the *fraction* of the operands that disappear after the transformation. As n tends to infinity it tends to $1/e$. So the fraction that remains, to give the variety, is $1 - 1/e$.

7/24. **1:** 3 states, $= 1 \cdot 58$ bits. **2:** By another $1 \cdot 58$ bits. **3:** "a and b" becomes, in succession, $5a$, $5a + 7$, $10a + 14$, $10a + b + 14$. If 14 is subtracted, $10a + b$ is left. Thus the hundred combinations of a and b (if 0 and 0 is allowed) is transformed one-one, after subtraction of 14, to the hundred numbers from 0 to 99. The variety is 100 states or $6 \cdot 64$ bits. **4:** All the two-number combinations that are suggested on such occasions. **5:** Zero. **6:** 2 states, 1 bit; either various circuits or one circuit at various times. **7:** No. They may be going together round the same cycle. Distinguish between (i) equality of state between machine and machine considered at one instant, and (ii) equality of state between time and time considered in one machine.

8/3. **1:** By no more than one cut can do.

8/4. **1:** Yes; "taking the antilog". **2:** No; the same value for x' is given by many values of x. **3:** The identical transformation. **4:** $n' = n - 7$. **5:** $x' = x - y$, $y' = -x + 2y$. **6:** $3 \log_2 26$ bits, i.e. $14 \cdot 1$ bits. **7:** $26^3 = 17576$. **8:** $\log_2 8 + \log_2 7$, i.e. $5 \cdot 8$ bits. **9:** Not quite: the variety would be $5 \cdot 7$ bits, which is insufficient ($\log_2 52 < \log_2 56$). **10:** 1 bit; the messages are "courting" and "not-courting", and there are two of them. The complexities of molecule and ritual are irrelevant here.

8/5. **1:** $A A C B D D B C B C C B$. **2:** $a c d b d c d$. **3:** $b d c d b a d$. **4:** Yes. **5:** 10, 8, 7, 10, 11, 9, 8. **6:** 10, 8, 4, 3, -1, -1, 3, 0, 1, 1, -1, ... **7:** $x = 2$, 1, 2, -11, 11, -2, 16, ... and $y = 1$, 4, -11, 13, -24, -13, -93, ... **8:** $x = \exp(-4t - \sin t)$. **9:** $x = \frac{1}{2}(e^{-t} + t e^{-t} - \cos t)$. **10:** x chases a, and follows it closer and closer.

8/6. **1:** No; in the table of transformations there must be 108 rows, so each column must have 108 elements; as only 100 are available, there must be repetitions. **2:** (i) 7, (ii) 5^{12}. **3:** Fitting some device such as a speedometer or tachometer that emits a number proportional to the time-derivative. **4:** No; for if the output is steady at zero (as will happen if it is started at zero) a's values cannot be deduced from x's transitions, which are $0 \rightarrow 0$ for all a.

8/7. **1:** It does not maintain all distinctions; a perfect inverter is fundamentally impossible with it.

2:

(b,B)	R	R	R
(b,C)	S	S	S
(b,D)	(will not occur)		
(c,A)	S	S	S
(c,B)	R	R	R
(c,C)	(will not occur)		
(c,D)	Q	Q	Q
(d,A)	(will not occur)		
(d,B)	Q	Q	Q
(d,C)	R	R	R
(d,D)	S	S	S

3: It must have diagram of immediate effects $u \to x \to y$, with y emitting u's values two steps later. x may be of the form

$\downarrow$	x_1	x_2	x_3	$\ldots$
u_1	x_1	x_1	x_1	
u_2	x_2	x_2	x_2	
u_3	x_3	x_3	x_3	
$\ldots$	etc.			

If now y has the form

$\downarrow$	U_1	U_2	U_3	$\ldots$
x_1	U_1	U_1	U_1	
x_2	U_2	U_2	U_2	
x_3	U_3	U_3	U_3	
$\ldots$	etc.			

then y will emit capital letters corresponding to u's original values.

If the two $(x + y)$ are regarded as one machine with state (x,y), the transformations must be

$\downarrow$	(x_1,U_1)	(x_1,U_2)	(x_1,U_3)	$\ldots$	(x_2,U_1)	(x_2,U_2)	(x_2,U_3)	$\ldots$
u_1	(x_1,U_1)	(x_1,U_1)	x_1U_1	$\ldots$	x_1U_2	x_1U_2	x_1U_2	
u_2	(x_2U_1)	x_2U_1	x_2U_1	$\ldots$	x_2U_2	x_2U_2	x_2U_2	
u_3	(x_3U_1)	x_3U_1	x_3U_1	$\ldots$	x_3U_2	x_3U_2	x_3U_2	
$\ldots$	etc.				$\ldots$	etc.		

In general, u_i takes (x_j, U_k) to (x_i, U_j), which goes, at the next step, to $(-, U_i)$, thus repeating the original u_i.

8/8. **1:** $p' = n$, $m' = c/d$; join by putting $d = n$ and $c = p$. **2:** $p' = n$, $m' = \frac{1}{2}(d - c) + 2$; join by putting $d = n$ and $c = p$. **3:** $p_1' = x$, $p_2' = y$, $m_1' = (c_1 + c_2)/2d_1$, $m_2' = (c_2 - c_1)/2d_2$; join by putting $d_1 = x$, $d_2 = y$, $c_1 = p_1$, $c_2 = p_2$. **4:** The equation cannot be solved for a and b separately, *or* a and b affect the equation only in the combination $a + b$ *or* their distinct effects do not appear distinctly in the output, and cannot therefore be traced back—these are different ways of expressing the same basic idea. Notice that the reason for the impossibility lies not in the lack of suitable gadgetry but in the fact that the output does not *define* the input—the necessary information is simply not there. **5:** The inverter requires speedometers to give $\dot{x}_1$ and $\dot{x}_2$ as outputs. Then any machine that forms the functions

$$a_1 = \frac{\dot{x}_1 x_2 - \dot{x}_2 - x_1}{x_1(x^2_2 - 1)} \quad \text{and} \quad a_2 = \frac{-\dot{x}_1 + \dot{x}_2 x_2 + x_1 x_2}{x^2_2 - 1}$$

will emit the original input. If an actual transformation is required, then (the functions of $\dot{x}_1$, etc. above being represented by A_1 and A_2) the transformation $a'_1 = k(A_1 - a_1)$, $a'_2 = k(A_2 - a_2)$ will give the required behaviour as closely as is desired if k is made positive and large enough (Ex. 8/5/10). **6:** -2 has no particular relation to (7,3), whereas 4 has, as the construction of the table showed.

8/11. **1:** t has 3 states; u has 2. **2:** t has 3 states; u cannot have more than 6; u actually has 5. **3:** T has 2 states; so has U. **4:** 3 states. They are (0,0,0,0), (0,0,1,0) and (0,1,0,1).

8/13. **1:** One bit per step, for r has two states only. **2:** The numbers of distinct states occupied, at successive states, were: Q: 9,4,3,3,3; R: 1,2,2,2,2; S: 1,1,2,3,5. **3:** Because the jump from 1 to 4 would have implied a gain in variety of 3, whereas R can supply only 2 at most.

8/14. **2:** The number of balancings cannot, whatever the method, be fewer than three. For the variety to be transmitted is $\log_2 27$ bits, and the transmitter can carry only $\log_2 3$ bits per step.

8/15. **1:** Four; the variety from A takes longest. **2:** Four steps; (the answer *must* be the same as to Ex. 1, for the two questions are really identical). **3:** Three; that from y takes longest. **4:** Two steps.

8/17. **1:** A was at (3,2). (Hint: A'' was at $(-1,0)$ and B'' was at $(1,0)$.) **2:** Yes; the output enables the sequence of input-vectors to be deduced, of which the sequence of first components is the α-message. **3:** No; Y's movement is simply A's with half the amplitude. **4:** If the letters a, b, etc. indicate the respective movements of A, B, etc., to right and left from suitable zeros, with common scale, then $l = \frac{1}{2}(a - b)$, $n = \frac{1}{2}(a + b)$, $y = \frac{1}{2}(l + n)$, and $z = \frac{1}{2}(-l + n)$, from which l and n are readily eliminated. "Decoding" corresponds to solving these simultaneous equations for a and b, the unknowns, in terms of y and z, the knowns.

9/2. **1:** The transformation so obtained is determinate; how it was obtained is irrelevant. **2:** Since each state must go to *some* state, the probabilities, and the numbers in each column, must add up to 1. **3:** No. **4:** 2^{10}, i.e. 1024. **5:** More than one arrow may leave each point.

9/4. **1:** The actual transition frequencies are

↓	A	B
A	6	17
B	17	10

As each column's probabilities must add to 1, the first column must be divided by 23 and the second by 27. The estimated probabilities are thus

↓	A	B
A	0·26	0·63
B	0·74	0·37

4:

↓	A	B
A	0·2	0·5
B	0·8	0·5

(This is the system that was, in fact, used to generate the trajectory in Ex.1.)

9/5. **1:** Once under a pebble it would stay there. **2:** B must be the paper (where the fly sticks), and D the stove (where it never stops). **3:** From protocol to matrix; the protocol gives a unique matrix, but the matrix can give only a set of protocols. Or, if the matrix is lost it can be restored from the protocol, but a lost protocol cannot be restored from the matrix.

9/6. **1:** (100,0,0), (25,75,0), (62,19,19), (32,61,7), etc., if taken to the nearest unit. **3:** Face 3 tends to come up, face 4 is tending to go down; therefore $x = 4$. **4:** Consider 100 molecules, and let x of the 100 A's be dissociated. Ignore the B's. Each A has two possible states, dissociated or not, and in each interval of time has the probabilities of staying in its state or changing:

↓	Dissociated	Not Dissociated
Dissociated	0·999	0·01
Not Dissociated	0·001	0·99

5: If x and y are the numbers dissociated and not, respectively, then for equilibrium:

$$x = 0.999x + 0.01y$$
$$100 = x + y;$$

Therefore, $x = 90\frac{10}{11}$. **7:** Each insect can be only in one of 3; if there are n insects, the number of distinct populations is $\frac{1}{2}(n+2)(n+1)$.

9/7. **1:**

↓	C	D
After C: C	0	5
D	11	6

↓	C	D
After D: C	11	7
D	0	5

Thus, transitions from C are markedly affected by what preceded the C.

9/10. **1:** $t'_i = \frac{x}{i}t_i$. **2:** No. **3:** Yes.

9/11. **1:** The probabilities are (so far as the evidence goes) 0·175 and 0·825; so the entropy is 0·67 bits. **2:** The probabilities are $\frac{1}{52}, \frac{1}{4}, \frac{19}{26}$; so the entropy is 0·94 bits. **3:** 2·6 bits. **4:** 5·2 bits. **5:** 2·6 × n bits. **6:** 0.

9/12. **2:** It always falls below 1 bit.

9/13. **1:** The terminal equilibrium is with all in B; and any sequence must eventually become $\dots BBBB\dots$. This has no variety, so the entropy must be zero. **2:** Entropy is calculated when the whole is at terminal equilibrium and in this case the terminal equilibrium does not permit the assumption "when it is at A".

9/16. **1:** Yes, for 62 is fewer than 3^{14}; 3^4 is 81, so four sugars might be sufficient if suitably chosen. **2:** Every number in it is the same, e.g. that at the end of S.9/10.

9/17. **2:** It must be at least 2000 bits per min., if the assumptions are correct. **3:** Each finger has variety of $\log_2 3$ in $\frac{1}{300}$ min, and $300 \log_2 3$ in 1 minute; so all 10, being independent, have $3000 \log_2 3$ bits in one minute; so the bound is 4800 bits/min. **4:** 5540 symbols/hour.

9/18. **1:** b can follow only a or b, not d; so Xb must be ab; similarly Xc must be ac; and XX must be dX.

9/19. **1:** (i) $\downarrow \begin{array}{ccc} A & B & C \\ 4 & 9 & 7 \end{array}$ (ii) $\downarrow \begin{array}{ccc} A & B & C \\ 2 & 1 & 5 \end{array}$

2: Only if the combinations of α and β are restricted to some three of the four possible.

9/20. **1:** A distortion, for a second inversion will restore the original without loss. **2:** A distortion if each tension evokes a distinct frequency. **3:** A corruption, for various tensions evoke the same (zero) output.

9/21. **1:** H_1 is $\log_2 9$. H_2 is found from:

Symbol received: 1 2 3 4 5 6 7 8 9
Probability: $\frac{1}{9}$ $\frac{2}{9}$ $\frac{1}{9}$ $\frac{1}{9}$ $\frac{1}{9}$ $\frac{1}{9}$ $\frac{1}{9}$ 0 $\frac{1}{9}$

and is 2·948; so the equivocation is 0·222 bits per symbol. **2:** Equivocation $= 0$; yes, the new messages are transmitted unambiguously. **4:** 0·00299. **5:** The table of events and probabilities is:

Actual cell:	L	L	M	M
Diagnosis:	L	M	L	M
Probability:	0·9405	0·0095	0·00025	0·04975

(The probabilities are most simply found by dividing 20,000 cells first into 19,000 and 1,000; and then dividing these into cells mis-diagnosed and the rest; finally divide by 20,000.) $H_1 = 0\cdot365$ bits/cell; $H_2 = 0\cdot324$ bits/cell. So equivocation $= 0\cdot041$ bits/cell.

10/4. **1:** The cat acting on, perhaps playing with, a dead mouse. **2:** If such were possible, it would correspond to the cat doing something that brings a dead mouse back to life! **3:** C is **lethal** to M if not one of $C(M_1)$, ..., $C(M_k)$ is in $M_1, ..., M_k$.

10/5. (i) Temperature and humidity; (ii) the oxygen in the climber's blood and all that depends on it; (iii) the directions of the light rays passing through; (iv) the illumination of the objects that would otherwise be invisible after sunset; (v) the temperature of the food and, consequently, the degree of its bacterial contamination; (vi) the intensity of illumination of the plant's leaves; (vii) the intensity of illumination of the retina; (viii) the pressure (at high intensities) on the sole; (ix) the contact-pressure, which is kept at zero; (x) the distance between shell and target, which is kept zero or small.

11/3. **1:** $\downarrow \begin{array}{ccc} 1 & 2 & 3 \\ \gamma & \beta & \alpha \end{array}$ **2:** D being given, R should take the value that satisfies $37 = R - 2D$; so R should take the value $37 + 2D$. **3:** The main diagonal (S.2/10) has the outcomes "skid corrected", the other two cells the outcomes "skid exaggerated". **4:** Zero—they will all be c's, whatever the variety in D's selections. **5:** Yes.

11/4. **1:** Yes.

2: $\downarrow \begin{array}{ccccc} 1 & 2 & 3 & 4 & 5 \\ \beta & \beta \text{ or } \delta & \alpha & \alpha & \alpha \text{ or } \delta \end{array}$

3: R simply plays γ on all occasions, without reference to D's move. **4:** Yes, and he should use the transformation

$\downarrow$	Mr. A	Mrs. B	Mr. C
	Sherry	Gin	Sherry

11/11.   1: Yes. D has a variety of 10 bits/sec, the optic nerve can transmit 200 times this. **2:** The capacity available for regulation is 0·63 bits/sec by telegraph and 5·64 bits/sec by the wheel. So evidently D does not usually emit more than 6·3 bits/sec. **3:** No, it is grossly insufficient. D provides 10^7 bits in each day, and the variety transmitted to the general is at most one-seventeenth of this. **4:** No, he can emit only $3·6 \times 10^5$ bits/day.

11/14.   1:

↓	1	2	3
a	β	α	γ
b	α	γ	β
c	γ	β	α

2: D is threatening to transmit to E at 2 bits/sec. To reduce this to zero the channel $D \to R$ must transmit at not less than this rate. **3:** $C \to E$ is to carry 20 bits/sec, therefore $C \to R$ must carry at least that amount. **4:** $R \to T$ must carry 2 bits/sec to neutralise D (from Ex. 2), and 20 bits/sec from C; as these two are independent (D's values and C's not correlated), the capacity must be at least 22 bits/sec.

12/8.   1:

↓	L	R
L	0	0·99
R	1	0·01

2: The systems are almost isomorphic; $β$, however, will occasionally jump from A directly to D, and will occasionally stay at C for a step. **3:** The successive probabilities for a at each step are: $0, \frac{1}{4}, \frac{7}{16}$ and $\frac{26}{32}$; b's probabilities are the remainder. **4:** The answer can be found by pre-multiplying the column vector $\begin{bmatrix}0\\1\end{bmatrix}$ by the matrix product prq; compare Ex. 2/16/3 and 12/8/4. **5:** The new system must have states that are couples, e.g. (b,e); so it will have six states. Now find the transition probabilities. What, for instance, is that for the transition $(b,e) \to (a,f)$? For this to occur, b must go to a, and it must do this while the other component is at e, i.e. at $β$. With input at $β$ the probability of $b \to a$ is 0·9. Similarly, with b (i.e. at $δ$) the probability of $e \to f$ is 0·3; so the probability of the whole transition (for which both independent events must occur) is 0·27. The other probabilities can be found similarly, and the matrix is (with brackets omitted for brevity):

↓	ae	be	ce	af	bf	cf
ae	0·06	0·63	0·25	0·14	0·15	0·12
be	0·12	0·07	0·25	·	0·35	0·08
ce	0·02	·	·	0·56	·	0·20
af	0·24	0·27	0·25	0·06	0·15	0·18
bf	0·48	0·03	0·25	·	0·35	0·12
cf	0·08	·	·	0·24	·	0·30

6: Yes.

12/10.   1: A possible matrix is:

↓	1	2	3	4	5	6	7	8	G
1	.	$\frac{1}{3}$	.	.	.	.	.	.	.
2	1	.	$\frac{1}{2}$	.	.	.	.	.	.
3	.	$\frac{1}{3}$	.	.	.	$\frac{1}{2}$	.	.	.
4	.	.	.	.	.	.	1	.	.
5	.	$\frac{1}{3}$	.	1	.	.	.	.	.
6	.	.	$\frac{1}{2}$	.	.	.	.	.	.
7	.	.	.	.	.	.	.	.	.
8	.	.	.	1	.	.	.	.	.
G	.	.	.	.	.	$\frac{1}{2}$	.	1	1

12/11.   1: G only.   **2:** "When at a or b it does not seem to know where it is, and it wanders at random; c is the only other compartment accessible from a or b; if it arrives in c it seems to recognise where it is, for it then always goes unswervingly through d and e to f, where it stops—perhaps it was always fed there."

12/12.   1: (i) Yes, (ii)

↓	B	G
B	–	$\frac{1}{2}$
G	–	$\frac{1}{2}$

There are no transitions after B.

2: Yes—for *my* essential variables!

12/14.   1: γ must be the identity; β must have no 1 in its main diagonal.

12/17.   1: (i) 26; (ii) 52 (see *Design for a Brain*, S.23/2; here $p = \frac{1}{32}$).

12/21.   1: Two; G's position is completely determined by P's, which has one; J's angle of rotation gives a second.   **2:** One way would be to move V to mid-way between L and K.   **3:** One way would be to re-route the air-tube so that it comes down to V instead of up to it.

13/15.   1: $3 \log_2 7$, i.e. 8·42 bits.   **2:** $3 \log_2 91$, i.e. 19·52 bits.   **3:** 3·3 bits is the minimum, for only 10 combinations are *distinct*.   **4:** 1 bit; the number of states and other details are irrelevant.   That the answer *must* be 1 bit can be seen by imagining that these are the only two machines possible (as is given), and then imagining that the designer must send his instructions by cable; clearly he need not pay much, for a simple 1-bit distinction is sufficient for the recipient's instruction.   **5:** (i) 49800 bits; (ii) 1·6 bits; no agreement is to be expected, for the values refer not to the one stamp but to two different sets of possibilities.   **6:** $n \log_2 n$ bits.   **7:** $in \log_2 n$ bits.

13/17.   1: 19 removed.   **2:** 26 removed.   **3:** 4·75 bits fell to 3·00, so 1·75 bits was removed.   **4:** As a_1 may go to any of $n - 1$, and a_2 similarly, the new number of transformations is

$$(n - 1)(n - 1) \ldots (n - 1) \quad (n \text{ terms}),$$

i.e. $(n - 1)^n$. Logarithmically the variety was $n \log_2 n$ and is now $n \log_2 (n - 1)$, so the variety removed by the restriction is

$$n \log_2 n - n \log_2 (n - 1).$$

5: $1\cdot4$ bits; more accurately it is $(1 + \frac{1}{2n} + \ldots) \log_2 e$.   **6:** Examination of the kth card in a pack of n gives information, or has entropy,

$$-\frac{1}{n-k+1} \log \frac{1}{n-k+1} - \frac{n-k}{n-k+1} \log \frac{n-k}{n-k+1}$$

if the drawing occurs. If success has occurred earlier the entropy is 0. These two events (and their entropies) have probabilities $(n-k+1)/n$ and $(k-1)/n$. So the weighted average entropy is

$$-\frac{1}{n} \left(\log \frac{1}{n-k+1} + (n-k) \log \frac{n-k}{n-k+1} \right)$$

which is $\frac{1}{n} \left[(n-k+1) \log (n-k+1) - (n-k) \log (n-k) \right]$.

7: At each drawing the entropy is the same—that of the probabilities $\frac{1}{n}$ and $\frac{n-1}{n}$, and the average information

$$\frac{1}{n}(n \log n - (n-1) \log (n-1)).$$

14/1.   **1:** An adequate supplementary input of water is, of course, necessary. The output comes from this, through a tap, which is controlled by the input. A possible method is to use piston or bellows so that the pressure set up when 0, 1 or 2 ml/sec are forced through a narrow orifice will move the tap to the appropriate position.

INDEX

(The number refers to the page. A **bold-faced** number indicates a definition.)

289

293